PMCA
Back to Basics
Confectionery Fundamentals

Volume 1: 2000–2006

PMCA
Back to Basics
Confectionery Fundamentals
Volume 1: 2000–2006

Published by

PMCA—An International Association of Confectioners
Annual Production Conference Committee
2980 Linden Street, Suite E3
Bethlehem, PA 18017 USA
Telephone: +1 (610) 625 4655 • Fax: +1 (610) 625 4657
Web: www.pmca.com • Email: info@pmca.com

Produced by the editorial staff of
MC/The Manufacturing Confectioner
711 W. Water Street • PO Box 266
Princeton, WI 54968
Web: www.gomc.com • Email: mcinfo@gomc.com

Library of Congress Control Number: 2007920540

ISBN 978-1-933430-12-6

PMCA, 2980 Linden Street, Suite E3, Bethlehem, PA 18017 USA

Printed in the United States of America

10 9 8 7 6 5 4 3 2 1

In Memoriam
RALPH LEE

As this book was going to press, we were shocked to learn of the sudden passing of Ralph Lee. Ralph was a PMCA Production Conference Program Committee member for several years and his presentation on "Nougat and Marshmallow Processing" in the 2006 Back to Basics session on Aerated Confections is included in this book. Ralph joined M&M/Mars in 1987 in Hackettstown, New Jersey (later to become Masterfoods, USA) where he was a senior process development engineer—most recently responsible for chocolate products. He also had management responsibilities for the pilot plant and R&D facilities in Hackettstown.

Very active in his local church, he was the capital campaign chair for the construction of a new religious education building, in addition to serving as treasurer and youth minister. Ralph is survived by his wife, Pat, and their two sons, Richard and Daniel.

Ralph's broad technical background and eagerness to participate in the Program Committee's activities made him an outstanding committee member. His contributions and infectious enthusiasm will be sorely missed.

Foreword

The first Pennsylvania Manufacturing Confectioners' Association (PMCA) Annual Production Conference was held at Lehigh University in Bethlehem, Pennsylvania, in September 1947, with a registration fee of $5.00 per day. The success of this forum (as it was called then) led to the annual conferences that are now held in the spring of each year.

The high quality of the presentations, on many technical aspects of product manufacture, led to the publication in 1970 of *Twenty Years of Confectionery and Chocolate Progress*, compiled from the proceedings of the 1947 to 1966 conferences. This 775-page book contained 66 complete papers presented during those 20 years, plus 259 abstracts of the remaining papers.

In the ensuing years there has been a great increase in product diversity and product development activities. Because of this, a need was identified for a source of basic information on core confectionery types and processes. This source would focus on core subjects and present basic information on proven manufacturing methods and developments from previous years.

At the PMCA conferences in 2000 and 2001, presentations were made on the basics of several topics (chocolate tempering, sugar confectionery and sugar crystallization). The success of these led to extended sessions in the following years.

Since 2002, the initial half day at each Annual PMCA Production Conference has been devoted to the presentation of basic information (with candymaking demonstrations and samples) required to cover the core technology of a single topic—to meet the basic technology needs of the industry on that topic. The Back to Basics era had begun!

This has been no simple task. Each Back to Basics session has required the Production Conference Program Committee and other members of the industry to first develop a comprehensive outline of the chosen topic. They then invited a range of experts to present their knowledge on the individual subjects. Equipment and ingredient companies donated their time and materials to help conduct the demonstrations. And there are even night-before rehearsals to ensure the high quality and smooth running of the various demonstrations.

This book comprises the first seven years of the Back to Basics presentations. It provides comprehensive—yet compact—access to basic information on core confectionery and chocolate technologies. In so doing, this book contributes to one of PMCA's key missions, which is to "educate and train current and future confectionery technical personnel worldwide."

This volume, containing the contents of the 2000 and 2001 presentations and the five full Back to Basics sessions since then, has involved the time and effort of many people. The PMCA extends its sincere thanks to all the industry members and others who have made this book possible.

We believe that making this information readily accessible to all segments of the industry will benefit the industry as a whole while working towards the PMCA objective of "Making Confections Better."

The PMCA Production Conference Committee

Contents

CONTENTS

Early Fundamentals

Fundamentals of Sugar Confectionery

Brian Jackson
Jackson Associates

This paper is intended for newcomers to the industry, and as a reminder of the fundamentals to the rest of us. It should form the basis for further investigation.

SUGAR CONFECTIONERY BASICS

We are agreed on these fundamentals:

- The confection must not undergo fermentation, mold growth or any other microbiological spoilage during a long storage life.

- The confection must not undergo any change in its physical properties during this storage.

- The confection must have the desirable physical properties normally associated with the particular confection. For example, it must not be too hard to eat comfortably; its texture and solubility must be pleasing to the palate; and, not least, it must be flavored correctly and be sweet tasting.

- The confection must be pleasing to the eye. This factor is determined by the art and skill of the confectioner.

Let us take each one and examine it in more detail.

MICROBIOLOGICAL SPOILAGE

While there is no clear-cut line, experience indicates that if the solids content is below 75 percent, certain molds and yeasts will grow in carbohydrate solutions and spoilage will result. Some examples are shown in Figure 1. If, on the other hand, the solids content is above 75 percent, then this is unlikely to occur. Remember that when considering sugar confectionery we are not dealing with a material kept under commercially sterile conditions, as with canned foods, for instance, but with a product that must be kept under normal nonsterile conditions. The confection must be self-preserving in its own right since every source of contamination cannot be kept away from it.

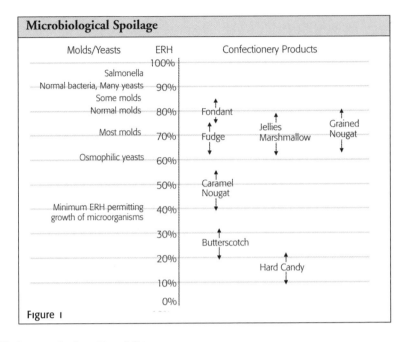

Figure 1

Equilibrium Relative Humidity

Equilibrium relative humidity (ERH) is the point at which the product neither gains water nor loses it to the atmosphere.

ERH is expressed as a percentage and water activity is expressed as a decimal A_w.

$$\text{ERH } 70\% = 0.7\ A_w$$

If we take a typical sucrose solution of two parts sucrose to one part water, what ERH would be required to keep this from gaining or losing moisture? Figure 2 shows the solution, and Figure 3 shows typical ERH values of a variety of sugar confections.

The saturation solubility of sucrose in water at 20°C (68°F) is 66.6 percent. Figure 4 shows the percentage at a range of temperatures.

ERH Value of Sucrose Solution
200 g of sucrose in 100 g water
Number of Moles = $\dfrac{200}{342}$ = 0.585
ERH = $\dfrac{100}{1 + 0.27\,(0.585)} = \dfrac{100}{1 + 0.158}$ = 86.7% ERH
Figure 2

Typical ERH Values of Sugar Confections	
Confection	ERH%
Hard Candy	>30
Caramels	45−50
Creams	80−85
Fondant	75−80
Fudge	65−75
Jellies	60−76
Licorice	57−65
Marshmallow	64−72
Turkish Delight	60−70
Figure 3	

Here are some useful rules of thumb to remember:

- At room temperature, 1 lb of water will dissolve 2 lbs of sugar.
- At boiling point, 1 lb of water will dissolve 4 lbs sugar.

THE SOLUBILITY OF SUCROSE

The rate at which crystallization proceeds depends on the degree of supersaturation and the temperature (Figure 5). The degree of supersaturation is the proportion (not the amount) by which the sucrose in solution exceeds the content at saturation. It is defined as a ratio. For example, at 20°C (68°F) a saturated solution of sucrose is said to contain 66.6 percent the degree of supersaturation.

So, a solution 66.6 percent the degree of supersaturation is 66.6/66.6 = 1.

A solution containing 75 percent of sucrose by weight will be 75/66.6 = 1.126 supersaturated.

Crystallization Zones

Consider the various zones of crystallization (Figure 6).

The metastable zone. It includes those concentrations of sucrose in solution that are conducive to the growth of existing crystals, but not to the formation of new crystals, i.e., crystallization progresses but no new crystals are formed.

The intermediate zone. This zone is just beyond the metastable. Here existing crystals continue to grow but also new crystals form. Crystals will form only in

Solubility

Sugar dissolves in water. The amount which dissolves depends on the temperature of the solution:

°C (°F)	% Sugar	°C(°F)	% Sugar
0° (32°)	64.4%	60°(140°)	74.2%
10° (50°)	15.3%	70°(158°)	76.5%
20° (68°)	66.6%	80°(176°)	78.8%
30° (86°)	68.2%	90°(194°)	81.0%
40° (104°)	70.0%	100° (212°)	83.8%
50° (122°)	72.0%		

Figure 4

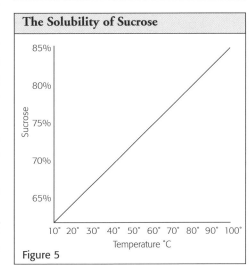

Figure 5

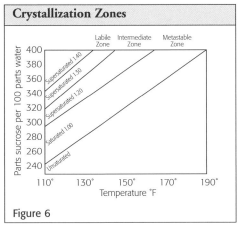

Figure 6

Crystallization Zones of Supersaturated Solutions			
Supersaturation	% Sucrose Concentration	Zone	Occurrences
S1.3 and greater	73	Labile	Spontaneous crystallization
S1.2–1.3	70	False grain	Rapid growth of crystals when external seeding takes place
S1.0–1.3	65–70	Metastable	No spontaneous crystallization but crystal growth can occur
S1.0 and below	67	Stable	No crystallization

Figure 7

the presence of other crystals.

The labile zone. This is the zone beyond the intermediate where crystals form spontaneously without the presence of others. (See Figures 7 and 8).

Sucrose alone cannot give us a product with a solids content sufficiently high to prevent microbiological spoilage without crystallizing.

What can be done to alter this, and to permit us to prepare a solution stable against crystallization with a solids content of 76 percent w/w or over at normal temperatures, i.e., 20°C (68°F)?

Boiling Point of Sucrose Solutions	
Sucrose Concentration Total Soluble Solids	Boiling Point °C (°F)
40%	101.4° (214.5°)
50%	102° (215.5°)
60%	103° (217.5°)
70%	105.5° (222°)
75%	108° (227°)
80%	111° (232°)
85%	116° (241°)
90%	122° (252°)
95%	130° (266°)

Figure 8

The answer is to have present in the solution with sucrose a sugar other than sucrose, a process known as *doctoring*.

PHYSICAL PROPERTIES

The main change in physical properties to be considered is the appearance of undesired crystals, which is called *graining*. This crystal formation in sugar confections, which should be free of any crystals, is normally due to the formation in the confection of sucrose crystals during storage.

Such crystals spoil the appearance of the product and, in addition, cause an unpleasant roughness on the tongue.

In the case of hard candy, it is obviously impossible (using the traditional proportions of sucrose and glucose syrup) to obtain a product of 97 percent solids content which is not supersaturated with respect to sucrose. However, it is well known that using 1.5 parts of sucrose to 1 part of 42 DE corn syrup, a hard candy can be prepared which can be stored for several years without any graining taking place.

This is possible because hard candies are an example of what physicists call the *glassy state*. They are solid, to all appearances, but they are in fact supercooled, non-crystalline liquids, liquids which are so far below their melting or softening points that they have assumed solid properties without crystallizing.

High-viscosity Liquids

As such, they can be considered as liquids of enormously high viscosity. High viscosity interferes considerably with the process of crystal formation. Consider what happens when a crystal forms. First of all, there must be a nucleus, that is, a completely sub-microscopic crystal, to act as a starting point for the crystal to form. These nuclei are formed spontaneously if the supersaturation is sufficient, but the higher the viscosity, the slower the rate at which they form.

The molecules of the substance crystallizing have to "hit and stick" to the nucleus, being brought to it by the continuous, very rapid movement of the molecules in all liquids and solutions. But this movement is very severely limited in a solid or in a liquid of extremely high viscosity. It is thus the extremely high viscosity and what one can call the pseudo-solid state of hard candy that in fact inhibits graining and there- . fore the crystallization of sucrose during storage.

Even if the supersaturation is high, graining can still take place, and this will happen if the doctoring is too low.

When the boiling has been poured on the slab and while it is being manipulated, its temperature is quite high, and it is a very thick liquid and not a solid at all. Its viscosity in this stage, while high, is not nearly so high as when the final candy has cooled to room temperature and solidified. In fact, during the cooling period on the slab and the later manipulation, an insufficiently doctored boiling will most definitely grain.

The stability of a confection, in particular a hard candy, is therefore due to the sugars present being in a glassy state. This state is metastable and once crystallization is started, graining is progressive. A change in the choice of raw material and the ratio of sugars in the recipe can affect the stability and the rate of graining.

When confections are held in a humid atmosphere they will immediately commence to absorb water. This is present as a film of water around the surface of the product, which rapidly dilutes the noncrystalline mixture of carbohydrates. Crystallization then commences, promoted by the lowered viscosity of the syrup film.

The solubility of carbohydrates increases as the temperature rises. Thus, the higher the temperatures experienced during a cooking process at atmospheric pressure means that the supersaturation with respect to sucrose is less than at the lower temperatures experienced during a vacuum cooking process.

This explains why a higher proportion of doctor must be used with a vacuum cooking process than is used with an atmospheric pressure cooking process. If this higher proportion of doctor is not used in a vacuum process, then graining during processing is always a danger.

In the case of caramels, the solids content (eliminating the fat from our calculations) is usually about 90 percent. The situation here, therefore, is rather different from hard candy, where the solids content is on the order of 97 to 98 percent. This lower solids content in caramels means that the viscosity of the sugary mass is very much lower. Thus caramels lack the antigraining effects of the very high viscosity of hard candy, and must be more highly doctored. For this reason, a sucrose/doctor to sugar solids ratio of 1.24/1 or even 1/1 is used.

In spite of this heavy doctoring, caramels usually have an appreciably shorter shelf life before graining sets in than is the case with hard candy.

PHYSICAL FORM

Hard candies, caramels and marshmallows are all examples of products where graining is normally detrimental to the appearance of the sugar confection. There are, however, certain confections which must have some grain for them to have their traditional form—for example, fudge and fondant.

In the manufacture of fondant, a greatly underdoctored mixture is boiled to a comparatively low temperature, cooled and then beaten to start off the crystallization of sucrose; the degree of doctoring, the temperature and the mechanical action ensure that a multitude of very fine sucrose crystals are formed. It is on the success of the production of a very large number of very small sucrose crystals that the smoothness of the fondant depends.

Fondant is a confection in its own right, but it is also used to promote crystallization in fudges. The principle of the manufacture of a fudge is that a boiling is cooled to a temperature found by experiment to give the correct degree of supersaturation, and then fine sucrose crystals in the form of fondant are added to start off the crystallization process. Obviously, details of manufacture and also the correct degree of doctoring are matters of great importance. Pulled candy (such as dinner mints) is another example of mechanical action being used to produce very fine sucrose crystals—in this case in much smaller numbers than in the case of fondant. Here the amount of doctor is much higher than in the case of fondant. The viscosity is also much higher owing to the much higher solids content. Both factors combine to reduce the number of sucrose crystals formed.

If sucrose and invert are present together in solution, a concentration can be reached whereby the sucrose content is only just prevented from crystallizing. Figure 9 shows the solids content of the solutions which are just saturated with sucrose.

From this it can be seen that sucrose itself is saturated at 67 percent solids and in a 50/50 mixture with invert sugar it becomes saturated with respect to dextrose at 76 percent solids (Figure 10). In the presence of corn syrup, however, it is shown that much higher solids can be obtained before saturation is achieved (Figure 11). This is not only important in hard candy but in products where microbiological stability is required (i.e., marshmallows) and where the control of graining is important, as in fondants and fudge formulations.

Prevention of Graining

All corn syrups exercise some control over sucrose crystallization in hard candy. In these confections, which are essentially highly supersaturated solutions of sucrose, the latter will always tend to recrystallize, both at the production stage and during storage. Unless this tendency is prevented by the addition of an inhibitor (or doctor as it is called, i.e., corn syrup), recrystallization will continue, resulting in graining. Because of the extremely low moisture content in hard candy, and the resulting high viscosity, graining may take place quite slowly under ideal storage conditions.

Once initiated, however, either by the picking up of moisture or by the

Solids Content of Solutions Saturated with Sucrose		
Sucrose Solids	Invert Solids	Solids Content*
100%	0.0%	67.1%
78.6%	21.4%	70.0%
67.6%	32.4%	72.0%
57.6%	42.4%	74.0%
48.8%	51.2%	76.0%
*at 20°C (68°F).		

Figure 9

Solids Content of Solutions Saturated with Dextrose		
Sucrose Solids	Invert Solids	Solids Content*
47.5%	52.5%	76.1%
40.0%	60.0%	73.6%
30.0%	70.0%	73.6%
20.0%	80.0%	67.7%
*at 20°C (68°F).		

Figure 10

Solids Content in Solutions with Corn Syrup		
Sucrose Solids	42 DE Corn Syrup Solids	Solids Content*
100%	0.0%	67%
78.6%	21.4%	70%
67.6%	32.4%	72%
57.6%	42.4%	74%
48.8%	51.2%	76%
40.9%	59.1%	78%
34.1%	65.9%	80%
28.4%	71.6%	82%
23.7%	76.3%	84%
*at 20°C (68°F).		

Figure 11

seeding of the confection with nondissolved sucrose, graining may take place very rapidly. The grain-inhibiting effect of corn syrup is twofold. The first comes from the increased viscosity in the glass of the hard candy, which prevents migration of sucrose molecules and nucleation, as described above. The second important property is the control of crystallization by increased sucrose solubility.

HYGROSCOPICITY

The relationship between a food product and its environment is important to the shelf life of that product and hence of great importance to its overall economy. The controlling factor is the equilibrium relative humidity (ERH) of the product. If the ERH is low the product will attract moisture and become sticky and is in some cases liable to microbiological spoilage. On the other hand, if the ERH of the product is high it will tend to lose moisture and become dry. This again is deleterious to the product.

The ERH at a given temperature is a function of the concentration of solids dissolved in the aqueous phase. If more molecules are dissolved in the aqueous phase the ERH is decreased.

Equilibrium relative humidity of a sugar confection can be quite accurately calculated by the use of the Money-Born equation:

$$ERH = 100 \times N_0/(N_0 + 1.5N)$$

where N equals the number of gram-molecules of the various carbohydrates present and N_0 equals the number of gram-molecules of water present.

The number of gram-molecules is obtained by dividing the weight of the substance present by its molecular weight, and the molecular weights we have to use are shown in Figure 12.

The molecular weights (which are obviously average molecular weights) for the two corn syrups are obtained by calculation elevations of these two products.

Consider three cases: one, a marshmallow taken as being 24 percent water, 48.8 percent sucrose and 51.2 percent doctor solids; one representing the conditions in the sugar portion of a caramel, which is taken as containing 10 percent water, 45 percent sucrose and 45 percent doctor solids; and one representing a hard candy, which is taken as containing 3 percent water, 63 percent sucrose and 34 percent doctor solids.

Applying the Money-Born equation to these cases, we get the results shown in Figure 13.

It will be seen that in all cases when

Average Molecular Weights	
Sucrose	342.3
Invert sugar	180.2
Dextrose	180.2
40 DE corn syrup solids	340.0
63 DE corn syrup solids	260.0
Water	18.02

Figure 12

ERH of Doctored Sugar Confections		
Type Case	Doctor	Equilibrium rH
Marshmallow	Invert	73.3%
	40 DE corn syrup	80.0%
	63 DE corn syrup	77.5%
Caramel	Invert	49.2%
	40 DE corn syrup	58.4%
	63 DE corn syrup	54.9%
Hard Candy	Invert	23.9%
	40 DE corn syrup	28.0%
	63 DE corn syrup	26.0%

Figure 13

invert sugar is used as a doctor, the relative vapor pressure of the confection is lower than when 40 DE corn syrup is used. This means that sugar confections doctored with 40 DE corn syrup will be less liable to pick up moisture from the atmosphere than when invert is used—a very important point in the relatively moist atmospheric conditions which apply in many other parts of the world.

If a slightly more moisture-retaining doctor than 40 DE corn syrup is wanted, then 63 DE corn syrup will be suitable.

Dextrose, since its molecular weight is the same as that of invert sugar, has the same effect on equilibrium relative humidity as the latter.

PLEASING TO THE EYE

This factor is determined by the art and skill of the confectioner.

CALCULATIONS FOR RECIPES, RECIPE FORMULATION

It is recommended that the confectioner compile information on production specifications, technical factors and nutritional data.

Figure 14 shows a typical example for a basic caramel recipe, indicating the theoretical yield and Figure 15 shows an extension to provide the bill of materials.

Theoretical Yield of Caramel

Description	Formula lbs/batch	Ingredient Moisture Content	Lbs of Water in Formula	Lbs of Solids in Formula	% Dry Solids Basis
Sugar, bulk extra fine granulated	56.0000	0.25%	0.1400	55.8600	46.6071
Corn syrup 42 DE	34.0000	19.30%	6.5620	27.4380	22.8931
Sweetened condensed milk	39.0000	27.50%	10.7250	28.2750	23.5914
Vegetable fat	8.0000	0.00%	0.0000	8.0000	6.6749
Emulsifier	0.0300	0.00%	0.0000	0.0300	0.0250
Salt, Morton Purex food grade	0.2500	0.05%	0.0001	0.2499	0.2085
Water	18.0000	100.00%	18.0000	0.0000	0.0000
Totals	155.2800		35.42713	119.8529	100.000

Figure 14

Bill of Materials for Caramel

Description	Process No.	Formula lbs/batch	Divide by Yield/Batch	MRP Qty. per	MRP Process Scrap %	MRP Adjusted Qty. Per
Sugar, bulk extra fine granulated	1	56.0000	129.4529	0.4326	3.00	0.4460
Corn syrup 42 DE	1	34.0000	129.4529	0.2626	3.00	0.2708
Sweetened condensed milk	1	39.0000	129.4529	0.3013	3.00	0.3106
Vegetable fat	1	8.0000	129.4529	0.0618	3.00	0.0637
Emulsifier	1	0.0300	129.4529	0.0002	3.00	0.0002
Salt, Morton Purex food grade	1	0.2500	129.4529	0.0019	3.00	0.0020
Totals	1	137.2800	129.4529	1.0605	3.00	1.0933

Figure 15

The spreadsheet can be extended to provide information such as cost per pound of ingredients and finished product, and nutritional information.

CONCLUSION

The successful manufacture of candy and troubleshooting often return to the basic fundamentals, which should be studied first before more expensive solutions are sought.

Questions & Answers

Q: Why is A_w more descriptive and are A_w and ERH exactly the same?

A: ERH is the equilibrium relative humidity expressed as a percentage. A_w (water activity) is a decimal of the ERH. For example, 70 percent ERH equals 0.7 A_w. Water activity is a descriptive word which clearly states that water is an active ingredient.

Q: Your ERH charts show mallows and other confections with ERH of 75 to 80 percent. These presumably are not microbiologically stable, with water activities above the critical 0.65 percent. How do you deal with this?

A: The ERH of 75 to 80 percent should not be confused with the total soluble solids content of the marshmallow. Solids above 75 percent are generally considered to be stable and marshmallow, for example, with an ERH of 80 percent, or an a_w of 0.8, would normally tend to dry out under normal storage conditions.

Q: Since most fondants, fudge, jellies, marshmallow and nougats fall into the growth range of yeasts and molds, why don't we see more spoiled confections?

A: In considering the ERH or A_w in the critical zone, it should be remembered that the soluble solids of the confection are the critical factor in controlling the microbiological stability. In particular, any confection that has a multiphase system, such as fondant or fudge, consists of a crystal phase and a liquid phase, and in the liquid phase it is important to have soluble solids above the 75 percent range.

Q: Is there any rule of thumb "on the floor" for telling where you are (approximately) on the sucrose crystallization zone? How do you just see it in the cooker/pot?

A: The crystallinity of a solution can normally be observed visually, showing a lack of transparency and a semi-milky appearance, and, at a more advanced stage, can be clearly appreciated on the palette. There is no rule of thumb except experience in deciding for a particular process (i.e., atmospheric vacuum, processing by forming or by depositing), what ratio is required between the rate of sucrose/sugar inversion and between sugar and corn syrup.

Chocolate Tempering Fundamentals

Terry Richardson
Richardson Researches, Inc.

This paper has two parts. The first part deals with some theoretical explanations about what happens when we temper chocolate. The second part will be concerned with the actual physical tempering of chocolate.

Most of the theoretical discussion is based on work that has been done by other people and, since there is no bibliography for this paper, I will give verbal attribution to S. Beckett, R. Cook, P. Dimick, W. Duck, R. Hartel, Hernqvist, K. Larsson, B. Minifie, R. Nelson, K. Sato, E. Seguine, G. Talbot, S. Vaeck and M. Weyland.

EFFECTS OF TEMPERING CHOCOLATE

Why do we have to go through the laborious exercise known as chocolate tempering? The process of tempering chocolate achieves the following results:

- It allows the chocolate to set quickly for practical processing.

- It sets the chocolate with a fine crystal structure, giving an attractive gloss and snap.

- It contracts the chocolate and permits moulded chocolate to release from moulds.

- It prevents the chocolate from showing signs of bloom under correct storage conditions.

What is so special about chocolate that it requires the tempering process and what do we mean by tempering?

Tempering is defined as the process of cooling and mixing substances (steel, glass, chocolate) to achieve the correct texture, hardness and appearance.

Chocolate contains cocoa butter fat. When cocoa butter is melted, cooled and agitated, depending on the way it is done, the cocoa butter can and will set up in six different crystal forms. Only one of these forms, as far as we confectioners are concerned, is sufficiently stable to allow us to properly process the chocolate and make our attractive-looking boxed chocolates.

What is so special about cocoa butter that it needs all this kid glove treatment?

First, and very fortunately, in its stable crystal form cocoa butter melts out at a few degrees below our body temperature, and yet at normal room temperature it is easily handled—it's not soft or sticky.

The majority of cocoa butter is comprised of triglycerides. These are substances that have different fatty acids connected to a glycerol molecule (Figure 1).

The common analogy to simply represent this is an elongated chair shape.

The glycerol part represents the chair seat; the back or number two position is occupied by oleic fatty acid; and, for the most part, the two legs are palmitic or stearic fatty acids, singly, in single or double conformation and that switch around in position.

Cocoa butter, being a natural substance, contains various ratios of the differently shaped chairs, and even chairs made from one or two fatty acids only, and with different length chair legs (Figure 2).

Cocoa butter from different growing areas and even different seasons will have

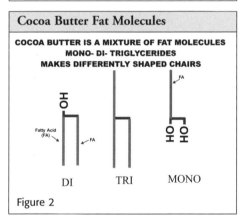

Cocoa Butter Triglyceride Molecule

THEORY OF COCOA BUTTER CRYSTALLIZATION
COCOA BUTTER HAS AT LEAST 6 CRYSTAL SHAPES
WE AIM FOR ONE (FORM V) DURING TEMPERING/COOLING

FATTY ACID 2 (OLEIC)

GLYCEROL

FATTY ACID 1 (EITHER PALMITIC OR STEARIC)

FATTY ACID 3

ONE COCOA BUTTER TRIGLYCERIDE MOLECULE CHAIR SHAPED

Figure 1

Cocoa Butter Fat Molecules

COCOA BUTTER IS A MIXTURE OF FAT MOLECULES
MONO- DI- TRIGLYCERIDES
MAKES DIFFERENTLY SHAPED CHAIRS

Fatty Acid (FA)

FA

FA

DI   TRI   MONO

Figure 2

different amounts of various triglycerides, diglycerides and, sometimes, traces of monoglycerides.

I say this not to confuse but to inform, since the ratios of the chairs to one another influence the tempering conditions. On top of this, since most chocolate contains milk fat (which brings in more differently shaped chairs), it makes tempering a little "artsy," especially if you are dealing with different chocolate formulas and different manufacturers.

FOUR STAGES OF CRYSTALLIZATION

Before we discuss the differently shaped crystals and their effect on tempering, let's look at the crystallization process in general.

Stage 1—Induction

First we liquefy all of the cocoa butter to about 130°F. At stage one we have all of the chairs in a state of vibration, bouncing off of one another and providing liquidity to the mass (Figure 3a).

Stage 2 – Nucleation

We then start to cool and agitate (temper) the chocolate and, by so doing, slow down the vibrating chair-shaped triglycerides. And after a time they slow down so much that they start to line up and stack together, the smallest stack being two chairs. Then on further cooling and agitating these stacks will form platelets which align with other platelets and become crystals (Figure 3b).

Stage 3 – Crystal Growth

With the liquid tempered chocolate there will be only a small amount of these crystals present (about 1%) based on the chocolate.

When we correctly set the chocolate, these shapes bridge together and dictate the final crystal shapes in the chocolate (Figure 3c).

Stage 4 – Hardening

Finally, during cooling these platelets bridge together and confer a set structure to the chocolate (Figure 3d).

That, then, is the mechanics of fat crystallization generally, but, again, cocoa butter is different from this.

POLYMORPHISM

As previously stated, the cocoa butter can set up in six different shapes, but for the everyday tempering process, we need

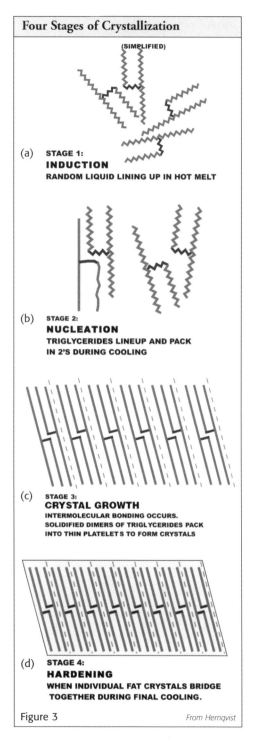

Four Stages of Crystallization

(SIMPLIFIED)

(a) **STAGE 1:**
INDUCTION
RANDOM LIQUID LINING UP IN HOT MELT

(b) **STAGE 2:**
NUCLEATION
TRIGLYCERIDES LINEUP AND PACK
IN 2'S DURING COOLING

(c) STAGE 3:
CRYSTAL GROWTH
INTERMOLECULAR BONDING OCCURS.
SOLIDIFIED DIMERS OF TRIGLYCERIDES PACK
INTO THIN PLATELETS TO FORM CRYSTALS

(d) STAGE 4:
HARDENING
WHEN INDIVIDUAL FAT CRYSTALS BRIDGE
TOGETHER DURING FINAL COOLING.

Figure 3   *From Hernqvist*

only concern ourselves with three of these shapes, Form II (alpha), Form IV (beta prime) and Form V (beta) (Figure 4).

When we temper chocolate, we aim for Form V, but, because of the cooling conditions that we use during tempering, possibly some Form II and most certainly Form IV will also form.

CRYSTALLIZATION AND MELTING RANGES FOR COCOA BUTTER POLYMORPHS

> ### Polymorphism
>
> ABILITY OF A SUBSTANCE TO EXIST IN MORE THAN ONE CRYSTAL FORM
>
> EXAMPLE: COCOA BUTTER HAS 6 FORMS UNLIKE SUCROSE ONE FORM ONLY
> Different forms have different properties.
>
> EXAMPLE:
> FORM I has a melt point of 63°F, GAMMA
> FORM II has a melt point of 74°F, ALPHA
> IV{ FORM III has a melt point of 78°F, BETA PRIME
>   { FORM IV has a melt point of 82°F, BETA PRIME
> FORM V has a melt point of 93°F, BETA ONE
> FORM VI has a melt point of 97.2°F, BETA TWO
>
> Contraction rates are different.
> Appearances are different at a given temperature.
>
> **Figure 4**   (From Willie & Lutton)

Let's talk more about Forms II, IV and V. For the sake of simplification and because the melt points of III and IV are close together, we'll ignore Form III.

Figure 5 shows crystallization and melting ranges for the cocoa butter crystal types. This heavily used chart is by Vaeck, with some of the melting points modified later by Willie and Lutton.

Let us see what we can deduce from Vaeck's chart.

First, Vaeck shows in a step fashion the progression of the different crystal forms toward the stable Form V. Note how the crystallization and melt point of the crystal forms increase as we proceed up the steps.

I want to caution you that these temperatures are to a specific cocoa butter (no milk fat being present), so these temperatures would be modified when either any changes in the natural chemistry of the cocoa butter occurred or if any amount of dairy butterfat were present in the chocolate.

Cocoa Butter Crystal Types

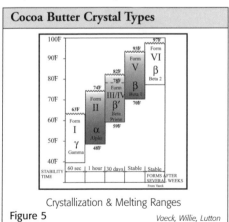

Crystallization & Melting Ranges

Figure 5   Vaeck, Willie, Lutton

Form I

Assume that the cocoa butter is melted to 130°F, then cooled to the various temperatures listed for each of the crystal forms.

The gamma (Form I) on the left of the chart forms between 39° to 60°F and melts out at about 63°F, but lasts only about a minute before changing up to Form II. We can, for practical purposes, forget about Form I except to say that if we did form some Form I crystals because of low-temperature cooling, these Form I crystals would accelerate the nucleation of Form II. Similarly, Vaeck shows the progress of the formation and melting ranges of the other different crystal forms until we get to Form VI.

Form II

As Figure 5 indicates, Form II forms between 48° to 72°F. The Form II chairs are beginning to stack together, albeit in a loosely stacked formation (Figure 6). When a stack of two chairs is formed, they are able to bond with another two-pack to form platelets and, once these platelets are of sufficient size, form the Form II crystal shape.

Since the chairs are only loosely stacked, they are easily melted at temperatures greater than 74°F. So they don't last that long in our chocolate, providing that there aren't too many of them to melt out. The fact that they existed at all aids in the growth of the next higher stable form, Form IV, the ubiquitous and very damaging beta prime crystal shape.

Form IV

In Figure 7 you can see that the chairs are stacked even closer together than the Form II, bestowing the Form IV with a higher melting point of about 82° to 83°F, which, since it is very close to our enrobing temperatures, makes it more difficult to eliminate.

Form IV can form from the Form II crystal shape or by itself at temperatures of about 73°/74° to 80°F, which is well within the range of the cooling medium that we use to quickly temper the chocolate. And, let's not forget the cooling air used to set the chocolate.

Form V

We now come to the desired Form V beta crystal shape (Figure 8). You will note that the two chairs are stacked even closer together, but in reality the Form V shape is three chairs stacked together

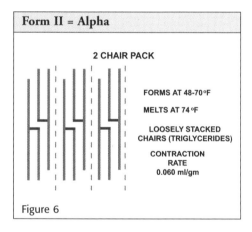

Form II = Alpha

2 CHAIR PACK

FORMS AT 48-70 °F

MELTS AT 74 °F

LOOSELY STACKED CHAIRS (TRIGLYCERIDES)

CONTRACTION RATE 0.060 ml/gm

Figure 6

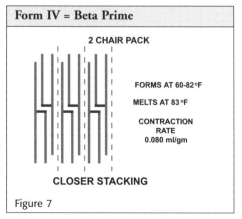

Form IV = Beta Prime

2 CHAIR PACK

FORMS AT 60-82 °F

MELTS AT 83 °F

CONTRACTION RATE 0.080 ml/gm

CLOSER STACKING

Figure 7

(Figure 9). There is a bending of the chair in the number two position which allows for an even closer stacking than the two-chair stacks found in the Form II and IV crystal shapes. This confers an even higher melting point to the Form V crystal.

Vaeck indicates that Form V forms out of IV (Figure 10) or it can form by itself between about 83° to 91°F (Figure 11), albeit very slowly since no prior Form IV crystals would be present to initiate the Form V crystallization.

For this discussion on tempering, we will not concern ourselves with the highest stable crystal shape, Form VI (since this can form only much later during the aging of the chocolate), except to say it has an even higher melting point than Form V, about 97.5°F.

Note also that the contraction rate is

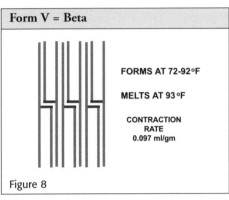

Figure 8

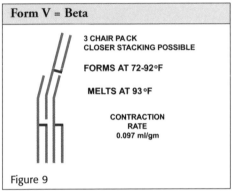

Figure 9

greater as we progress from Form II to V. This factor is very important for the demoulding process of moulded chocolates.

TEMPERING

Now we come to the actual process of tempering the chocolate. As indicated earlier, because of the complexity of the natural cocoa butter and milk fat, the process of tem-

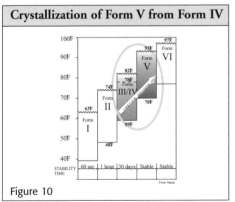

Figure 10

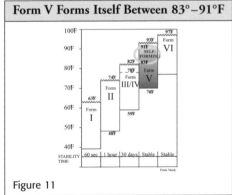

Figure 11

pering is a little artsy. It is because we generally use the same chocolate day in and day out, only changing from milk to dark, that we are able to get some process control over the manual tempering process.

The following tempering variables then make the process of tempering artsy:

- Fat composition in cocoa butter.
- Amount of fat in chocolate.
- Amount and composition of dairy butter in formula.
- Whether it is "bound" or free.
- Temperature of cooling medium.
- Speed of agitation.
- Residence time on reheat cycle.
- Method of tempering.
- Machine design.
- Method of hand-tempering.
- Mush, traditional or adding seed.
- Particle size and amount of solid ingredients in the chocolate.
- Amount of residual seed before tempering.
- Age of chocolate (Form VI crystals) before tempering.

If you are looking for specific temperatures for chocolate tempering, you are in the wrong place. But (as Ed Seguine has said), when we temper chocolate we are aiming for the largest number of the smallest possible crystals and of the Form V beta crystal form.

There are dozens of ways that we can achieve these goals, but usually we wish to do this in the fastest and most convenient possible way. Hence, we have to make our first "mistake" by supercooling the chocolate; that is, reducing the temperature of the chocolate to a point where it is almost set up and encouraging the nucleation of unstable crystal Forms II and IV.

Tempering Profile of Milk Chocolate

The first consideration for tempering chocolate is whether it is milk or dark chocolate.

We need to melt block milk chocolate to at least 125°F (for most common enrobing milks) and at least 130°F for dark chocolate, then hold it for at least 60 minutes, but preferably overnight, to ensure that all of the fat crystals have been melted. Follow your chocolate manufacturer's recommendations.

Using chocolate in the liquid form directly from your supplier means that you can start at a lower temperature since the chocolate would have been processed above 125°F and constantly held at elevated temperatures, certainly above crystal-forming temperatures.

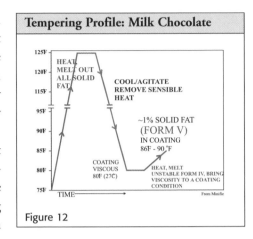

Figure 12

Having melted out all of the solid fat crystals, begin the cooling and crystallization cycle (Figure 12). To accelerate the cooling cycle we would use a cooling medium temperature anywhere between 40°F (machine) to 70°F (hand).

At first, sensible heat is removed until we come within the temperature range at which the fat can start to crystallize, about 92°F for Form V only.

We continue to drop the temperature down to about 83°F for dark and 80° to 81°F for milk to induce more fat to crystallize. Because of the low temperature of the cooling medium, we now would have produced unstable Form IV crystals too. This is okay because Form IV aids in the formation of Form V crystal.

The viscosity at this point is relatively high, too high for coating, so we increase the temperature, not only to increase the liquidity of the chocolate, but also to melt out any Form II and IV unstable crystal forms.

We now should have about 1 percent of the stable Form V crystals in our coating chocolate, which on proper cooling will allow the remaining liquid cocoa butter that will crystallize at these conditions to line up in the correct Form V crystal shape.

Here it might be instructive to draw an analogy between the crystallization of sugar from a supersaturated sugar solution to make fondant and the crystallization of solid fat from the liquid mass.

Having put the correct amount of sugar in solution during the heating of our basic fondant syrup, we cool the sugar solution to a temperature at which the sugar becomes supersaturated and will crystallize out with a fine crystal if it is agitated vigorously, or a coarse crystal if no or slow agitation takes place.

And so, too, with our fat system in the chocolate.

You will note in Figure 13 that at 125°F for a regular milk chocolate we have 0 percent solid milk fat crystals. As we cool the chocolate mass down, we then reach temperatures at which solid fat crystals can form (so, like our fondant syrup with sucrose molecules, the chocolate becomes supersaturated at lower temperatures with fat molecules that are ready to nucleate and form crystals).

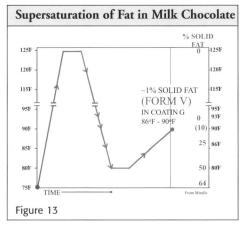

Supersaturation of Fat in Milk Chocolate

Figure 13

You will see from Figure 13 that on the right side I have entered in a percentage of solid fat in the milk chocolate at the temperatures which are critical to the tempering process.

This data was obtained on chocolates held at these various temperatures in a static condition for 48 hours before the analysis was done. And, under these conditions, higher solids will result compared to chocolate that was held, say, one hour during the tempering process. Unfortunately, I don't have any data for percent solid fat after one hour for the whole tempering range used in tempering; various researchers, however, have reported between 0.5 to 5 percent solid fat in chocolate held in a dynamic state at coating temperatures. For simplicity, we will assume the percent solid fat at 1 percent in the tempered coating.

Although the numbers may not br exactly correct, the concept is. As we reduce the temperature below about 93°F for milk chocolate, we come into the range of fat crystallization. At 90°F we have potentially 10 percent of the fat (static conditions, Minifie) that wants to crystallize but, as indicated, this is more likely to be about 1 percent (dynamic conditions).

As we drop the temperature down to, say, 80°F, the chocolate will then be very viscous and mushy with about 50 percent of the fat crystals present wanting to crystallize out of the liquid mass.

Chocolate is different than sugar in that during a forced cooling process (as Vaeck indicates in Figure 5), unknown quantities of the unstable Form II and IV crystals will certainly start to form.

We will be using 70°F water to cool the chocolate for our physical presentation and will, therefore, initiate a quick crystallization to the mass. But, as you can see from Figure 5, not only will the 70°F temperature produce Form IV crystals, it could also produce Form II.

This is one reason why we must raise the temperature to above 83°F to ensure that we have melted out all of the II and IV crystal forms.

Unfortunately, just raising the temperature up to 83°F will not necessarily completely melt out the unstable Form IV crystals. We need to hold and stir for a while to ensure that any unstable crystals are melted. (We call this *residence time*, and it is similar to stirring sugar into our coffee!) Fortunately, we are able to feel loose sugar crystals in the bottom of the coffee cup; unfortunately, we cannot see or feel unstable Form IV crystals being melted.

For manual tempering operations, part of the art is knowing when you have melted out the Form IV crystal form.

But then you might think, looking at Vaeck in Figures 5 and 11 again, if we just cool and agitate the dark chocolate to about 85°F, which is above the melt temperature for Form IV crystallization, we shouldn't have any Form IV crystals in our chocolate. This is not true if you force-cooled the chocolate and use any temperature below, say, 81°F to cool it. From Vaeck you can see that you would still form some IV, which have to be eliminated from the chocolate by reheating it and holding it above the melt temperature of 85°F for a period of time.

Let's arrange to hold the chocolate after first remelting to 125°F, and then let it naturally cool overnight to 85°F so no IV can form and the chocolate is ready to go straight into Form V on agitating (Figure 11).

This is okay and, in fact, was and still is a method used by enrober operators to put their machines in a tempered condition, but Form V crystals could start slowly forming overnight. Since they were left to crystallize on their own, the crystal size will be larger than one which was agitated from a force-cooled chocolate.

It is easier to form smaller crystals from a IV to V transformation by agitating a force-cooled mass than by crystallizing Form V from the slowly cooled mass.

Tempering Profile of Dark Chocolate

Our first tempering experiment (Figure 14) with a dark chocolate will be to heat the chocolate to 130°F; hold it for a period of time to ensure that all of the solid fat crystals are melted; then cool and agitate it in a double-jacketed kettle, using water at 70°F, to about 82° to 83°F until sufficient crystallization has taken place of both IV and V. Then raise the temperature to between 88° to 91°F; hold it for a few minutes to melt out the unstable Form IV crys-

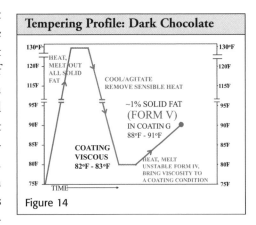

Tempering Profile: Dark Chocolate

HEAT, MELT OUT ALL SOLID FAT

COOL/AGITATE REMOVE SENSIBLE HEAT

~1% SOLID FAT (FORM V)

IN COATING 88°F - 91°F

COATING VISCOUS 82°F - 83°F

HEAT, MELT UNSTABLE FORM IV, BRING VISCOSITY TO A COATING CONDITION

TIME

Figure 14

tals; and check for degree of temper, both by tempermeters (to be discussed later) and physical examination.

To physically check for the degree of temper, we will be looking for the following:
• Will the chocolate hold a mark/string without the mark/string collapsing into the

chocolate? This is an indication of yield value or fat crystallization in the chocolate. It is accompanied by an increase in viscosity as the percentage of liquid fat is decreased.

• How quickly does it set under standard conditions of, say, 65°F under a moderate fan? I would expect a fairly good set within five minutes. Unfortunately, this is a subjective evaluation.

• How glossy and even is the surface appearance of the chocolate? It should have a reasonably good shine and no gray streaks.

• And finally, the snap takes much longer to evaluate, probably 30 to 45 minutes.

The second method that we are going to use is the mush method. This will be done on the milk chocolate.

This time the main mass of chocolate will be cooled from 125°F to between 92° to 94°F. At this temperature it will contain very few fat seed crystals, but, as previously mentioned in Figure 13, it is getting close to the temperature range when Form V crystals will begin to nucleate.

About 20 percent of the chocolate will then be removed at this point and "mushed" on a Formica board (or marble tabletop) at room temperature (72° to 76°F) until a thick, viscous paste results. The temperature of this paste is usually about 79°F and it will definitely contain unstable Form IV crystals.

This mush is then transferred back into the chocolate being held at 92° to 94°F. It is mixed in evenly for a few minutes. The temperature will now be about 88° to 90°F and should not contain any unstable Form IV crystals.

The product is evaluated for degree of temper as for the dark chocolate.

Another common method used by operators that don't have tempering machines is to seed untempered chocolate which is at 92° to 94°F with about 5 to 10 percent of tempered chocolate shavings that have been shaved away from well-tempered blocks of chocolate.

Since this pretempered chocolate contains only stable Form V crystals and the main mass of chocolate is about 92° to 94°F, this will be above the unstable IV melt temperature and only Form V crystals can be present in the chocolate. This works quite well, but, because of the relative slowness in effecting an overall crystal structure, it tends to give a coarse and duller-looking chocolate than the mush method.

We now have our temper seedbed in our chocolate.

Whatever method we use for manually tempering chocolate, we maintain the temper viscosity of the chocolate by adding unseeded chocolate that has been cooled from 125° to 130°F down to 92° to 94°F (dark) or 90° to 92°F (milk) at the same rate as chocolate is being drawn away from our tempered seedbed to coat the centers. The unseeded warm chocolate is being drip fed into the tempered bed—not the enrobing curtain—otherwise you will have hot streaks in your chocolate. This way the viscosity and degree of temper of the chocolate will stay quite constant and your percent chocolate pickup will be under control.

Remember that constantly agitating the chocolate enrobing temperatures will cause more crystallization of the fat, which will increase the viscosity of the chocolate and make it more difficult to work with.

We can either counteract this buildup of seed by gently warming the enrober (not a practice I recommend) or, as explained, by adding warm, unseeded chocolate in stream fashion.

Now we are coating our centers with our well-tempered chocolate. We have to cool the chocolate to set it up so that we can handle it at the packing station.

Remember that tempered chocolate at the enrober contains about 1 percent crystallized fat. Since milk chocolate will contain up to 70 percent solid fat when left to fully crystallize after about two days at 65°F, this means there is at least 69 percent of the fat that has to be set up in the correct stable crystal form, V.

Which brings us back to Vaeck (Figure 5) yet again. He says that cooling temperatures less than about 80°F are likely to encourage the formation of unstable IV. Worse still, temperatures less than about 73°F produce the Form II crystal form, but don't forget he is referring to straight 100 percent cocoa butter.

When a tempered chocolate starts to crystallize during the cooling process, changing from a liquid fat to a solid, latent heat is evolved which has the function of raising the temperature of our chocolate coating. So we need to blow or cool air to carry this heat away from our setting chocolate, otherwise the chocolate surface will be dull and blooming.

Since the major part of the setting or crystallization takes place in about the first three minutes of cooling, and as long as we don't use too low of an air or center tem-

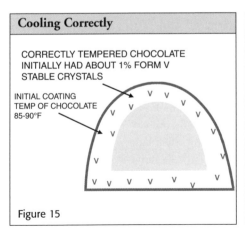

Cooling Correctly

CORRECTLY TEMPERED CHOCOLATE INITIALLY HAD ABOUT 1% FORM V STABLE CRYSTALS

INITIAL COATING TEMP OF CHOCOLATE 85-90°F

Figure 15

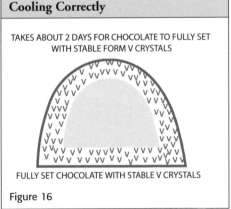

Cooling Correctly

TAKES ABOUT 2 DAYS FOR CHOCOLATE TO FULLY SET WITH STABLE FORM V CRYSTALS

FULLY SET CHOCOLATE WITH STABLE V CRYSTALS

Figure 16

perature, then the temperature of the cocoa butter should not be within the range for forming unstable Form IV or Form II crystals.

If the correct temperature profile of the chocolate is used during cooling, then only Form V crystals can form. If we use too cold of air temperatures at the beginning of the cooling, then more Form IV can form, which subsequently will cause bloom in our products.

See Figures 15–18 for pictorial representations of correct and incorrect cooling.

We should point out that if the center temperatures are also too low (below about 75°F), then again there is a danger that unstable IVs or maybe even Form II crystals will start to form in the setting chocolate, which will result in a dull appearance to the chocolate and will create the same shelf-life problem as illustrated in Figure 18.

TEMPERMETERS

We have been talking a lot about precrystallization or tempering of cocoa butter and the release of latent heat of crystallization.

When melted fats are cooled and agitated under controlled conditions (Figures 19 and 20), at first sensible heat is withdrawn from the mass and the temperature curve will show a steady decline in its shape. But as the fat changes from its liquid state into its crystallized solid form, latent heat is released, which causes a rise in temperature before falling off again as the amount of latent heat being released from the sample mass is less than the temperature of the surrounding conditions.

If we monitor this temperature drop against time, a cooling curve can be obtained that characterizes the fat or any precrystallization that has taken place within the fat. You will also note the lowest point that the temperature reaches (inflection point) before it starts to rise again to a maximum point (recalescence point) from the latent heat being evolved. Then the temperature again drops off.

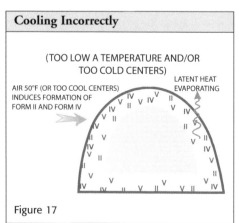

Figure 17

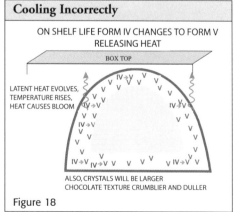

Figure 18

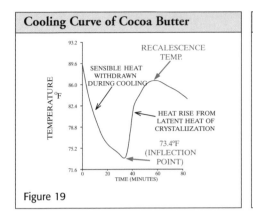

Cooling Curve of Cocoa Butter

Figure 19

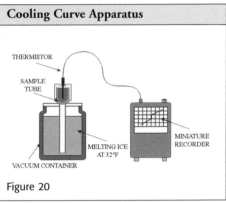

Cooling Curve Apparatus

Figure 20

When we temper chocolate we are altering the amount and type of crystallization of the fats in the mass to such a degree that when we determine the cooling curve, a differently shaped curve will result, depending on the initial amount of precrystallization (temper) in the chocolate.

Undertempered

For instance (Figure 21), if we have only a partially precrystallized chocolate, we would have fewer crystal nuclei and initially a slower crystallization rate; thus, consequently, a slower release of the latent heat of crystallization. The temperature drop will be faster than a chocolate that contains a higher amount of initial crystals.

The inflection temperature will be lower, the maximum temperature rise or recalescence point will be higher and the cooling curve might be something like Figure 21.

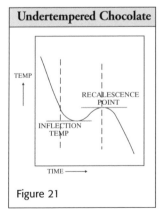

Undertempered Chocolate

Figure 21

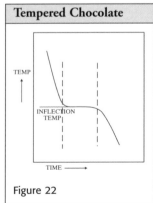

Tempered Chocolate

Figure 22

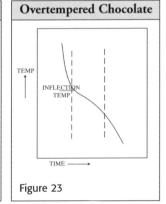

Overtempered Chocolate

Figure 23

Tempered

As we increase the amount of precrystallization or tempering (Figure 22), we will remove more latent heat during the tempering process. There will be less latent heat to remove during the measurement of our chocolate cooling curve, so the inflection point will be higher up the scale. The curve could look something like Figure 22 and may now show no recalescence point.

Overtempered

Finally, when we have a substantial amount of precrystallization initially in our chocolate (in fact, what we would characterize as being overtempered), the inflection point will be much higher than the well-tempered sample. Since the overtempered or highly precrystallized chocolate has the ability to initially seed off a much higher amount of the liquid fat, the latent heat comes off earlier during the determination of our cooling curve (Figure 23).

You can see that each curve and inflection point will be different for each degree of temper. These two data allow us to characterize the chocolate as under-, correct or overtempered.

You must appreciate that these curves are arbitrarily shaped and each tempermeter device functions differently and will show differently shaped curves for the same chocolate.

Tempering Methods

1. Traditional cooling from 130°F: Dark Chocolate.

Melt dark chocolate to 130°F and hold for at least 60 minutes.
Cool dark chocolate to about 82° to 83°F using 70°F water bath.
Agitate for about five minutes before raising temperature to 88° to 90°F.
Check temper.
Coat samples.

2. Mush Method: Milk Chocolate.

Cool chocolate from melt at 125°F to 92° to 94°F using 70°F water bath.
Take out about 20 percent and separately mush to a thick paste, matte-like appearance.
Return this mush to chocolate being held at 92° to 94°F.
Mix in until paste is completely dispersed. Adjust temperature to 86° to 88°F.
Check temper.
Coat samples.

A word of caution is that for each chocolate formulation you will get different inflection points. If, for instance, a formula contains a different amount of dairy butter oil, any amount will lower the inflection point due to the eutectic effect of mixing oils of different molecular shapes.

Different tempering machines will also alter the inflection point. Machines that have the ability to form a high amount of fine crystals will show higher inflection points than machines that give a coarse crystal, even though they both could show satisfactorily shaped curves.

A last word of caution is that the tempermeters are measuring the release of latent heat of crystallization under controlled cooling conditions. Even though they give a satisfactory cooling curve, this does not mean that the chocolate contains the stable Form V crystal form. You need X-ray diffraction for this. It is my recommendation that you use tempermeters in conjunction with a physical determination of the degree of temper.

Questions & Answers

Q: Conventional wisdom would indicate that the less stable crystal forms, alpha and gamma, can only exist at and below 62.6°F. It should follow that if the temperature does not fall below 62.6°F in the tempering process, then these forms cannot be created. Some tempering machines, particularly small units in use with stringers and decorating machines, use direct expansion Freon systems where the gas temperature can be as low as 22°F with a plate surface temperature of 30° to 34°F. Would this not preclude the creation of a good temper?

A: Not if the alpha and gamma crystal forms are subsequently melted out during the reheat/residence process. Remember that by forming crystals of a lower form, higher crystal forms are nucleated from these forms and the crystallization of the higher forms proceeds at a faster rate.

Q: Do (or should) different chocolate formulations have different tempermeter readings when good temper is achieved?

A: Yes, tempermeter readings, especially inflection points, are formulation specific.

Q: What is the best way of determining that you have the "right" crystal form in different formulations on the manufacturing line?

A: Look at how even the surface appearance is (no streaking) and how quickly the sample sets.

Q: You had mentioned that CTU or SLOPE does not tell you crystal type. Does that mean a zero slope could indicate a chocolate has a large number of unstable crystals? (Forms II, III, instead of Form V.)

A: We set up a tempering experiment essentially to trick a tempermeter to give a correctly tempered curve, yet for the chocolate to have a Form IV crystal appearance and feel.

We tempered (by the mush method) our seed at ambient conditions of 50°F, purposely inducing the formation of some Forms II, IV and V. This seeded portion was then added back to the melt at 94°F and mixed. A tempermeter recorded a perfect slope for temper, yet the set chocolate was duller and greasier to feel than chocolate tempered at 70° to 75°F (normal method).

Q: Is it true that finer chocolate tempers faster than coarser chocolate? (At constant composition viscosity will vary dramatically.)

A: I assume you mean finer crystallization. Yes, all else being equal, it will temper faster since there will be a higher amount of crystal surface area for the remaining oil that will potentially crystallize to crystallize on.

Q: What temper-measuring tool could you recommend that could tell us the quality of temper based on crystal type (polymorphic form), crystal size or even crystal population?

A: X-ray diffraction analysis.

Q: Please comment on the effect of lecithin on tempering chocolate.

A: Any dilution of cocoa butter with "foreign" fatty substances will have an inhibitory effect on the rate of crystallization.

Q: Under what condition do you achieve better contraction in moulding: overtemper or undertemper?

A: It depends on the degree of each.

Q: Even though the tempering process only produces 1 to 3 percent Form V seed crystals, why is there such a large increase in viscosity with such a small phase volume of crystals? What size are the tempered Form V seed crystals?

A: There is some confusion about the actual amount of solid fat seed crystals in the tempered chocolate. Some researchers report the amount of fat at 1 to 3 percent of the fat phase, some say 1 to 3 percent of the coating is in the crystal form. Let's assume that the tempered coating has 3 percent of the fat phase in the stable crystal form, or 1 percent of the coating which has about 33 percent fat when the coating is tempered. The liquid fat content is reduced to about 32 percent and simultaneously there is an increase of 1 percent in the solid phase. These amounts are sufficient to cause viscosity differences observed during the tempering process.

Sugar Crystallization

Sugar Crystals

An Introduction

Walter Vink
Vink Associates, Inc.

Sugar is purchased in many forms but primarily by particle size. For the most part that particle size is achieved through crystallization. Figure 1 shows three typical sizes of sugar crystal.

Coarse Granulated

Coarse granulated (the least used in candy of the three sizes) is used where purity and color are of extreme importance to the finished product. The larger crystal size delivers these properties because the natural impurities, such as ash, are occluded on the surface of the crystal. Coarse granulated, with its smaller total surface area, contains less impurities than the same sugar in a smaller crystal. Coarse-granulated sugars are generally more expensive.

Fine Granulated

Fine granulated is the most commonly used because of lower price, ease of flow, rapid dissolving and syrup clarity.

Baker's Special

Baker's special is a very uniform, small crystal and is used where the size and crystal uniformity is important. The most important use of this sugar to the candymaker is in the production of soft sugar-panned goods such as jelly beans.

SUGAR AND CANDY TECHNOLOGY

We often describe candy technology as the art and science of controlling crystallization in confectionery. Our products are based on this. In chocolate we control the crystallization of cocoa butter. In sugar candy we control the crystallization

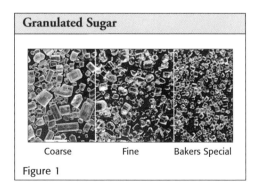

Granulated Sugar

Coarse   Fine   Bakers Special

Figure 1

of sucrose. In fudges and creams we control the size and amount of sugar crystals. In hard candy and caramels we prevent crystallization altogether. While this may seem to be an oversimplification, it is what we as candy technologists are about.

WHAT IS SUGAR?

Let's take a look at just what sugar is. Sugar has many definitions, some of which are quite useful, and at least one of which is politically expedient and makes little sense (that being the NLEA definition of sugar as only mono- and disaccharides). For the purposes of this paper we are talking about sucrose.

Just what is it about sugar that sets it apart from the other saccharides? Sucrose has the same empirical formula of other disaccharides, such as maltose and lactose. Yet we all know that there is a world of difference in the performance and functionality of these three examples. If we could remove all of the water from them, we would be left with the same pure carbon. So, what is it, structurally, that is responsible for the utility and taste of sucrose?

THE STRUCTURE OF SUGAR

Sucrose has two monosaccharides—dextrose and fructose—linked together by an ether linkage. We are all too familiar with the results of splitting this molecule into its two component parts—the process known as inversion.

Chemically the process is more correctly referred to as hydrolysis, but the term *inversion* has come to mean, specifically, the hydrolysis of sucrose. Inversion occurs when sucrose is hydrolyzed the specific rotation goes from a positive number, + 66.5, to a minus number, -19.5. In other words, the optical rotation, as observed in a polarimeter, is inverted. There was a time when polarimetry was used as the standard for measuring sugar quality and composition, with its own set of standards and a special polarimeter equipped with a sugar scale called a saccharimeter.

The unique structure of sucrose is also responsible for its characteristics of solubility, sweetness and flavor retention. What separates sugar from other common disaccharides is the fructose end of the molecule. The fructose end, with its five-member ring, is the reason sucrose, unlike maltose and lactose, is not a reducing sugar. This is also why sucrose is relatively nonhygroscopic in its crystalline form, while its component parts are very hygroscopic. For example, crystalline sugar has an equilibrium relative humidity (ERH) of about 88 percent, while dextrose monohydrate has an ERH of about 35 percent and crystalline fructose considerably below that. This is the reason grained confections require some kind of humectant to prevent drying out.

One of the best, and earliest, studies on the structure of the sucrose crystal was conducted by Brown and Levy in 1963, using neutron diffraction. The key elements of the study were the findings that all but one of the hydroxyl groups were involved in hydrogen bonding and that two of these bonds were intramolecular (inside the molecule) and the remainder intermolecular (between molecules).

It is important to note that hydrogen bonding is at the heart of how sugar can be manipulated to make the wide variety of candies that we manufacture. By mixing sucrose with other carbohydrates, we can prevent crystals from forming or we can control the speed and extent to which crystals do form. Another factor which is often overlooked is that the hydrogen bonds between the hydroxyl groups and other sources of oxygen are probably at the heart of why sugar retains flavors. Most of the flavoring components are aldehydes or ketones, or contain hydroxyl groups of their own, so it doesn't take a very large stretch of the imagination to see that these compounds would also be attracted to sugar, possibly resulting in the wide variety of flavorings that can be achieved in candy. In fact, there has been considerable research on why sugar both binds and potentiates flavor.

As mentioned earlier, Levy and Bown determined that one of the hydroxyl groups is not involved in the single crystal formation. Further research by Vavrinecz showed that this hydroxyl group was involved in the formation of twin crystals and that there are three types of twin crystals. By using lucite models we can picture the three types (Figure 2). The importance of twins to us as candymakers is that they are found in poorer-quality sugars and tend to retain impurities by occluding them in the interface between the crystals. They are also formed from highly supersaturated solutions which promote rapid nucleation and large crystal growth. If twins form during fondant manufacture, the fondant will be coarse in texture.

Besides twins, there is a fourth type of crystal known as a conglomerate. It is a large irregular-shaped double crystal and, like twins, is present in poorer-quality sugars. As with twins, the conditions which promote conglomerates are high supersaturation and rapid crystal

Sugar Twin Crystal

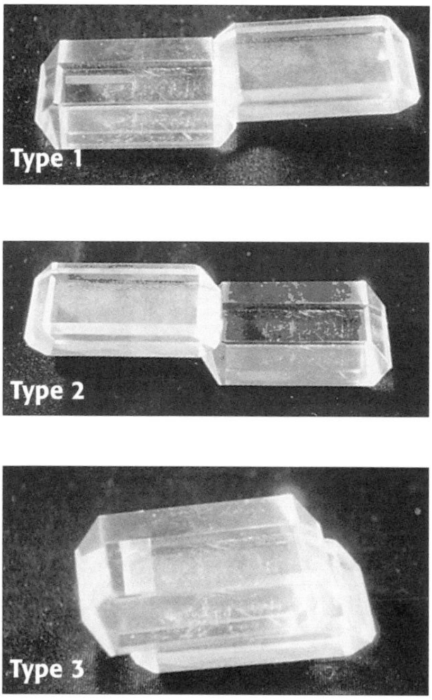

Type 1

Type 2

Type 3

Figure 2

growth. Poorly made fondant from highly supersaturated syrup can have a coarse texture which suggests the formation of conglomerates (Figure 3).

Sugar Conglomerate

Figure 3

The mechanism of sugar crystallization has been covered by many in the literature and we will not spend time on this other than to look at some of the reasons why sucrose is so easy to use in our processing. There are three key items necessary for crystallization:

• Supersaturated solution

• Syrup viscosity sufficiently low to permit crystal growth

• Source of seed (nucleation or added)

SUPERSATURATED SOLUTION

First, let's take a look at the solubility of sugar. In the range of temperatures normally encountered, sugar has a solubility ranging from 64 to 72 percent. Under most normal conditions, the standard sugar solubility is 67 percent solids. If we go much beyond 70 percent solids, we have a syrup which quickly becomes supersaturated and will begin to crystallize at room temperature (Figure 4).

Solubility of Sugar

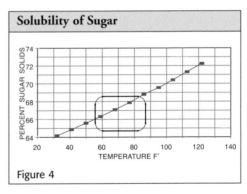

Figure 4

Second, if we look at the boiling point of sugar syrups, we see that concentrations as high as 90 percent can be achieved at temperatures which cause very little color formation and, depending upon the acidity of the solution, very little inversion (Figure 5). This allows the candymaker a processing range which permits controlled crystallization.

Boiling Point of Sugar Solutions

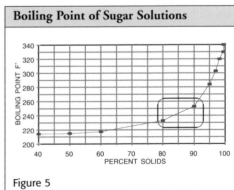

Figure 5

Syrup Viscosity

The beauty of sugar is that once the syrup becomes supersaturated, the viscosity is low enough over the range of solids to permit crystallization, provided sufficient seed is present. Consider pure sugar hard candy: it appears to have a high viscosity at room temperature yet it has a very short shelf life, measured in days. The candy viscosity is low enough to permit dry graining due to the seed generated in the process of tempering to cool the candy.

A Source of Seed

A 70 percent sugar solution will begin to crystallize when merely sitting out exposed to the atmosphere at 70°F, simply because there are dust particles in the air which can settle on the syrup surface and cause nucleation. In most candy processes we do not leave crystallization to such chance and happenstance. We deliberately manipulate the syrup to form the desired degree of crystallization by beating it or adding a seed source.

Production of Crystallized Sugar Candies

By adding other carbohydrates, such as corn syrup and invert sugar, we can change the viscosity and degree of supersaturation. By doing this we can control the size, quality and degree of crystallization. A wide variety of fondants can be produced, which can be extruded, rolled or cast without difficulty. All that is needed is the proper seeding, either by agitating or direct addition of seed crystals.

For further reading on the subject, obtain a copy of *Sucrose, Properties and Applications*, M. Mathlouthi and P. Reiser, published by Blackie Academic and Professional.

REFERENCES

Brown, G.M. and H.A. Levy. Sucrose: Precise Determination of Crystal and Molecular Structure by Neutron Diffraction. *Science* 141: 921–923, 1963.

Vavrinecz, G. *Atlas of Sugar Crystals*. Verlag. Dr. A. Bartens, Berlin, Germany, 1965.

Questions & Answers

Q: *Why is baker's sugar mostly used in panning and not baking?*

A: I cannot speak for the baking industry, but the use in panning is related to the uniformity of crystal size and the small crystal size. Baker's special is about as fine a sugar size as can be achieved by crystallization. Finer sugars are made by grinding, such as 6X and 10X confectioners sugars. The ground sugars are prone to lumping and, in some applications, are difficult to use. In soft panning, such as jelly beans, the baker's special results in the desired shell structure, whereas a 6X or 10X would tend to dry out, resulting in a crunchy shell.

Some sugar suppliers sell a "fruit" sugar grade which has similar properties to baker's special.

Q: *What is the best choice for invert sugars in a glucose/sucrose hard candy?*

A: Both invert sugar and a high fructose 45 can be used, as well as honey. The key is to control the final reducing sugars of the candy to less than 20 percent (dry solids basis) in order to control the hygroscopicity of the candy. This includes the reducing sugars contributed by the corn syrup.

Q: *What is the shelf life of the sugar/honey confection?*

A: The shelf life of the sugar/honey candy will depend on how the product is packaged. It will be slightly more hygroscopic than a comparable sugar/corn syrup candy. A good moisture barrier package can keep the candy in excellent condition for up to a year. Sugar sanding can also keep the candy for up to a year by establishing an artificial layer of nonhygroscopic sugar grain.

Unprotected in a candy dish the product will last 1 to 3 months depending on the ambient humidity.

Basics of Grained and Ungrained Confections

Maurice Jeffery
Jeffery Associates

Confectionery can be broken down into two basic types: fat-based confections and syrup-based confections.

FAT-BASED CONFECTIONS

In fat-based confections, the glue that holds the confection together is fat. Bound together by the fat is a whole variety of ingredients, including sugar. These are technically called fat-phase confections. In order to understand the technology of these products, it is important to understand the properties of the fat (its melting characteristics, mouthfeel, etc.), the nature of the particles mixed into it and its contribution to taste, texture and the rheology of the confection.

Chocolate is the most important example of this type of confection and a major part of our industry. Compound coatings and nut pastes, such as peanut butter, are also fat-based confections, some examples of which are shown in Figure 1.

SYRUP-BASED CONFECTIONS

Syrup-based confections range from hard candy to soft marshmallows. In these confections, syrup is the glue which holds the confection together, i.e., they are all syrup-phase confections. The structure, composition and properties of the syrup have to be understood when dealing with the technology of syrup-based confections. The interaction between particles, particularly sugar crystals, dispersed through the syrup and the effect they have on the texture, structure and rheological properties of grained confections are the main topics.

Examples of Fat-based Confections

Figure 1

Whereas fat-based confections are relatively narrow in their type, syrup-based ones have many variables. This leads to the enormous range of delicious confections and confectionery centers covered in chocolate that is the basis of our industry. Until relatively recently, the main ingredient has always been sugar—the traditional sweetener and bulking ingredient. Sugar replacers and intense sweeteners have now extended the range of sugarfree confections.

Structure of Syrup-based Confections

Honey is the simplest and earliest confection known to humans. It is nature's invert sugar, consisting mainly of two simple sugars, dextrose (sometimes called glucose) and fructose (fruit sugar), dissolved in water to form the familiar, deliciously sweet syrup.

Honey is normally a clear liquid with a pale amber color, but it sometimes becomes opaque. It changes in character from a free-flowing liquid to a paste, sometimes called honey butter. The least soluble of the sugars in honey butter, dextrose, has crystallized because its solubility in water is only 48 percent at 70°F, compared with fructose (79.3% at 70°F), and the syrup is said to have grained. The dextrose crystals reflect light, so that the syrup becomes opaque. They also have a large surface area which has to be lubricated by the remaining syrup still holding the structure together, so that the grained product does not readily flow.

There are fundamental differences between syrup-based confections with uncrystallized syrup holding or gluing the confection together and those in which one or more of the ingredients dissolved in the syrup have crystallized, changing its character in several ways. This simple example demonstrates clearly the change in physical character from a thermoplastic material that will flow to one with internal friction between crystallized particles that inhibits flow.

Honey butter is the earliest example of a fondant—a dextrose fondant. We will be examining sugar versions of this and discussing the technology of fondants and cremes, examples of which are shown in Figure 2.

We can also change the character of a syrup by taking some of the water out of it. As we do so, it becomes more and more viscous. Finally, when we

Examples of Fondants and Cremes

Figure 2

reduce the water below 3 to 4 percent, the syrup becomes so viscous that when it is cooled it forms a glass-like product, forming the basis of the hard candy section of our industry. In hard candy, the viscosity of the syrup is so high that the sugar molecules in it cannot come together to form crystals, and it has thermoplastic characteristics—glass-like when cold and softening when warmed. If we warm it enough to agitate or mix it, some sugar microcrystallization can take place, and we use this in pulled-sugar products to change the texture and appearance of the hard candy, examples of which are shown in Figure 3.

If we take a simple syrup, add air and a protein material—a whipping agent—to help air mix into it, numerous small bubbles are formed, which weaken the syrup glue. Its density is also decreased and at the same time it becomes opaque, because the air bubbles reflect light. This gives us marshmallow confections. We can also cause some of the sugar in the syrup to crystallize, further weakening the syrup and changing its texture, producing grained marshmallows, examples of which are shown in Figure 4.

We can also take this whipped syrup, uncrystallized or crystallized, add fat and flavoring ingredients (such as cocoa powder) to produce the ever-popular nougats or nougatines. These vary in texture from hard torrone to the soft nougats that make up a major part of bar lines—*Snickers, Milky Way, Baby Ruth* and many

Examples of Hard Candy

Figure 3

Examples of Marshmallows

Figure 4

other products, as shown in Figure 5.

When we add milk to the syrup and cook it, characteristic flavors are produced. Milk protein and reducing sugars (such as dextrose, maltose or fructose), along with the sugar in the milk (lactose), react together via the Maillard reaction to produce the flavor of caramel confections.

When the syrup is made to crystallize to break up its structure, the texture becomes short and less chewy, leading to the whole range of fudges. Their texture varies with the amount of crystallization of the syrup, ranging from a grained caramel with sufficient crystallization to give the product good standup properties and machinability, to heavily grained hard fudge. Examples of caramel and fudge products are shown in Figure 6.

Finally, if we add a gelling agent (such as gelatin, starch, pectin, etc.) the syrup is changed from one that flows to one that is immobilized in a gel structure. The resulting texture depends mainly on the gelling agent used.

The molecules of sugar are effectively locked in place and cannot move around freely or come together to crystallize. These jellies remain uncrystallized gelatinized syrups and not grained ones. This produces the wide range of jelly confections which are another major part of our business, examples of which are shown in Figure 7.

Faced with this wide variety of syrup-based confections, it is important to pick

Examples of Nougats and Taffy

Figure 5

Examples of Caramels and Fudges

Figure 6

out items which are common to all of them before exploring the technology of those in which sugar crystals break up the syrup glue that binds their structures together.

Common Features

Syrup-based confections all contain

Examples of Jellies

Figure 7

water. For the same recipe, the higher the water content, the softer the confection. Controlling the water content in finished products, both in their manufacture and on their way to the consumer, is essential for consistent quality. This requires that we properly formulate, process, protectively pack and distribute to achieve this goal.

For a normal shelf life of 6 to 9 months, these products must have an equilibrium relative humidity of less than 65 percent. This translates into a water activity of below 0.65. Water activity is a measure of how available the water is to bacteria, yeasts and molds to allow them to be active and propagate. It can be measured by a water activity meter. Pure water has a water activity of 1, but as we dissolve other materials in it (such as sugar, invert sugar and particularly small molecules of such things as salt) the availability is reduced or locked up and the water activity falls. We cannot put enough salt into a confection without making it inedible to get down to 0.65, so we have to rely on sugar, corn syrup and other materials (such as sorbitol, fructose, etc.) dissolved in the water to reduce the water activity down to a safe level. To do this, a total of at least 76 to 78 percent of these materials must be dissolved in the water (the soluble solids) to form the syrup which binds the confection together.

Water activity is often confused with moisture content and total solids in the confection, but it is only those solids which are dissolved in the water that reduce water activity.

This is why it is important to know the solubility of sugar (68% at 70°F), fructose (79.3% at 70°F) and corn syrup solids (82% at 70°F generally) in formulating stable confections. As you can see, it is not possible to produce a shelf-stable syrup-based confection from sugar alone. This is why we generally use corn syrup and other more soluble sugars in confectionery recipes.

This is very important to understand as we move on to confections where we deliberately make sugar crystallize from the syrup binding the confections together, reducing its soluble solids. We must formulate the recipes to end up with sufficient soluble solids left in the water, after crystallization has taken place, to keep the water activity below 0.65, to produce a stable, grained confection.

CRYSTALLIZATION OF SYRUPS

Before reviewing specific ungrained and grained confections and their recipes and manufacturing processes, it is important to examine the key factors that affect the crystallization of syrups.

Concentration

The concentration of each of the ingredients in the syrup and its solubility in water at room temperature must be known. If any of them are more concentrated than their solubility, they potentially can crystallize to precipitate the excess, leaving the syrup saturated with the ingredient. Although the ingredient potentially can crystallize, it may not if its molecules cannot come together to form crystals because, for instance, a gelling agent prevents them from moving, or some of the other factors listed below are having a similar effect.

The situation is complicated by the interactions between all of the ingredients, all competing for the water in the syrup. Thus it is their mixed solubility which is important to know in evaluating their ability to crystallize.

For most of the grained confections we will discuss, sugar is the ingredient which crystallizes from the syrup binding the confection together, leaving up to 68 percent sugar, at room temperature, still in solution to help stabilize the product.

Viscosity of the Syrup

Gelling agents effectively immobilize the sugar molecules in jellies and prevent sugar crystallization from taking place. Other ingredients, particularly the long-chain dextrins in corn syrup, increase the viscosity of a syrup. The higher their concentration, the more viscous the syrup becomes and the more difficult it is for crystallization to take place.

The extreme effect of viscosity is shown in hard candy where the moisture content is so low (2% to 3%) that the sugar in the recipe should crystallize, but the viscosity of the sugar glass is so high that it cannot.

However, when standard hard candy is left unwrapped, it picks up moisture from the atmosphere. The syrup formed on the surface is lower in viscosity and sugar crystals can form to give a grained skin on the product. If the dextrin content of the recipe is high enough by using, for instance, a recipe with 50 percent low 36 DE corn syrup in it, surface graining may not take place but the surface gets sticky.

Viscosity is also affected by temperature. It increases as the temperature is lowered. If products are stored in cold rooms or in freezers, crystallization can be inhibited even though the solubility of sugar is reduced as the temperature is lowered. It is like goldfish in a fishbowl. When the water is at room temperature, the fish can swim around happily and collect together, but when the bowl is put in a freezer, the fish are locked in ice and cannot move. Thinking of the sugar molecules in a syrup as the fish, one can visualize the effect of temperature on crystallization.

Seeding of the Syrup

Crystallization is made easier when the sugar molecules are given a pattern to follow in forming crystals. If sugar crystals are mixed into the syrup, crystallization is initiated. The more that are added, the greater the chance of graining taking place. This is similar to seeding chocolate by tempering to provide a pattern for cocoa butter to crystallize. Seeding with fine sugar crystals, in the form of fondant, is an important part of grained-confections technology.

Mixing

Crystallization of a syrup is helped considerably by agitation or mixing it to assist the sugar molecules to come together to form crystals. Generally, the more vigorous the mixing, the faster the syrup will grain and the smaller the sugar crystals which form. Slow crystallization generally produces large crystals.

Cooling and Temperature

When sugar crystallizes from a syrup it gives out heat. If this is not removed by cooling, the syrup temperature will rise, affecting the crystal size and amount of crystals formed. Generally, the higher the crystallization temperature the larger the sugar crystals which are formed.

This leads us to specific grained confections, which hopefully will reinforce these general factors.

FONDANTS AND CREMES

Fondants are the simplest of grained confections. They are normally based on sugar, although sugarfree fondants based on maltitol or other polyols are being made. Their structure consists of sugar crystals dispersed in a saturated solution of sugar and other carbohydrates such as invert sugar and corn syrup.

Those other carbohydrates are sometimes essential to the shelf stability of the product. Normally there is 50 to 60 percent sugar crystals dispersed in 40 to 50 percent syrup.

Fondant recipes consist of three main ingredients: sugar, water and corn syrup. These are combined with other ingredients such as invert sugar, fructose, sorbitol and glycerol. Sometimes mold-inhibiting chemicals, such as sorbic acid, are added where a formulation gives a product with a water activity greater than 0.65. You can avoid this by using the correct formulation, if possible.

Moisture Content

The water content of the finished fondant is the most critical variable, because it affects the efficiency of using it, and its shelf life. Generally water content is in the range of 12 to 15 percent but should be controlled accurately, i.e., within ± ½ percent of that specified.

Type of Corn Syrup

Corn syrups now cover a wide range of compositions. The major components are dextrose, maltose and dextrins—mainly consisting of long molecular chains of dextrose.

The quantity of dextrose plus maltose on a dry solids basis is expressed as dextrose equivalent (DE). Now that enzymes are also used to produce corn syrup, it is possible to change the ratio of dextrose to maltose and achieve higher DE. High-maltose and high-dextrose corn syrups can also be produced. In addition, it is possible to produce high-fructose syrups, which are sweeter. These are increasingly used in confectionery, although mainly in the beverage industry.

High-DE syrups have fewer dextrins in them; they are particularly important in fondants because they affect the viscosity and the crystallization of sugar from the fondant syrup. Low-DE corn syrups lead to more viscous fondant syrups with slower crystallization of sugar from them, and high-DE corn syrups do the opposite. The choice of corn syrup therefore is a very important variable.

Amount of Sugar

The sugar content of the recipe, which increases the ratio of sugar to corn syrup, is a key variable. The higher the sugar content the more sugar crystals are formed and the harder the fondant, for a given water content.

Amount of Other Materials

The quantities of humectants, such as sorbitol, glycerol and invert sugar, are also important. They reduce the viscosity of the fondant syrup, increase sugar crystallization rates and lower water activity.

Commercially available fondants are generally made to simple recipes, using sugar, water and 42 DE acid-converted corn syrup. They are often referred to by the ratio of sugar to corn syrup, e.g., 8:1 fondant contains eight parts of sugar and one part of corn syrup. The soluble solids of the syrup in the finished product are below 75 percent. Because this recipe is unstable, a small quantity of sorbic acid or potassium sorbate is added to inhibit mold growth. The higher the sugar content of fondant, the higher the water activity, with the greater danger of mold growth and yeast fermentation. This is why black spots of mold are sometimes found on the surface and inside high-sugar fondants. This will not happen with a 3:2 fondant using standard 42 DE corn syrup. There are many ways of eliminating this using the newer corn syrups and incorporating ingredients that lower water activity, such as sorbitol or glycerol.

Making Fondant

Making fondant can be broken down into a number of steps as shown in Figure 8.

Essentially, the cooking temperature controls the final moisture content of the fondant and must be controlled accurately, including compensating for the effect of atmospheric pressure on the cooking temperature, cooking higher on dry days when the pressure is high and lower on wet days when the pressure is low.

Figure 9 shows a typical cooking-temperature compensation chart for a sugar syrup, indicating the cooking temperature required for a specific water content.

The crystallization temperature and the mixing or shear rate control the size distribution of the sugar crystals. In general, the higher the syrup temperature when it is mixed to cause sugar to crystallize, the larger the crystals produced. Generally, also, the faster the syrup is mixed, the smaller the crystals.

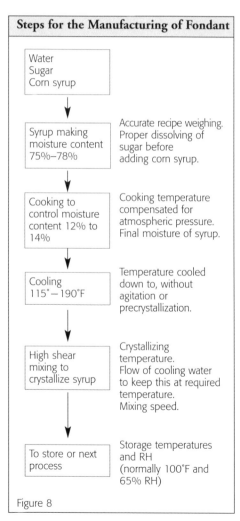

Steps for the Manufacturing of Fondant

Water
Sugar
Corn syrup

↓

Syrup making moisture content 75%–78%

Accurate recipe weighing. Proper dissolving of sugar before adding corn syrup.

↓

Cooking to control moisture content 12% to 14%

Cooking temperature compensated for atmospheric pressure. Final moisture of syrup.

↓

Cooling 115°–190°F

Temperature cooled down to, without agitation or precrystallization.

↓

High shear mixing to crystallize syrup

Crystallizing temperature. Flow of cooling water to keep this at required temperature. Mixing speed.

↓

To store or next process

Storage temperatures and RH (normally 100°F and 65% RH)

Figure 8

Barometric Pressure						
in inches						
Moisture Content	29.42°F	29.67°F	29.92°F	30.17°F	30.42°F	30.67°F	30.92°F
14.0%	236.5	236.8	237.2	237.6	238.2	238.5	239.0
13.0%	238.8	239.1	239.5	240.0	240.5	240.8	241.3
12.0%	240.8	241.2	241.5	242.0	242.4	242.8	243.4
11.0%	243.1	243.5	244.0	244.4	244.8	245.8	246.2
10.0%	245.8	246.2	246.6	247.0	247.5	248.0	248.5
9.0%	248.6	249.0	249.5	250.0	250.5	251.0	251.4
8.5%	250.1	250.5	251.0	251.5	251.9	252.4	252.8

Figure 9

When you make fondant either by hand or by machine, there is not just one size of sugar crystal produced but a whole range.

The sugar crystals, in addition to sweetness, contribute texture and surface area, which considerably govern the viscosity of the fondant and affect its use. The human palette can only detect particles greater in size than 12 to 16 microns. Below this all particles taste smooth, like water. Bigger particles control the detectable texture of the product. When they reach 50 microns and above, they start to become sandy and too coarse to be pleasant. Generally, fondants intended for very smooth cremes have sugar crystals below 12 microns. For some applications where coarser textures are desired they range up to 40 to 50 microns.

Whatever texture is required, it is important to get a consistent particle size distribution because it affects the viscosity of the fondant. When it is used for starch and starchless moulding, particularly single-shot depositing, viscosity control is critical. Sugar particle size also affects the setting rate of the deposited fondant or cremes in which it is used. This is particularly important in starchless moulded products where setting times, ready for demoulding, are 10 to 15 minutes, instead of the hours available in starch moulding.

Controlling particle size distribution requires the following:

• Accurate recipe control

• Accurate water content control

• Accurate control of crystallization temperature

• Consistent mixing speed/shear rate

To illustrate this, we are going to discuss fondant-making both by hand and by machine using three recipes, to illustrate the effect of recipe on crystallization rate and the effect of recipe on water activity. We will also show the effect of mixing rate on particle size distribution.

Commercial Equipment

Fondant can be made on a relatively small scale by batch methods using cooking kettles and cooled batch mixers to crystallize the syrup. The old ball beaters are still in operation doing this.

On a larger scale continuous methods are used, consisting basically of four parts:

- A recipe batching system to put together an uncooked 75 percent soluble solids syrup.
- A cooker to boil the syrup to the correct moisture content.
- A cooling drum or other means of cooling the syrup as a thin unagitated film to a controlled uniform temperature.
- A water-cooled mixer to vigorously mix the cooled syrup to crystallize it and remove the heat of crystallization given out as the sugar crystals are formed.

Accurate control of each stage for consistent product and efficient operation of this and subsequent processes is essential.

Uses of Fondant

Fondant is used in several ways:

- For making starch or starchless moulded units, often flavored with peppermint or fruit flavors and sugar crusted to give a glistening appearance.
- For making cremes, which are generally softer than fondants and used as centers for chocolate enrobing, or as fillings for shell-moulded or single-shot moulded products.
- To control the crystallization of other confections, such as fudge or nougat, by adding it to seed their graining.

Moulded Fondants

Moulded fondants vary in texture from crisp, hard ones used for coating in sugar crystals to softer ones coated in chocolate. The final soft texture is made by adding the enzyme invertase to the recipe.

Moulded fondants are made by reheating the base fondant to the required depositing temperature, generally 160° to 170°F, and adding a thinning syrup to adjust its viscosity. A typical recipe is shown in Figure 10.

The thinning syrup is similar in recipe to the fondant but has a higher moisture content, and often a humectant such as

Moulded Fondant Recipe	
Fondant (4:1)	60.0%
Thinning Syrup	39.5%
Color and flavor	0.5%
Thinning Syrup Recipe	
Sugar	70.0%
Corn Syrup (42 DE)	20.0%
Sorbitol (70% solution)	10.0%
Cooked to 84% soluble solids.	

Figure 10

sorbitol added to it. The temperature of the mix is finally adjusted to the depositing temperature. Color is mixed in before the fondant is deposited into starch or starch-less moulds. Starch-moulded fondants are left for 6 to 8 hours in a conditioned room to cool and set before demoulding.

Starchless moulding requires some adjustment of the recipe and depositing temperature to enable the fondant syrup to be cooled and set in 5 to 10 minutes to demould efficiently. Generally, the moisture content of the deposited fondant is 0.5 percent lower than that used in starch moulding because no loss in moisture takes place in the starchless mould, as it does in starch. The depositing temperature is also raised to 185° to 190°F to ensure rapid setting of the fondant induced by the higher supersaturation of sugar in the syrup at this higher temperature.

Often the hot thinning syrup is used to reheat the fondant by the so-called Hot Bob or Baker Clay process, the syrup being called the *bob syrup*. This old process is often adopted in modern, continuous high-output fondant and creme processes.

Cremes

Fondant forms the base for cremes, which are usually soft in texture and used as centers for chocolate products. For these a fondant with a 3:1 or 3:2 sugar-to-corn syrup ratio is typically used. The type of corn syrup chosen gives the final texture required in the creme. The thinning syrup has humectants such as invert sugar, sorbitol or glycerol added to it to prevent the creme from drying out in the final product.

An aerated or whipped syrup, often called a frappé, is also added to the mix to give the creme more whiteness and opaqueness for brighter colors when the coloring materials are added. The frappé also softens the texture of the final creme. A typical creme recipe is shown in Figure 11.

The final temperature adjustment in the recipe depends on the way the creme will be used, generally 170°F for starch moulding, 185°F for starchless moulding, 95°F for chocolate shell filling and 85° to 90°F for single-shot depositing, depending on whether it is used with milk or dark chocolate. Good depositing characteristics are essential to avoid tailing (which leads to moulded mis-shapes) and leakers in shell (particularly in single-shot units).

Extruded Cremes

Extrusion makes a grained product by an entirely different way from those in which sugar is crystallized from a supersaturated syrup.

In the extrusion process premade fine sugar crystals are mixed with a syrup or glue to form a paste suitable for extrusion. The sugar crystals are made by milling standard sugar to give particles in the range of 6 to 30 microns, and generally are supplied as dry fondant, containing eight parts of sugar and one part of dry corn syrup or dextrin solids.

The dry fondant is then mixed with sufficient syrup. Often this is just corn syrup and water, but generally also containing butter and/or vegetable fat to give a paste of the required consistency and moisture content. They are mixed at the correct extrusion temperature, 95° to 100°F. The enzyme invertase is added and mixed in thoroughly, followed by color and flavor. The paste is then extruded into ropes that are cut into the correct lengths by a wire or vibrating blade as the ropes leave the extruder nozzles. The units drop onto a plastic-coated canvas band which conveys them through a cooling tunnel and then onto a bottomer and enrober to be covered in chocolate. After 2 to 3 weeks, the invertase in the center breaks down the sugar to produce a soft, shelf-stable creme. A typical recipe for extruded cremes is shown in Figure 12.

As with most confections there are numerous recipes used, including those containing special starches, crystalline fructose and a whipping agent.

The role of invertase in fondant and creme technology has already been mentioned under moulded fondants and is essential in the manufacture of soft extruded ones. It is important that we understand how it works and what we have to do to ensure that it does work. Invertase is an enzyme that, under the right conditions, specifically breaks down sugar into its two simple sugars (dextrose and fructose), making available the very soluble fructose to dissolve in the syrup and increase its soluble solids to a stable 75 to 76 percent, lowering its water activity to below 0.65. When it is used in fondant, the amount of sugar crystals is reduced as the fructose goes into solution and the fondant softens to a creme texture.

Cream Recipe

Fondant (3:1)	54%
Frappé	10%
Thinning syrup	36%
Color and flavor as desired	

Frappé Recipe

Egg albumen (spray dried)	6%
Water	7%
Corn syrup (63 DE)	87%
Whipped to a density of 0.5.	

Thinning Syrup Recipe

Sugar	40%
Water	20%
Corn syrup (63 DE)	27%
Invert sugar	13%
Cooked to 84% soluble solids.	

Process
The fondant is reheated by adding most of the hot thinning syrup to it and mixing thoroughly, raising the temperature of the mix to 200°F.

The frappé is then mixed in, followed by the color and flavor.

Finally the temperature is adjusted and more syrup added as required to obtain the correct viscosity for depositing.

Figure 11

Extruded Creme Recipe

Dry fondant	83.7%
Butter	4.0%
Water	10.0%
Vegetable fat	2.0%
Invertase	0.3%
Color and flavor as desired	

Figure 12

Several factors have to be controlled to make invertase work properly to give a stable, soft-textured product:

Water Sufficient water is needed in the deposited fondant or extruded creme, but not so much that there is not enough sugar to break down and raise the soluble solids and reduce the water activity to below 0.65. Invertase to some extent is automatic in that if there is enough water and sugar solids present it will continue breaking down the sugar until the water activity drops to 0.68 to 0.70, when inversion slows down or stops.

Temperature Invertase starts to be deactivated at 140°F, slowly at first but more rapidly as the temperature rises. Above 180°F it loses most of its ability to invert sugar. This is not a problem with extruded cremes, which are formed at 95° to 100°F, but does limit the depositing temperature of moulded fondants to 165° to 170°F. The storage temperature after the cremes are packed is also important. If they are put directly into cold storage, this will inhibit the invertase from doing its job, and potentially result in unstable, unsaleable rocks.

Extruded cremes are sometimes regarded as too coarse in texture compared with deposited ones, which can give them a lower-quality image. The coarse texture is the result of using an impact-milled sugar powder, which generally has a coarser particle size distribution profile than that of a crystallized fondant. The problem of coarseness can be overcome by using standard high-sugar fondant to replace powdered fondant in the extruded paste, making adjustments to the amount of corn syrup used in the paste recipe to give the right texture for extrusion.

MARSHMALLOWS—UNGRAINED AND GRAINED

Marshmallows consist basically of a syrup (with a moisture content of typically 17% to 20%), an aerating agent (egg albumen, soya protein, milk protein isolate or gelatin) and air (which reduces its density to 0.2 to 0.6). The aerating agent is a film-forming material which efficiently mixes air into the syrup, forming small air bubbles dispersed throughout the syrup, and stabilizing them so that they do not coalesce. The density of marshmallows and their air bubble size distribution play a key part in their quality.

Egg albumen, soya or milk protein is generally used for soft, tender mallows, whereas gelatin is used where a rubbery, chewy texture is needed, typical in extruded mallows. Sometimes modified starches, agar agar and gum arabic are also used in marshmallow recipes to give the required texture. These are used mostly in combination with egg albumen or one of the other aerating agents.

The amount of aerating agent required ranges from 1 to 1.5 percent of the final product for egg albumen, soya protein, lactalbumen and agar; 2 to 6 percent for gelatin; and 8 to 10 percent for starch. The aerating agents have to be properly resolubilized in water to be effective. This involves mixing in water without forming lumps, and then allowing them to stand for ½ to 1 hour before use. Starch and agar require cooking to solubilize them into the mallow syrup.

The composition of the syrup that holds the whole structure together is a critical variable and allows a wide range of mallow products to be made. When the syrup is formulated with a high proportion of 42 DE corn syrup, typically equal to the sugar content, it doesn't crystallize, resulting in ungrained mallows.

A typical ungrained marshmallow recipe, suitable for moulding, and process is shown in Figure 13.

When a short-textured marshmallow is required, the ratio of sugar to corn syrup is increased and fondant is added to the recipes to induce the syrup to grain. If the syrup crystallizes too early, aeration becomes more difficult because it loses its elasticity, and the final product is inconsistent.

A typical grained deposited marshmallow recipe is shown in Figure 14.

Aeration of marshmallow syrups can be done in several ways:

- A conventional planetary batch mixer of the Hobart type, fitted with a whisk to whip in air at atmospheric pressure, which is the traditional method suitable for relatively small-scale production. It is limited in reducing the density below 0.5, and generally gives a product with a wide air bubble size distribution.

Ungrained Marshmallow Recipe

Corn syrup (42 DE)	38.0%
Sugar	22.0%
Water	6.0%
Invert sugar	9.0%
Sorbitol	7.0%
Gelatin	1.5%
Water for gelatin	6.0%
Egg albumen	1.0%
Water for egg	3.0%
Corn syrup (63 DE)	6.5%
Color and flavor as desired	

Process
The gelatin is dunked in cold water, with rapid mixing, and then allowed to stand for 30 minutes.

The egg albumen is dissolved in water and warm 63 DE corn syrup, first forming a smooth paste with the egg and a small amount of water, and then adding this to the remaining water and corn syrup.

The sugar is dissolved in water, the 42 DE corn syrup, invert sugar and sorbitol added, and the syrup cooked to 84% s.s.

The syrup is then cooled to 190°F and the gelatin mixed into it, followed by the egg solution.

Color and flavor are added and the syrup then whipped to a density of 0.5–0.6 and deposited into starch moulds.

The units are removed from the starch in 24 to 48 hours ready for finishing and packing.

Figure 13

Grained Deposited Marshmallow

Sugar	40%
Water	10%
Corn syrup (42 DE)	28.5%
Gelatin	1.5%
Water for gelatin	6%
Egg albumen	0.5%
Water for egg	3%
Fondant (4:1)	10%
Color and flavor as desired	

Process
Processed in a similar way as in the ungrained marshmallow recipe, with the fondant being added and mixed in well immediately before depositing.

Figure 14

- Batch pressure whisks whip the syrup under air pressure so that when the pressure is slowly released the air bubbles expand without bursting, to give light densities down to 0.2.
- Very efficient continuous-pressure beaters produce low-density products consistently for larger-scale production.

The recipes and processes must avoid any contact with fat or emulsifiers, which lower the surface tension of the syrup and make it very difficult to aerate. This requires that utensils and process equipment must be free from fat and properly rinsed with clear water to avoid detergent residues. Even using oil-based flavors, such as citrus oils, can have an adverse effect on aeration, particularly when making light-density marshmallows.

NOUGATS

Nougats are similar to marshmallows in that they contain an aerated syrup but they have the following differences:

- They are used generally for sheeting and cutting and not for depositing.
- Their moisture content varies from 6 percent for hard torrone or French nougats, to 15 to 17 percent for the soft nougats.
- Their density is generally higher than marshmallows, in the range of 0.5 to 0.8.
- They generally contain 3 to 5 percent fat, which helps lubricate them for cutting, and keeps them from sticking to the teeth. Fat also affects the texture of the nougat and its standup properties.

We have seen that fat can seriously affect aeration of syrup. This is particularly important in nougats, where it is deliberately added to the recipe. The way fat is added to nougat to avoid deaeration and densification is a key part of nougat technology. The fat and fat-containing ingredients, such as cocoa powder (6% or 12% fat), are always added as the last ingredients to the aerated syrup, and mixed in gently with minimum shear and with as short a mixing time as is consistent with adequate dispersion. Some densification will always occur even under the best conditions. This restricts achieving light densities, unless a fat-free or low-fat nougat is the final product.

Nougats are a very broad topic to cover adequately at this time, except to emphasize that the lower the moisture content the harder the nougat, and that hard chewy ones are generally ungrained. Short-textured soft nougats often include fondant seed in the recipe, and are formulated to grain after being coated in chocolate. If they grain too early, they lose elasticity and are more difficult to sheet and cut.

Nougats often contain nuts, particularly peanuts, almonds and filberts (hazelnuts), raisins and cereals. Some of these ingredients can contain the fat-splitting enzyme lipase. This can make any lauric fats used in the recipe taste soapy.

Typical recipes are shown in Figures 15 and 16.

Torrone Nougat (Ungrained) Recipe	
Sugar	33.0%
Corn syrup (42 DE)	35.0%
Water	13.0%
Egg albumen	1.5%
Water for egg	3.0%
Honey	12.0%
Vegetable fat	2.0%
Color and flavor as desired	0.5%

Process

The egg albumen is made into a paste with water and then mixed into warm (150°F) honey and allowed to stand for ½ hour.

This mixture is then whipped to a density of approximately 0.5.

The sugar is dissolved in water, the corn syrup added and then the syrup cooked to 268°F. It is cooled to 210°F and then mixed into the egg whip. The combined materials are then whipped to a density of 0.4.

The color and flavor are then mixed in, followed by the fat, which is mixed in carefully.

The finished nougat is sheeted, cooled and cut into units.

Figure 15

Soft Chocolate Nougat (Grained) Recipe	
Sugar	36.0%
Water	10.0%
Corn syrup (63 DE)	36.0%
Egg albumen	1.0%
Water for egg	2.0%
Corn syrup (63 DE)	9.0%
Cocoa powder	2.0%
Fondant (4:1)	2.0%
Vegetable fat	2.0%
Flavor as desired	

Process

The egg albumen is solubilized in its recipe water and warm corn syrup. It is then aerated to a density of approximately 0.5.

The sugar is dissolved in water, the corn syrup added, and then the syrup is cooked to 255°F.

The syrup is cooled to 210°F, added to the egg whip, and aerated to a density of 0.3–0.4.

The warmed fondant is then mixed in, followed by the cocoa powder and flavor.

Finally the fat is mixed in carefully and the nougat sheeted, cooled and cut into units.

Figure 16

CARAMEL AND FUDGE

The technology of caramel and fudge is also a very broad topic to cover adequately. Generally, caramels are ungrained, chewy soft glasses, and fudges are deliberately designed to grain—to give a short, less chewy texture. They both contain milk protein. In the cooking process the typical caramel flavor is developed from the Maillard reaction between the protein and reducing sugars—dextrose, maltose and lactose—in the syrup.

The number of variables available leads to a very wide range of caramel and fudge products. Caramels all have the following things in common:

• They all have Maillard reaction flavor—the true caramel flavor.

• They all contain milk protein, generally at levels between 1 to 4 percent.

• They all contain fat, generally dairy fat and a hardened vegetable fat, with a total level of 5 to 15 percent.

• Caramels are all soft glasses, so that they flow and distort at a rate which depends on the following:

–Their milk protein content. The more milk protein, generally, the better their standup properties.

–Their moisture content. The greater this is, the more they flow, ranging from 7 to 8 percent for hard caramels or toffee, to 18 to 20 percent for caramel syrups used on ice cream desserts, etc.

–The type of corn syrup used, where the higher the dextrin content (i.e., the lower the DE of the syrup), the less the caramel flows.

–The higher the temperature at which the caramel is held, the more it will distort.

Until they have grained, fudges share the first three characteristics with caramel. Once the syrup binding the ingredients together crystallizes, the fudge is no longer a sugar glass, and resists flow and distortion at normal temperatures. The remaining saturated syrup binding the fudge together is a soft glass. It is only the friction of the sugar crystals that prevents flow. Consequently, at warmer temperatures fudges will distort, particularly in a large pack, from the pressure of their weight on each other.

Crystallization of fudge is normally controlled by adding up to 10 percent high-sugar fondant to the recipe after cooking and partially cooling the fudge, to seed the syrup. The rate and extent of crystallization and the crystal size distribution are all very important. They depend on the recipe and the other factors—crystallization temperature, shear rate, etc.—already discussed.

Fudges range widely in texture, from hard, coarse, heavily crystallized tablets to soft, fine, spoonable fudge, often cut from a bulk display in retail shops.

Partially grained caramels, where only a small amount of sugar crystals is incorporated into the caramel glass structure (often added as fondant), are used where better standup properties and some shortness is needed, but where it is also important to retain the chewy properties of caramel. Cut-and-wrap caramels are often partially grained, for both good machining characteristics and the final product.

Typical caramel and fudge recipes are shown in Figures 17 and 18.

Sodium bicarbonate is often added to caramel recipes to adjust the pH of the syrup to 6.0 to 6.5 to ensure that the milk protein does not coagulate during cooking, which produces a slightly coarse texture in the product and changes the functional properties of the protein. A similar effect can be produced if there are high calcium and magnesium salt levels in the syrup coming from hard water or from other ingredients. To overcome this, often a small amount of sequestering salts, such as sodium di-hydrogen phosphate, is added to the recipe water at the beginning of the process, producing a much smoother caramel.

It normally takes several days for fudge to finally crystallize, so that it can be shaped

Milk Fudge Recipe	
Sugar	28.6%
Water	10.0%
Corn syrup (42 DE)	28.6%
Full cream sweetened	
condensed milk	17.6%
Vegetable fat	8.5%
Lecithin	0.2%
Sorbitol	2.0%
Salt	0.2%
Fondant	2.8%
Sorbitol	1.4%
Vanilla	0.1%

Process

The syrup is formed from the sugar, corn syrup, milk, fat, lecithin, sorbitol and salt and properly emulsified.

It is then cooked to 250°F over a period of 20–30 minutes, and then cooled to 200°F.

The warmed fondant, mixed with its recipe sorbitol is then mixed in thoroughly, followed by the flavor.

The final fudge is then sheeted and cooled.

Figure 17

Caramel Recipe	
Sugar	22.50%
Water	7.00%
Corn syrup (42 de)	36.00%
Full cream sweetened	
condensed milk	22.80%
Vegetable fat	11.00%
Lecithin	0.22%
Sodium bicarbonate	0.02%
Salt	0.22%
Vanilla	0.24%

Process

The sugar is dissolved in the water to which the sodium bicarbonate has already been added. The corn syrup, condensed milk, fat, lecithin and salt are added and mixed thoroughly to emulsify the fat into the syrup.

This is then cooked to 250°F over 20–30 minutes to properly develop the caramel flavor and color.

The flavor is mixed in and the finished caramel poured onto a cooling table or belt.

Figure 18

by extrusion, sheeting and cutting or other means before it becomes too short to pass through this type of equipment.

CONCLUSION

This was designed to be a basic review, and in many respects we have only scratched the surface of what is fascinating technology, getting even more complicated and exciting as the ingredients and tools we have to work with proliferate. The advent of sophisticated polyols, sweeteners, tailored fats and refined proteins and the growth of functional confections will offer even more potential.

Questions & Answers

Q: At how high a temperature can fondant be deposited in starch moulds? Would 200°F or higher be acceptable? What happens to the finished products?

A: The normal range of depositing temperatures for fondant into starch is 160° to 190°F.

The higher the depositing temperature, the more sugar goes into solution and the faster the fondant sets for demoulding. This, however, can lead to coarser sugar crystals being formed

and grittiness in the finished product, because there are not enough fine sugar seed crystals left in the fondant above 190°F to ensure the sugar in solution crystallizes into small crystals.

Q: How can a typical creme formula be extruded, without the use of dry fondant, to make a better product? What formula would you recommend?

A: Replace the dry fondant with an 8:1

sugar/corn syrup standard fondant with a fine crystal structure (below 12 microns) and 12 to 13 percent moisture content. Mix this thoroughly at 110° to 115°F with 5 to 10 percent butterfat or other hardened (92°F melting point) fat, together with whatever flavor or color desired, and finally add and mix in thoroughly 0.2 percent invertase. Extrude the resulting paste in the normal way, cool to 70° to 75°F and enrobe in chocolate. After 1 to 2 weeks storage at 70°F, it should soften to a creme. Approximately 5 percent of a standard frappé can also be added to the mixture to improve whiteness and give brighter colors. Always check the water activity or soluble solids of the final inverted creme to ensure it is below 0.65, which normally needs a soluble solids of at least 76 percent. Sorbitol (5%) or glycerol (2%) can be added to the mix to lower the water activity and reduce drying out of the finished creme.

A typical recipe:

Fondant (8:1)	80%
Butter oil	10% (or hardened palm kernel oil)
Frappé	5%
Sorbitol	5%

Color and flavor as desired.

Q: Can you make nougats on a continuous system and what would you recommend?

A: Most large-scale production of nougat is made continuously so that moisture content, density and final temperature, ready for sheeting and cutting, can be accurately controlled.

The process involves the following:

- Make a syrup from sugar, corn syrup and other ingredients such as honey, invert sugar, sorbitol, etc., and then cook it accurately and continuously to a controlled moisture content, using a coil cooker, plate evaporator or scraped tubular cooker.
- Dissolve spray-dried egg white or a similar aerating agent in water and corn syrup, to completely dissolve the egg albumen.
- Meter the cooked syrup and egg syrup through two separate metering pumps and tubes into a continuous high-shear pressure aerator (Mondomix, Hansal, Ter Braak, GEI, etc.) and whipping it at 80 to 100 psi to form an aerated syrup of 0.4 to 0.5 density.

- Mix the continuously aerated syrup with cocoa powder, nuts, raisins, etc., in a continuous cylindrical water-jacketed mixer, preferably a double shaft type for efficient but low-shear action.
- Finally, mix in 5 to 10 percent hardened fat toward the end of the mixing to avoid densification of the resulting nougat, which should have a density of 0.6 or 0.7.
- This can then be continuously sheeted, cooled and cut into units for enrobing in chocolate, or for hard nougats, cut and wrapped.

The hardness depends largely on the final moisture content, 5 to 6 percent for hard nougats, 13 to 15 percent for soft. This is controlled by the syrup cooking temperature.

Q: Can you explain just what is 4:1, 8:1, 3:2, etc., in actual finished composition as to sugar, corn syrup, dry solids and moisture content?

A: The ratios 4:1, 8:1, 3:2, etc., generally refer to the ratio of sugar to wet corn syrup (80 percent solids) and the moisture content in the finished fondant is normally 12 to 14 percent, controlled by the cooking temperature of the sugar, water (to dissolve the sugar) and corn syrup mixture.

For example, a 4:1 fondant at 14 percent final moisture content would have this composition:

71.68%	Sugar
14.32%	Corn syrup solids
14.00%	Water

Q: What type of fondant is best for seeding nougat, dry or regular fondant?

A: Dry fondant tends to be larger in particle size distribution and can give a coarser texture to the nougat. It is, however, easier to meter and mix into the nougat.

Wet fondant has generally a finer particle size distribution and 90:10 (9:1) is marginally more efficient than 80:20. Both have to be fed warm into the nougat to mix it in thoroughly, without densification of the nougat. Both powder and wet fondant should be added into the aerated syrup before the fat to minimize densification.

Q: *When using invertase, how do you reconcile the required water activity of 0.7 to 0.75 for the invertase to work with an activity of less than 0.65 for stability?*

A: For invertase to work, there has to be sufficient free water in the fondant or confection and generally a water activity of 0.75 to 0.85 ensures this. As the sugar in the recipe is inverted, the fructose, which has a high solubility (79% at 68°F), dissolves in the water, raising its soluble solids to 75 to 76 percent and lowering its water activity to 0.65, if the recipe has been properly formulated. It is then stable against microbial attack.

Q: *What process conditions do you measure in the factory? How are those measurements made?*

A: This is a large question to answer simply but I will try to give the key process measurements as follows:

Moisture content of all syrup-based confections, because it affects texture and eating quality, as well as efficient production. This needs accurate cooking temperature measurement and control, which, for low- and medium-boiled confections need to be adjusted for atmospheric pressure variations, cooking higher on dry days, lower on wet.

Recipe formulation All recipe ingredients should meet precise specifications, and be weighed accurately. A "bucket of this" or a "cup of that" just does not meet accuracy requirements if you want to control the process properly.

Density of mallows and nougats because this affects the final texture, and rheology for depositing or sheeting. A density cup is often sufficient for this purpose, comparing its weight full of water with it full of the confection. The density is then the weight of the confection divided by the weight of water.

Particle size distribution in fondants, cremes and fudges because this affects again the final texture and rheology of the confections. This can be measured in several ways but is often controlled by controlling crystallization temperatures, seeding conditions and mixing rates.

Air and water quality This includes air temperature and humidity in processing areas together with potential air-born contaminants (yeasts, molds, bacteria, etc.). For water, it must ensure consistent salt levels, particularly calcium and magnesium in jelly production, as well as potability.

Water activity is normally controlled by using stable recipes and controlling moisture content, etc. However, it pays to check this regularly on potentially high-water-activity recipes such as soft creme, soft caramels, fudges and particularly truffles. This can be done with a water activity meter, made by a number of companies and designed to give results in 15 to 20 minutes.

Sanitation monitored on a regular basis by swabbing and microbiological testing.

Q: *What cooling temperature and/or time will optimize fudge crystallization at the point of adding fondant for slightly soft/flowable texture, but with standup within 1 to 2 hours?*

A: Generally, this requires cooling the cooked fudge syrup to 160° to 170°F before adding warm (130° to 140°F) fondant and mixing it in thoroughly so that the fudge will remain flowable and soft. If this is then deposited into a tray or spread onto a belt, it should then be cooled with air that is not too cold, because this inhibits crystallization. An air temperature of 70° to 75°F with plenty of air movement over the trays or belt is required to set the fudge in 1 to 2 hours. If it takes longer, raise the temperature of the fudge after the fondant is mixed in.

Generally, the higher the depositing temperature the faster the setting time, if sufficient air cooling is uniformly used.

Q: *What is the common range in grained confections for the ratio of crystals to syrup?*

A: This depends on the confection and its recipe. For instance, in a 9:1 fondant, the sugar crystal content is very high (at 14% moisture content approximately 70% with 30% syrup) but in a 3:2 fondant it is lower (40% with 60% syrup). For fudges, it depends on the final texture required but generally is in the range of 10 to 30 percent crystals to 90 to 70 percent syrup, and similarly for nougats.

Q: How would you recommend measuring the moisture content in syrups? Is there a practical way to determine moisture content during the cook? What instruments do you recommend (refractive index, microwave, other)?

A: The accurate way is the lab-based Karl Fischer titration, which is normally used for calibrating other instrumental methods. In the factory, an accurate refractometer, regularly calibrated, is probably the most useful, practical and reasonably accurate method for measuring the moisture content of low- to medium-cooked syrups.

Near infrared (NIR) instruments can give a rapid, fairly accurate measurement but they have to be calibrated against Karl Fischer moisture measurements.

Microwave or infrared drying instruments can also give a result in 10 to 15 minutes on some confections.

Q: How can I control sugar settling out in sweetened condensed milk?

A: It is generally the lactose in condensed milk which crystallizes because of its low solubility (18% at 68°F).

It must be seeded in the milk-processing operation to ensure that fine lactose crystals form and not large ones, which settle at the bottom of the drum container.

Q: What is more critical for nougat graining—moisture content or amount of fondant?

A: You need to control both for a consistent product; but, as with all syrup phased confections, variations in moisture content have a significant effect on their crystallizing properties.

Seeding fondant is normally only 10 percent of the total recipe so that small variations in this are not so significant.

Q: What was the temperature of the plate that you worked with?

A: The cooking plate is thermostatically controlled and can be varied from low (approximately 100°F) to high temperature (approximately 288°F).

Q: Why use fondant instead of sucrose as a seeding agent?

A: Fondant normally has very fine sugar crystals in it, generally below 12 microns, so that it provides a large number of fine seeds. Impact-milled sugar is generally coarser, and more variable in particle size distribution.

Q: What percentage of seed is suggested to give fine grain to caramels?

A: In the range of 5 to 10 percent of a fine (below 12 microns) 9:1 fondant.

Q: Do other ingredients, like cocoa powder, affect the crystal formulation of sugar?

A: Only marginally if fondant or powdered sugar is used as the main seeding agent. If there is too little of these, cocoa can act as an inefficient seeding agent.

Q: How does shearing cause the sugar to crystallize?

A: Simply by helping to bring the sugar molecules together and overcome the viscous forces which prevent this, so allowing crystals to form.

Q: What does FCSCM stand for?

A: Full cream, sweetened, condensed milk.

Fats and Oils

Processing of Oils and Fats

Alan Brench, PhD
A&L Shatto, Inc.

The theories and practices of oil and fat processing have been developed over a number of decades, culminating in the very large continuous refineries in use in the North American soybean industry with throughputs of up to 2,000,000 lbs per day. Located close to the oilseed growing areas, and frequently linked to extraction plants, these refineries are assured of consistent supplies of optimum-quality oils that, with extended production runs, are used to generate a range of high-quality liquid and solid oil products. Specifications for these products tend not to be overly complex, focusing predominantly on flavor, keepability and solids profile.

The confectionery industry presents the oil processor with a very different series of challenges. The specifications for many of the confectionery fats are among the most complex in the world of oils and fats, involving dynamic functional performance tests such as the Jensen cooling curve. While the raw materials for the confectionery industry do include commodity oils like soybean oil, they also encompass the more exotic oilseed crops like illipe and shea fat. These are jungle crops that are not cultivated, but rather harvested from their natural environment with wide variations in annual availability. The remoteness of the oil sources from the extraction and refining facilities also provides ample opportunity for raw material quality deterioration. Where the confectionery industry does employ commodity oils as the source of ingredients, product specifications necessitate an extension of conventional refinery operations to include interesterification and fractionation to meet the exacting functional performance criteria.

This paper will first examine the current sources of oils and fats for the confectionery industry, placing particular emphasis on the characteristics of the oils that need to be considered in their processing to yield the functional ingredient. This will form the basis for a critical review of the current theory and practice of oil processing and modification as applied to confectionery fats, highlighting the key aspects of each process step. The paper will conclude with a discussion of potential product defects and strategies employed to minimize their impact on the final confectionery product.

CONFECTIONERY OILS AND FATS

The functional fats used in confectionery products can be readily classified into four groups based on how the functional performance of the fats is achieved: cocoa butter, exotic oils, lauric fats and domestic hard butters.

Cocoa Butter

Cocoa butter can be considered as the fat that initiated the concept of fat-based confectionery and as such is the standard by which the performance of alternative fats is assessed. Cocoa butter is obtained from the seeds of the *Theobroma cacao* tree, which is grown as a tropical plantation crop in a number of regions in the world within 10° to 15° of the equator. The two key distinguishing features of cocoa butter are that it possesses the unique property of melting very sharply at mouth temperature and has a very pleasant flavor and aroma.

Like many tropical fats, cocoa butter is rich in saturated fatty acids, as can be seen from Figure 1. It also has a relatively simple triglyceride structure, with the symmetrical triglycerides POSt, StOSt and POP typically accounting for approximately 80 percent of the triglycerides present in the fat. As these triglycerides all have melting points around body temperature, this explains the sharp melting behavior of the fat.

Typical Triglyceride Composition of Cocoa Butter	
Fatty Acid	%
Palmitic (P)	25
Stearic (St)	36
Oleic (O)	34
Arachidic (Ar)	1
Linoleic (L)	3
Triglyceride	%
PStSt	1
POSt	39
StOSt	26
POP	16
StOAr	2
PLSt	4
StLSt	1
PLP	2
StOO	4
POO	4
Others	2
Figure 1	

The cocoa butter flavor owes its origin, at least in part, to the extensive and unique processing the beans receive, which includes a 3 to 8 day fermentation period followed by drying and then roasting at 100° to 140°C. The final roasted bean material (nibs) has an average fat content of approximately 55 percent which allows the cocoa butter to be expelled from the seeds, typically leaving either a 22 percent fat cake (high-fat cocoa) or a 10 to 12 percent fat cake (medium-fat cocoa). To preserve its flavor and aroma, cocoa butter is not subjected to conventional oil processing but may, on occasion, be treated with an aqueous solution of sodium or potassium carbonate to improve its color and flavor. Such products are often referred to as dutched or alkalized. Cocoa butter is also frequently given a very light form of deodorization, again to reduce off-flavors and acidic notes. Typical conditions for this treatment are a pressure of 5 mbar at 140°C (c.f. 200° to 270°C in conventional deodorization), thus minimizing the loss of aroma components and the risk of damaging the triglyceride structure. An additional benefit of this light deodorization is that it also sterilizes the cocoa butter, reducing the risks of microbial activity.

Conventional oil processing is applied to old or damaged cocoa beans starting with a hexane extraction of the beans. The extracted fat then undergoes conventional neutralization, bleaching and deodorization to yield a bland fat with the same solids profile and triglyceride composition as the expelled oil but no flavor or aroma. Processing temperatures are again carefully controlled to avoid structural damage to the triglycerides. Cocoa butter from this source usually finds application as an add-back in food uses to adjust color and flavor or in nonfood roles where the melting behavior is its selling feature.

Natural cocoa butter exhibits an elevated resistance to deterioration by oxidation and rancidity, which is due to the low levels of polyunsaturated fatty acids in the fat and the high levels of natural protecting compounds left in the fat by its limited processing. In general, the more processing an oil receives, the greater the removal of natural antioxidants and other materials from the oil and the more vulnerable it becomes to deterioration.

Exotic Oils

Since the functional performance of cocoa butter originates from the blend of monounsaturated symmetrical triglycerides it contains, similar physical performance can be expected from other fats containing elevated levels of the same triglycerides. Of necessity these fats are tropical in origin since they have to contain high levels of saturated fats, and include illipe, shea, kokum, aceituno and sal fats. The source and geographical origin of these various oils are summarized in Figure 2. None of them contains exactly the same triglyceride composition as cocoa butter (Figure 3), but they do offer blending opportunities to formulate products that are cocoa butter equivalents (CBE) with respect to functional performance.

The above fats are not cultivated plantation crops, but rather harvested from their natural jungle environments. This imposes a number of inherent difficulties on the use of the oils, including irregular fruiting/harvesting and quality deterioration due to

Exotic Oils Sources

Oil	Source	Location
Palm	*Elaeis Guinneensis*	Malaysia, Indonesia, West Africa, S. America
Illipe	*Shorea stenoptera*	Borneo
Shea	*Butyrospermum parkii*	West Africa
Sal	*Shorea robusta gaertn*	India
Kokum	*Garcinia indica choisy*	India
Aceituno	*Simarduba glauca*	Central America

Figure 2

Typical Exotic Oil Composition

Fatty Acid	Cocoa B.	Palm	Illipe	Shea	Sal	Kokum	Aceituno
P	25	45	16		5	2	12
S	36	5	46	43	44	57	28
O	34	38	35	45	40	40	54
L	3	10		7	2	1	4
Ar	1		2		7		2
Triglyceride							
PStSt/PPP	1	5					
POSt	39	3	35	5	11	5	
StOSt	26		45	40	42	72	
POP	16	26	7		1		
StOAr	2		4	2	13		
PLSt	4	2					
StLSt	1	2					
PLP	2	7					
StOO	4	3	3	27	16	15	
POO	4	19		2	3		
Others	2	33	6	24	14	8	

Figure 3

the distance between harvesting areas and extraction/refinery plants. Flavor is generally not an issue with these oils, since they are subjected to conventional neutralization, bleaching and deodorization to provide bland fats.

A closer examination of the triglyceride compositions in Figure 3 shows that shea oil has an elevated level of StOO triglyceride, which considerably softens the oil. To make it suitable for use as a CBE component the oil must be fractionated via crystallization to yield a stearin fraction that is rich in the required symmetrical triglycerides and possesses a suitable solids profile. This is an appropriate point to explain the inclusion of palm oil in Figure 3. While it is a cultivated plantation crop, palm oil shares many of the other features of the exotic oils and via the plantation process has been converted into a tropical commodity oil. It offers a source of the symmetrical POP triglyceride via fractionation.

Compared to experience with indigenous crops in Europe and North America, the tropical oils present very different challenges to the oil processor. Compared to a crude soybean oil free fatty acid (FFA) level of 0.5 percent in Europe and North America, illipe fat is likely to arrive at the refinery with a FFA level of 5 to 15 percent and even the cultivated palm oil may have a 5 percent level. This has major implications for the operation of the neutralization plant and can have a significant impact on process economics via oil loss. Along with the free fatty acid, the crude oils often contain significant levels of diglycerides (illipe 4–10 percent, palm oil about 3 percent), which is of little consequence to commodity oil processing but can have a major impact on the CBE formulator due to their effect in slowing down crystallization rates. In addition to sharing the same FFA and diglyceride picture as illipe and palm oil, shea oil contains 5 to 10 percent of unsaponifiable material, which has no commercial use, and approximately 2.5 percent of a polyisoprene gum which is admirably suited to blocking filters during fractionation. To complete the picture of tropical oils, sal fat frequently exhibits a very dark green color due to chlorophyll, which must be addressed by an aggressive bleaching process. The performance of sal fat can also be adversely affected by the presence of epoxy and di-hydroxy derivatives of oleic acid in the symmetrical triglycerides, which appear to have a synergistic effect with the diglyceride present on triglyceride crystallization.

In view of the extensive processing most of the above oils experience in becoming usable fats, their stability to oxidation and rancidity is less than that exhibited by cocoa butter. It is, however, still very acceptable for most applications due to the very low levels of polyunsaturated fatty acids in the refined oils and blends.

Lauric Fats

While the exotic fats exploited the same triglycerides to match the performance of cocoa butter, the lauric fats achieve the same crystallization behavior and solids profile by exploiting triglycerides that contain shorter chain saturated fatty acids and exhibit the same crystallization characteristics as the monounsaturated symmetrical triglycerides. This approach makes palm kernel and coconut oils valuable in confectionery applications as cocoa butter substitutes (CBS). As can be seen from Figure 4, lauric acid is the key to the functional performance of these fats.

Using hydrogenation to fully saturate lauric fats generates fats that melt very rapidly, and by combining this technology with interesterification and fractionation it is possible to generate fats with a range of melting points and solids profiles for use in the confectionery industry (Figure 5).

Palm kernel oil and coconut oil are cultivated plantation crops so that, in general, their quality and supply are well controlled. As a result of hydrogenation processing, the oils typically have a low level of unsaturated fatty acids in their triglycerides and

Typical Lauric Fat Compositions								
Fatty Acid	Ca	C	La	M	P	St	Ar	O	L
Coconut	7	8	48	16	9	2	tr	7	1
Palm Kernel	4	5	46	16	8	2	tr	15	2

Fatty Acids: Ca = Caprylic; C = Capric; La = Lauric; M = Myristic

Figure 4

Typical Lauric Fat Solids Profiles						
Temperature (°C)	10°	20°	25°	30°	35°	40°
Cocoa Butter	90	81	73	53	0	0
Palm Kernel Oil	69	45	21	0	0	0
PK Stearin	90	83	67	28	0	0
PK Olein	48	10	2	0	0	0
Hydro PK	92	81	56	25	7	2
Hydro/Inter. PK	86	72	49	21	3	0
Figure 5						

as a consequence offer a high degree of oxidative stability. The presence of the shorter chain fatty acids does, however, make them more prone to hydrolysis than fats containing only the 16 and 18 carbon atom acids. This vulnerability leads to what is frequently referred to as hydrolytic, soapy or lipolytic rancidity. Organoleptically the shorter chain fatty acids can impart a soapy characteristic to the fat if they are liberated from the triglyceride molecule, with lauric acid having a flavor detection threshold level of 0.07 percent. As a consequence, processing of lauric fats requires the oil processor to pay particular attention to hygienic processing, avoiding contact with potential sources of lipase enzymes and vigorously restricting fat contact with free water. One feature of lauric fats that has emerged in recent years has been the occasional contamination of parcels of oil with polyaromatic hydrocarbons (PAH). This is a range of compounds that are formed during the incomplete combustion of a number of materials and are thought to originate at the plantation. Interest in these compounds stems from the fact that they have been identified as carcinogenic and need to be reduced to the 1 ppm range. The compounds can be broadly classified as light and heavy PAH, according to the number of aromatic rings in the compounds. Light PAHS are normally removed during the deodorization of the oil, but the heavy ones require inclusion of an activated-carbon step during the bleaching process.

Domestic Hard Butters

This final group of products makes use of the commodity oils such as soybean and cottonseed, and modifies them to match the solids profile of cocoa butter by converting the *cis* double bonds in the unsaturated fatty acids to the *trans* configuration. The *trans*-fatty-acid-containing triglycerides have melting points around body temperature. The transformation is achieved by adjusting hydrogenation conditions so that the conversion selectively generates elaidic acid or one of the other *trans* forms of oleic acid from the more unsaturated acids but stops short of forming stearic acid. By combining this approach with interesterification and fractionation, a range of cocoa butter replacers (CBR) can be generated with properties that approach those of cocoa butter (Figure 6). Frequently a blend of oils is used as a feedstock for the hydrogenation process with palm or cottonseed oils being included in the blend as a source of palmitic acid.

Typical CBR Solids Profiles						
Temperature (°C)	10°	20°	25°	30°	35°	40°
Cocoa Butter	90	81	73	53	0	0
CBR	85	69	51	30	15	4
Fractionated CBR	96	86	68	36	6	0
Figure 6						

The oxidative stability of these products is difficult to forecast. The reduction in the level of polyunsaturated fatty acids in the products improves their resistance to oxidation in comparison to their original oil feedstock, but the extensive processing employed can result in depletion of the natural antioxidants present in the oil. Experience would also suggest that CBRS benefit from the fact that the *trans* configuration of a fatty acid appears to be more resistant to oxidation than its *cis* counterpart.

OIL PROCESSING

The conversion of a crude vegetable oil into an edible functional ingredient involves the use of a number of unit operations that can be broadly classified into two groups, refining and fat modification. The refining operations—neutralization, bleaching and deodorization—have as their collective target the generation of fat products of a suitable color that are organoleptically acceptable and have sufficient shelf life for their end use. The refining unit operations do not, however, affect the functional performance of the oil. This is the province of the fat modification unit operations, which achieve their effects as follows:

• By changing the nature of the fatty acids in the triglyceride—*hydrogenation.*

• By changing the position of the fatty acids in the triglyceride—*interesterification.*

• By separating the triglycerides according to their melting points—*fractionation.*

Under normal circumstances oils will be neutralized and bleached before undergoing a fat modification unit operation, but on occasions there are advantages to fractionating oils in their crude state. The final unit operation in all oil-processing sequences is the deodorization step.

Refining

Neutralization The main purpose of neutralization is to remove the free fatty acids present in crude oils. This can be achieved using either physical refining or chemical neutralization.

Physical refining is a development of deodorization (see section later in paper) in which the free fatty acids are separated from the oil by steam distillation. The advantage of this approach is that it generates less oil losses than conventional chemical neutralization, particularly with high-free-acid oils. This gain can, however, be frequently offset by an increased bleaching loss as a result of the need to compensate for the beneficial effects of alkali treatment on other components in the crude oil (see below). The disadvantage of physical refining is the risk of structural damage to the oil as a result of its exposure to the high temperatures used in the process. As a consequence, the technique is limited to continuous deodorization plants. From the confectionery industry perspective, this technique is most commonly used on palm oil and the lauric fats, which have both high free-fatty-acid levels and low nonhydratable phosphatides.

In chemical neutralization the free fatty acid, a weak organic acid, is reacted with a strong inorganic alkali, sodium hydroxide, to generate soap:

$$C_nH_mCOOH + NaOH \Longrightarrow C_nH_mCOONa + H_2O$$

For example:

$$C_{17}H_{33}COOH + NaOH \Longrightarrow C_{17}H_{33}COONa + H_2O$$

Oleic acid + sodium hydroxide $\Longrightarrow$ soap (sodium oleate) + water

In addition to removing the free fatty acid, the chemical neutralization step also removes phospholipids, various glucosides and polysaccharides, trace metals, some oxidation products (like peroxides) and certain color substances.

The sodium hydroxide is dosed at a specific concentration and excess to compensate for its reaction with other components (phosphatides, monoglycerides) and to improve separation of the water phase. The neutralization reaction itself is a very fast reaction, but it only takes place at the oil/water interface, since oil and water are almost immiscible (water in oil solubility ~0.2%). As a consequence, the size of the water (alkalia) droplets has a significant effect on the reaction and the reaction product, soap, which is colloidally suspended in the water phase after the reaction.

Chemical neutralization is routinely carried out as both a continuous process and a batch process. The continuous process utilizes continuous automatic desludging centrifuges with capacities of up to 90,000 lbs per hour to separate the soap from the oil. Subsequent processing may include a warm water washing stage with further centrifugation or a passage through a silica gel bed to remove residual traces of soap. This type of processing is normally applied to the commodity oils such as soybean oil where FFA levels are low and very large batches of consistent-quality oil are processed.

Batch neutralization is carried out in a standard multipurpose vessel (typical size 25 to 40 ton capacity), which can also be used for bleaching and interesterification. The vessel is a pressure vessel equipped with a conical bottom, which can be connected to vacuum for oil drying. Most vessels are equipped with gate-type stirrers, consisting of a bottom plough in the cone and two helical-shaped stirring frames in the cylindrical part of the vessel to ensure adequate mixing. Heating with steam or cooling with water is achieved via multiple spiral bundle coils or vertical tube bundles in the vessel. The caustic solution or water is dosed into the vessel via splash plates or nozzles to achieve the optimal drop size. One of the major attractions of the batch process is its flexibility in dealing with a range of free acid levels, and a number of variations on the neutralization process using both dilute and concentrated alkali solutions have been developed to meet the needs of different oils. Normally the most critical stage in the process is breaking the emulsion that forms between the oil and water phases to achieve a clean separation of the phases and a good process yield. This type of process is typically used to process the exotic oils, which are frequently neutralized as blends with palm mid-fraction to both reduce the free fatty acid (FFA) level of the blend and reduce losses of the more expensive oils.

Bleaching The bleaching process was originally a process to remove (partially or completely) the color from oils and fats by contacting the oil with a suitable bleaching earth. Subsequently, it was established that the process also significantly influenced the taste and stability of fully refined oils and fats via a number of different mechanisms. The adsorption of polar components from the oil appears the most important mechanism for the decolorizing and cleaning of the oil, with typical examples of adsorbed material including chlorophyll (green color in sal fat), carotene (red color in palm oil), iron (oxidation catalyst), phospholipids (mainly in seed oils), soaps (after alkali neutralization) and polyaromatic hydrocarbons (PAH in coconut oil). The activated bleaching earth also acts as a catalyst with respect to the degradation of hydroperoxides and other oxidized components, generating some volatile components, which can be removed during deodorization while leaving the triglyceride structure of the oil intact.

The traditional adsorbents used during bleaching are bentonite-clay-based products, which primarily contain the mineral montmorillonite, an aluminum hydrosilicate ($4\ SiO_2.Al_2O_3.H_2O+n\ H_2O$). To obtain an active earth, the amount of montmorillonite content of the earth needs to be as high as possible (>80%). Most of the commercially available bleaching earths are activated by an acid treatment during production, which dissolves aluminum and other metals present, thus enlarging the available surface area of the earth. The larger the surface area, the more active the bleaching earth becomes. A range of commercial bleaching earths is available with differing levels of activity, surface area and particle size.

Alongside the traditional bleaching earths most refineries today also make use of activated carbon and silica gel in bleaching processes. Activated carbon is produced by the carbonization of wood, coal, lignite or coconut shell, and activated at high pressure with steam to generate a very large surface area. Active carbons have internal surface areas in the range from 500 m^2/g up to 1,500 m^2/g, which is essential for their adsorptive capacity. Since the average pore size of active carbon is in the range of the molecular dimensions of organic molecules, its main use is the adsorption of poly-aromatic hydrocarbons and pesticides.

Silica hydrogels are synthetic amorphous materials formed by a reaction of silica sol (Na_2O $nSiO_2$) with sulfuric acid. Silica gels have a surface area of 800 to 1,000 m^2/g, are chemically inert, do not adsorb coloring agents and do not promote any chemical changes in the oil. They do, however, have excellent adsorption capacity for polar compounds like soaps, phospholipids and metals. The bleaching process required depends on the refining process applied:

- Chemical neutralization (bleaching of neutralized oils) requires a one-step bleaching process.
- Physical refining requires a two-step bleaching process, which includes both a wet and a dry bleaching step.

In the one-step bleaching process, dry bleaching after alkali neutralization is used to remove residual soap, metals and phospholipids, and to obtain a sufficient color reduction of the oil.

The two-step bleaching process combines a treatment with 50 percent citric or phosphoric acid, addition of water, addition of bleaching earth to the wet oil and then subsequent removal of the water while the bleaching earth is still in contact with the oil. This complex regime is necessary for physically refined oils to remove the phospholipids and metals that would normally be removed during chemical neutralization.

Bleaching is normally carried out either as a batch or a continuous process depending on whether the neutralization step was operated in a batch or continuous manner. The standard vessels used for batch neutralization are also used for batch bleaching with the addition of a bleaching-earth dosing system and the acid/water measuring and dosing device. In order to reduce cycle times, a drop tank is frequently placed between the bleaching vessel and the filter used to separate the bleaching earth from the oil.

The continuous two-step bleaching system consists of two compartmented stirred reactors, the first of which runs at atmospheric conditions and the second under vacuum. A dryer is used to dry the oil before the acid and water is mixed inline with the oil. A buffer vessel is again frequently installed between the bleaching system and the filtration system to handle flow irregularities. Bleaching earth is added continuously to the oil. In the case of one-step bleaching, the acid/water dosing system and the first atmospheric reactor are omitted.

Deodorization The major purpose of deodorization is to remove the strong natural flavor of oils and generate bland vegetable oils that can be used in a variety of products. The major contributors to the odiferous and flavor compounds found in vegetable oils are long chain aldehydes and ketones, together with breakdown products formed during the thermal decomposition of peroxides caused by exposure of the oil to air. These compounds are more volatile than triglycerides but still have relatively high boiling points, making their removal difficult.

As the temperature of an oil is raised, the odiferous and flavor compounds will evaporate first, leaving behind the higher-boiling-point triglycerides. By reducing the pressure of the system, the temperature at which the evaporation of these more volatile components occurs can be reduced, to avoid thermally damaging the triglycerides. The use of steam as an inert stripping agent effectively enhances the vaporization of the volatile components, and analysis of deodorizer performance shows that for every order of magnitude reduction in the volatile component concentration the steam consumption doubles.

Besides the odiferous and flavor compounds, deodorization also readily removes the residual free fatty acids in the oil, which formed the basis for the development of physical refining. From the practical perspective, the need to remove all of the free fatty acid in a crude oil during physical refining greatly increases the demands on both the heating and condensing systems associated with the deodorizer, and dictates the use of stainless steel as the construction material of choice. The risk of thermally damaging the oil also effectively restricts physical refining to continuous or semicontinuous plants. The success of physical refining, however, depends less on the deodorization step of the process than on the degumming and bleaching step that precedes it to remove phosphatides, metals, etc., and generate an oil suitable for stripping that will not be vulnerable to flavor reversion or color problems. In addition to the free fatty acid, a number of other compounds present in vegetable oils are influenced by the deodorization process, either as a result of the stripping process or due to chemical reaction under the stripping conditions, as shown in Figure 7.

Deodorization can be operated as either a batch, semicontinuous or continuous process. Batch deodorization is best suited to CBE and CBS production where the flexibility of the process can be exploited, handling a multiplicity of oil products with minimal cross-contamination. Vessel sizes range from oil capacities of 25,000 to 50,000 lbs. The typical issues associated with this type of installation are the high steam usage occasioned by the continual need to reheat the equipment, the poor opportunities for heat recovery and the peak demands on services that operating a number of batch units in parallel can develop. The stripping steam is normally introduced into the vessel via a circular sparger ring located at the bottom of the deodorizer.

A semi-continuous deodorizer can effectively be considered as a number of batch operations interlinked to handle a larger throughput than can be processed by the individual batch units. The advantage of the design is that it can readily handle changes in feedstocks while minimizing cross-contamination and offers better thermal efficiency. The semi-continuous deodorizer is better suited to handling the typically larger volumes of CBRS and CBSS produced. In a continuous deodorizer, although the equipment superficially looks very similar to that in a semi-continuous unit, the flow of oil through the unit is continuous, with the oil retention time on each tray or in each compartment simply being a function of the tray/compartment volume. While this type of unit offers good thermal efficiency, it does not handle changes in feedstock without significant risk of cross-contamination and as a consequence is unlikely to be found in the production of confectionery fats since it is better suited to bulk liquid oil production.

Deodorizer operating conditions need to be carefully selected to minimize detrimental effects on oil quality. In addition to removing unwanted compounds,

Deodorization Influence on Minor Components	
Physical Removal	
Odor Compounds	Reduced to acceptable levels
Tocopherols	Partially removed
Sterols	Partially removed
Methyl/Ethyl Esters	Almost completely removed
Antioxidants (BHA, BHT)	Completely removed
Pesticides	Partially removed
Polycyclic Aromatic Hydrocarbons	Partially removed
Monoglycerides	Partially removed
Chemical Reaction	
Oxidized Fatty Acids	Partially decomposed
Carotene	Partially decomposed
Hydroperoxides	Partially decomposed
Soaps	Completely decomposed
Unsaturated Fatty Acids	Some cis/trans isomerization

Figure 7

over-deodorization can lead to excessive losses of tocopherols and a reduction of oxidative stability. Accompanying such extensive stripping of tocopherols, it is not unusual to see the deodorization process generate *trans* fatty acid levels as high as 6.4 percent with liquid soybean oil. (By careful management of deodorizer temperature, it is possible to generate neutralized, bleached, deodorized soybean oil with a *trans* fatty acid level consistently below 1 percent.) Of even greater significance to CBE manufacture, low levels of residual soap can catalyze some interesterification during high-temperature deodorization and lead to a loss of valuable triglyceride structure.

Fat Modification

Hydrogenation Hydrogenation involves saturating the double bonds in the unsaturated fatty acid chains of triglycerides with hydrogen. This is a catalytic process carried out in a three-phase system comprising gaseous hydrogen, liquid oil and solid catalyst. The catalyst is usually a heterogeneous nickel-on-carrier catalyst and has a complex porous structure with a high specific surface area. The reaction can be driven to completion with all double bonds saturated or partial with some of the double bonds left in the fatty acid chains. This second form of hydrogenation is most important in the confectionery industry since it leads to the formation of *trans* fatty acids via the *cis-trans* isomerization reaction. The hydrogenation process yields harder fats than the starting feedstock and generally leads to an improvement in oxidative stability and the development of off-flavors due to the reduction in unsaturated fatty acids present in the oil.

The reaction scheme for the hydrogenation of an oil can be viewed as the conversion of linolenic acid (C18:3) to stearic acid (C18:0) as follows:

$$C18:3 \longrightarrow C18:2 \longrightarrow C18:1 \longrightarrow C18:0$$

Cis-trans isomerization can occur at any stage in the chain of reactions and is promoted by a relative shortage of hydrogen at the catalytic surface. This shortage can be the result of process conditions (e.g., lower hydrogen pressure and higher temperature) and poisoning of the catalytic surface with sulfur, either during the catalyst manufacture or by recycling spent catalyst. (Sulfur is the major catalyst poison found in vegetable oils.) High levels of *trans* isomers in an oil lead to the steepness of the melting curve of partially hydrogenated products.

During the course of hydrogenation the *trans* content rises until a peak is reached and then drops as both *cis* and *trans* monounsaturated fatty acids are hydrogenated to saturated fatty acids.

The hydrogenation reaction is carried out on a batch basis using a pressure vessel of 10 to 40 tons oil capacity. The hydrogen consumed by the reaction is supplied to the reactor via a distribution ring near the bottom. A specially designed stirrer system sucks in the hydrogen from the head space into the oil and disperses this together with the gas entering the reactor via the distribution ring. The oil has to be heated to initiate the reaction, but since the hydrogenation is an exothermic reaction, thereafter it has to be cooled. Adequate cooling is essential to control the reaction temperature profile and achieve good batch-to-batch reproducibility. Catalyst is added to the reactor as a slurry in the oil and, at the end of the reaction, removed by filtration and, if necessary, chelation to avoid passing nickel into the food supply.

Hydrogenation plants are constructed to very specific standards since hydrogen is highly inflammable and mixtures of hydrogen with oxygen (air) are highly explosive even at relatively low temperatures or ignition energies. Hydrogen escaping from a pressurized vessel or pipe into air may auto ignite (static electricity) and burn with a high-temperature flame.

Interesterification Interesterification is used to modify the physical properties of an oil blend, primarily to alter its melting and crystallization behavior. However, interesterification does not impart a unique change in physical properties of an oil blend, since the solids profile and crystallization behavior of the blend can either increase, decrease or remain unchanged depending on the feedstock composition. Chemically, it is an ester-interchange reaction, which results in a random distribution of fatty acid groups over the triglyceride molecules. (*Note:* any free hydroxyl groups, such as diglycerides and monoglycerides, are affected in a similar way.) The reaction depends on time, temperature and the effective catalyst concentration.

The most common catalyst used to speed up the reaction is sodium methoxide (NaOMe) at approximately 0.06 percent by weight. The catalyst is, however, susceptible to poisons, with 0.1 percent FFA poisoning 0.02 percent NaOMe, and 0.01 percent water poisoning 0.03 percent NaOMe. As a consequence, the feedstock for interesterification normally contains less than 0.1 percent FFA and less than 0.01 percent water, hence emphasizing the importance of proper neutralization and drying prior to the reaction. To meet this water level target typically requires heating the oil to 110°C at a pressure of 15 mbar, and typically takes up to 3 hours unless oil circulation is used. The interesterification reaction normally only takes approximately 30 minutes and is followed by further neutralization and bleaching steps to deactivate the catalyst and remove reaction by-products (soaps, methyl esters, etc.). The reaction is typically carried out in a multipurpose vessel equipped with the necessary vacuum system and a suitable means of adding the catalyst.

The catalyst used for interesterification, sodium methoxide, is a hazardous material, which, with moisture (even humid air or skin), produces sodium hydroxide (caustic, corrosive) and methanol (flammable and toxic). Contact with hot surfaces and ignition sources must also be avoided since it has an auto ignition temperature of 40° to 70°C.

Fractionation Fractionation was originally developed to produce clear liquid oils and was developed from the winterizing process, i.e., allowing the oil to cool during the winter, the solids to grow and settle, and decanting the clear liquid as the product (olein). More recently, however, with the demand for CBES and CBRS there has been a growing application for the crystal/solid part of the fractionation process (stearin).

A fractionation process is comprised of two distinct operations—crystal growth and solid/liquid separation.

Crystal growth is a complex process and is not easy to control. It is essentially driven by cooling the oil below the temperature at which the more saturated triglycerides come out of solution in the less saturated triglycerides, thus generating a supersaturated solution. The level of supersaturation influences both the rate and type of crystals generated and can be manipulated via the oil temperature and the coolant temperature. The picture is, however, complicated by the existence of polymorphic states for many of the crystallizing triglycerides and the impact of crystal damage by the process equipment on the crystallization process. The objective for controlling the crystal growth is to produce large, dense crystal agglomerates from which the liquid oil can easily flow out and aid the solid/liquid separation step. As a side issue, crystal growth is exothermic with 1 percent crystal production causing about a 1°C temperature increase in the solution. This makes heat removal a critical process issue.

Fractionation processes have been developed along two differing routes—continuous solvent fractionation and batch dry fractionation.

The continuous solvent fractionation route involves dissolving the oil in a solvent, acetone being the most common. This inherently increases the cost of the process due to the need to recover the solvent from the fractions produced, remove any accumulated water from it and build the entire plant to meet flameproof standards. The advantages offered by the solvent, however, include a much increased crystallization rate and a greatly reduced viscosity for the trapped liquid "oil," thus aiding the solid/liquid separation efficiency. The solid/liquid separation can be further enhanced by washing the crystal mass on the filter with fresh solvent to displace additional trapped liquid oil from the crystal mass. The use of a solvent like acetone has the additional advantage that it is more polar than vegetable oil and as a consequence tends to concentrate FFA, diglycerides and other polar compounds in the olein fraction. This makes it attractive to solvent fractionate palm oil and shea oil in their crude states, although in the case of shea oil the polyisoprene gum must be separated from the solvent/oil mixture before it is crystallized. Typically the process is carried out using scraped surface crystallizers and moving belt filters to accommodate the wash solvent sprays.

The batch dry fractionation route commonly uses stirred tanks as crystallizers. These are equipped with either cooling coils or plates and stirrers that can handle the very viscous crystal suspensions generated during the crystallization process. The critical issue in controlling the crystal growth process is to be able to control the temperature difference between the cooling oil mass and the coolant circulated through the cooling coils. With too low a temperature difference, extended batch times occur, while if the temperature difference is too large, the cooling surfaces become coated with fat and lose their heat transfer capability. Typically batch crystallization times are approximately 10 hours as compared to the solvent route residence time of 30 minutes. Most modern dry fractionation plants use membrane filter presses to separate the solid and liquid fractions. These enable the filter cake produced by simple filtration to be squeezed, thus forcing out the liquid oil trapped between the crystals to both increase the yield of olein and produce a harder stearin. Simple filtration of an oil/crystal slurry generates a stearin that consists of 20 percent solid fat and 80 percent trapped liquid oil, while use of a membrane press can generate a stearin containing 65 to 80 percent solid fat.

Both the solvent and dry fractionation routes can be used in multistage processes where it is necessary to recover a mid-fraction as in the recovery of the POP triglyceride from palm oil.

Processing Limitations

As can be seen from the above, the oil processor has a fairly broad range of tools that can be used to generate high-quality products and manipulate the performance of oils to meet the customer's requirements. There are, however, limitations to what can be achieved.

In the hydrogenation process it is not possible to partially hydrogenate vegetable oils without generating *trans* fatty acids. This is a function of the thermodynamics of the *cis-trans* isomer equilibrium, which, under hydrogenation conditions, favors the formation of the *trans* isomer. While the confectionery industry exploits the *trans* fatty acids for their melting characteristics, this has implications for other food users of partially hydrogenated oils as a consequence of their nutritional impact. This has impacted the confectionery industry where the *trans* fatty acid content of CBRS has to be labeled.

For the fractionation process, even exploiting the enhanced characteristics of the solvent process, it is very difficult practically to achieve a clean separation between triglycerides that have a melting point difference of 10°C or less. Hence the separation of symmetrical monounsaturated triglycerides from their diunsaturated counterparts represents the best that can be achieved and the success of the separation depends very much on the feedstock composition.

With respect to diglyceride removal from the exotic fats and the reduction of the levels of hydroxy/epoxy triglycerides in sal fat, the oil processor is left largely without tools. Solvent fractionation offers the best opportunity to mitigate their effects by pushing some of these compounds down into the olein fraction but the effect is limited. The use of other separation techniques has been investigated but commercially attractive routes have yet to be identified.

QUALITY STRATEGY

The best quality strategy with vegetable oils and fats is to avoid the development of problems which have to be corrected at a later time, since deterioration is a one-way street. Where possible, control of oil quality needs to begin with the harvest of the crop. In the case of the exotic oils, their jungle origin and uncertain cropping makes this difficult but the earlier the crop can be dried the less the hydrolysis damage, which causes both yield loss at neutralization and a functional performance loss from the diglycerides formed. For the lauric fats, avoidance of PAH contamination at the plantation improves yield by avoiding the need for activated carbon treatment.

Moving into refinery operations, protection from oxidation is a key issue. The use of the minimum effective processing conditions can enhance the retention of natural antioxidants in the oil, which can be valuable where local regulations prevent the addition of antioxidants to finished products. Removing metals that act as oxidation catalysts via the use of process aids such as citric acid (a chelating agent) can also improve product oxidative stability. In addition to its flavor and aroma impact, oxidation can also impact the functional performance of oils. While it is possible to reduce the peroxide value of an oil to zero via bleaching, the residual components left in the oil after such a treatment lead to a tailing of the solids profile of a partially hydrogenated oil, when compared to a nonoxidized oil.

In the case of the lauric fats, rancidity rather than oxidation is a key problem, and major emphasis must be placed on vigorously avoiding fat/water contact, particularly in storage tanks where extended contact times at moderate temperatures may occur. The risk here is that any water trapped at the bottom of a storage tank becomes contaminated with a lipase-generating microorganism, which can accelerate the liberation of FFA and the development of a soapy off-flavor.

Questions & Answers

Q: Are lauric fats more prone to hydrolysis than domestic oils or is it that the C12 fatty acids have a stronger aroma/flavor due to their higher volatility? Why is lauric-acid-containing fat so prone to hydrolysis compared to stearic-, oleic-acid-containing fats?

A: The shorter chain fatty-acid-containing triglycerides are more reactive with water than their C18-containing counterparts, due to their slightly higher water solubility. They are also more susceptible to the action of lipase found naturally in the environment than their longer chain counterparts. The problem is exacerbated by the human sensory system, which shows a marked sensitivity for C12 fatty acids as compared to C18 ones.

Q: Are illipe, sal and shea used much in the United States?

A: Typically these fats are used as blends rather than individual oils. Current consumption in the United States is virtually zero, and in Canada on the order of a million pounds. Traditionally a significant volume of these products has been used in Europe, and the *trans* fatty acid labeling regulation may lead to further development of their use in North America.

Q: Are there any fats/oils/fractions that have all of the following attributes?
• *Liquid at room temperature.*
• *Fairly stable to oxidation.*
• *If used at less than 5 to 10 percent do not cause softening or incompatibility with hydrogenated palm kernel oil.*

A: No. While moderately stable liquid oils are readily available, any liquid oil or fraction will tend to dissolve solid triglycerides to some extent when mixed with hydrogenated palm kernel oil. As a consequence, the solid content of the blend will decline and the product soften. In the case of the lauric fats, differences in the fatty acid type in the liquid oil as compared to the hardened oil cannot be avoided and this causes further crystallization problems.

Q: Where does the PAH come from?

A: The exact origin of the polyaromatic hydrocarbons (PAH) found in some oils is unclear. PAH is generally associated with the partial combustion of a number of materials. Its presence in parcels of oil may be a reflection of the general "housekeeping" standards in some of the plantations, particularly as the level of PAH in samples of oil can vary from batch to batch of the same oil from the same source.

Q: What are the average nickel catalyst and solvent residues in oils?

A: Typically the residual nickel content of a hydrogenated oil, after filtration, is less than 0.1 ppm. In the event of difficulties in reaching this level, a chelation step may be incorporated into the posthydrogenation oil processing. For solvent fractionated oils, the final products have effectively a zero solvent content. For safety reasons in solvent fractionation plants, the solvent recovery systems are equipped with steam strippers to ensure that when the oil leaves the plant its solvent content is below the lower explosive limit for the solvent. The final oil deodorization removes any residual solvent traces that may have persisted after the solvent recovery operation.

Q: During the fractionation of an oil, does pressing the oil out (of the cake) affect the integrity of the remaining crystals?

A: No. The pressing process, both in terms of equipment and operating procedure, is designed specially to minimize damage to the crystal mass. If the crystals are damaged, this tends to collapse the channels through which the liquid oil flows out of the crystal mass and makes it more difficult to achieve a clean solid/liquid separation. Fragments of crystals also tend to blind the filter cloth, and make it more difficult to achieve adequate liquid oil drainage during pressing.

Q: In fractionation, what solvent should be used?

A: A number of different solvents have been used in fractionation, each with its own advantages and disadvantages. Acetone comes close to being an optimum solvent since typically, for confectionery fats, fractionation temperatures are in the 0°C (32°F) to 20°C (68°F) range, which can easily be achieved with ammonia cooling. It has the advantage of pulling diglycerides and free fatty acids away from the coating fat fractions but does concentrate them in the liquid fraction, which can cause usage problems. Water from the incoming oil accumulates in the solvent, which can lead to problems in controlling the crystallization process. Recovery of this accumulated water from the solvent does, however, require a fairly substantial distillation column due to the water/acetone vapor equilibrium behavior.

Isopropanol shows similar characteristics to acetone when used as a fractionation solvent, but being more polar has a larger impact on the fraction location of diglycerides and free fatty acids. Water presents more of an issue, since at comparable water levels to those encountered in acetone fractionation the isopropanol and the fat can form two liquid layers, thus negating many of the advantages of using a solvent. Water removal is also an issue due to the existence of an isopropanol/water azeotrope. Hexane use simplifies the water recovery issue since water readily separates from the solvent as a second liquid layer. However, unless water is rigorously excluded from the process this behavior can occur during crystallization and complicate the solid/liquid separation during the filtration step. Oil solubilities in hexane are such that fractionation temperatures tend to be lower in hexane than acetone, which can lead to difficulties in controlling crystal morphology and growth.

Q: Which fractionation process, dry or solvent, would be best for producing a trilaurin-free hardened palm kernel oil?

A: Without knowing the oil composition and which fraction is of interest, it is not obvious which route could potentially offer the most economical process. In general, solvent fractionation will offer the most selective fractionation opportunity, but, depending on the other triglycerides present, it may be necessary to accept a large yield loss to substantially remove all of a single triglyceride.

Q: Could you please briefly explain the technology of using enzymes in interesterification and fat tailoring?

A: The lipase group of enzymes, in the presence of water, catalyse the hydrolysis of fats to yield glycerol and free fatty acids. If the concentration of water present is reduced, eventually the direction of the reaction can be effectively reversed so that the enzyme will catalyse the formation of triglycerides from free fatty acids and glycerol. Under these restricted water conditions, the enzyme will also act as an interesterification catalyst and rearrange the configuration of the fatty acids on the glycerol backbone in a triglyceride.

Hence, using a lipase as an interesterification catalyst requires very precise control of the water content of the system if yield losses due to the formation of partial glycerides and free fatty acids are to be minimized during the rearrangement reaction. This, coupled with the fact that the lipases normally react at water/oil interfaces, favors the use of an immobilized enzyme, where the support can both hold the enzyme in a suitable reaction zone and provide water buffering to maintain enzyme activity. Enzymes are susceptible to poisoning from a variety of compounds routinely found in vegetable oils, so, in view of their cost compared to the chemical catalysts, careful cleaning of the oil is a necessary prerequisite to enzymic interesterification to prolong the active life of the catalyst. The main attractions of adopting enzymic interesterification over the chemical route are the mild processing conditions, which minimize by-product formation, and the opportunity to exploit the 1,3 specificity of some lipases for which there is no chemical option.

Characterization of Fats and Oils

Specifications and Technical Bulletins

Carl B. Heckel and Ed Wilson
Aarhus, Inc.

Characteristics of finished vegetable oils can fall into two categories: those that reflect how well the oil has been processed, and those that reflect important functionality characteristics. This paper discusses the lab tests that relate to these two categories. It is hoped that a better understanding of what the lab analysis can, and can't, tell us will help us all work with more meaningful specifications.

From a refiner's perspective, well-processed oil is colorless, tasteless and odorless. The degree of success depends partly on the specific oils being used. For instance, palm oil has high levels of beta-carotene. It is, therefore, red. To some extent, these color bodies can be removed, but palm oil can be expected to have some level of red color. Refining under specific conditions can be expected to yield specific criteria that can be measured in the lab and should consistently fall within a certain range that is specified in a quality specification. Color can be measured against specific standards; odor and taste are more subjective. Those conditions that lead to the removal of odor and taste, however, also affect parameters that can be nonsubjectively measured.

Functionality can be a more difficult characteristic to define. Ask one of your coworkers exactly what fat they are using, or looking for, or how it should function, and you'll see what I mean. The same oil may be used in a variety of products that have slightly different demands from the fat. The user has to first identify what is important, then, together with the oil refiner, ascertain certain measurable, physical properties that are related to the desired characteristics. These measurable properties would then be incorporated into a specification.

TESTING RELATED TO PROCESSING QUALITY

Refining and bleaching (or neutralizing and bleaching) and deodorization are processes that "clean" an oil. They do little to change its functionality. A number of tests are performed to monitor these processes. Particularly in combination, they reflect that the proper conditions existed for creating a colorless, odorless and tasteless product, as well as expected levels of stability, or shelf life. Certain criteria ought to be on every specification sheet, although the actual values may vary from oil to oil.

Fractionation, hydrogenation and interesterification, on the other hand, are specifically done to obtain different functional characteristics. A number of tests are available to reflect the effects of these operations.

Iodine value is a parameter that could arguably reflect processing quality, as well as purity of the oil. It is altered by two of the mentioned function-altering processes. Iodine value and other tests that relate to those processes will be discussed later.

Free Fatty Acids

Free fatty acids (FFAS) impart undesirable flavors, and are a reflection of poor processing. The analysis of an oil for the presence of FFAS is a simple titration using a weak caustic to neutralize an acid. A low value is desirable, but too low a value can indicate over-processing—excess losses, loss of desirable minor components such as antioxidants and increased costs. In the United States, almost all refiners standardize their solutions to read directly in terms of oleic acid. A typical specification will call for a maximum of 0.05 percent FFA as oleic acid (which equates to about 0.04% as lauric acid). This is a reasonable value, easily obtainable without over-processing and reflecting sufficient fatty acid removal.

Peroxide Value

Peroxides are degradation by-products from the oxidation of an oil. These impurities catalyze further degradation. Once they start to increase, they take off exponentially. As long as the oil starts with a low peroxide value (PV)—below 1 milliequivalent of peroxide per 1,000 grams—and is properly handled peroxides are not normally a problem. Peroxides are removed during deodorization, as are natural antioxidants found in those oils most susceptible to problems. Freshly deodorized oil should have a PV very close to zero. The PV should be less than 1 meq/kg at time of receipt by a customer.

Appearance

Appearance is not as readily quantified as other tests. The thought of a customer subjecting oil to the same conditions that we refiners subject oils to could make a refiner cringe. During processing, dirt (bleaching clay) is added, as well as caustic, acid, metals and water. The removal of these materials is important to the shelf life, aroma, taste and general acceptability of the oil as a food. Refiners expend considerable resources removing these undesirables once their purpose has been served. Appearance is often seen on specification sheets. Exactly what is meant probably varies from person to person. However, this is not a parameter to be taken lightly. Low levels of residual bleaching clay can shorten the shelf life of an oil significantly. One of the most sensitive, and underrated, analytical devices is the human eye. When trained to look for a deviation from the norm, it can be relied upon to flag a potential problem. There are tests—from the simple shining of a flashlight through a sample, to expensive turbidity meters, to intermediate filter tests—that can augment the subjective evaluation. How sophisticated do you need to be? Bear in mind that the refiner knows the importance of controlling the situation. Generally they do a good job. When they mess up, they usually mess up all the way. If you're looking for a potential problem, it will be fairly obvious. Just don't ignore the importance of appearance.

Flavor

Likewise, organoleptic evaluation for flavor (and aroma) may be difficult to define, but is definitely a legitimate reflection of the quality of the processing of an oil. By mentioning flavor at this point in this paper, I am in no way implying that it is not a functionality parameter of importance. People in the chocolate industry constantly evaluate the flavor and aroma of cocoa butter and in so doing create a sensory profile. This practice can also be adapted for fats and oils, and after a short time the sampler will be able to catch a potential problem before the product enters your facility.

Color

The color of an oil can be a reflection of minor components, and is potentially a functional parameter that should have been taken into account when the oil was selected for a particular application. Whole palm oil is red as a result of naturally occurring carotinoids; soybean and other oils may also have natural tinges of color that you should be aware of. Bleaching removes many color bodies, which can be destroyed to some extent in hydrogenation and deodorization. Unlike FFA and PV, what can be considered a good color will be dependent on the mother oil. The need then exists for a color specification, because a high color can be an indication of a number of potential problems, including heat abuse, age, trace metals and other impurities.

A reflection of proper processing can be obtained from certain tests such as FFA, PV and color. In addition, flavor and appearance are important analyses which should appear in specifications, even if only to the extent that they should be typical.

The question arises then, "What happens if the oil is out of specification?" The answer depends on what is out of spec, and why. At times, the intended use of the oil will have to be re-evaluated. Stability problems such as high peroxide may be improved by rebleaching or re-refining. The oil may have to be stabilized by hydrogenating it—in which case the physical characteristics are changed. If an oil is burned, and the flavor is permanently affected, it may have to be scrapped. In some cases if or solids profiles are off, blends can be altered or put aside for use in other blends. Hydrogenation is a one-way street; overprocessed batches, however, can sometimes be blended with slightly less hydrogenated oil to bring them into specification without impacting functionality. If an unintentional blend of different oils occurs, there are ways to convert these problems to usable products. There is a demand in this industry for customers that want to pay lower prices for blends, rather than single-source oil products. These blends come with slightly lower prices and while the specifications are usually wider and performance consistency may be an issue, they are widely used and accepted. Please note that not all blends are a result of mistakes: most blends are specificallydesigned for functional purposes and are not a result of mistakes.

TESTS RELATING TO FUNCTIONALITY

A number of analyses can be used to define important functionality aspects of confections. We'll look at two important aspects: tests defining the physical characteristics that will be seen in the finished product, and those defining the energy of transition that can help us identify processing conditions. Some tests are related to both.

Melting Point

The melting point is critical in establishing operating parameters for processes such as enrobing and depositing. The solids profile gives indications of important physical characteristics, such as heat resistance, snap and flavor release. Tests relating to the heat given off during crystallization of the fat may be critical in areas such as processing design that are necessary to establish a stable product. Another way to look at this is to assure a selected fat will work within an existing system design. For example: if you have an existing cooling tunnel that has only one zone and one entry point of air velocity, avoid selecting a fat that may require different temperature zones. You may otherwise end up running your equipment at considerably less than designed efficiency.

It needs to be noted that the tests being discussed here are all looking at fat melting, not solidifying. Fats are composed of many different molecules with different melting points. Several different crystalline structures (a polymorphic characteristic) are possible for many of these molecules. With a temper fat, it's necessary to obtain a fairly consistent, reproducible crystalline structure by tempering the sample to obtain reproducible, meaningful results. Polymorphic changes during melting itself are not a concern as long as we have a stable starting point.

In order to have reproducible results, these tests measure the transition from a solid to a liquid. The *AOCS Methods* manual has about five methods for determining the temperature at which a fat melts. Unfortunately, these different melting-point tests neither generate the same results, nor is there a fixed correlation between the results of different tests. Two common tests in the United States for confections are the Mettler drop point (MDP) and the Wiley melt point (WMP). While the WMP is officially discontinued by the AOCS, it still is widely used and accepted in the U.S.

Although the MDP method is supposed to be less subjective, there is a lack of commercially available standards, this makes it difficult for labs to check the calibration of the equipment. Adherence to the procedure is critical if reproducibility and agreement between labs are going to be maintained. The test itself involves casting up a small sample of well-melted oil in a small crucible. The sample is placed in a furnace and heated at a set rate until it is liquid enough to flow. As a drop passes an electric beam, the temperature is recorded.

This equipment is considerably more expensive than the beaker, thermometer and hot plate needed to run WMP or any of the capillary melting tests. While we have found excellent reproducibility within our own lab, we have found disappointingly inconsistent agreement between labs.

In the early '90s we ran an unofficial collaborative with approximately a dozen labs which ran both Mettler and Wiley tests. Surprisingly, there was better agreement with the more subjective Wiley test.

As mentioned, the WMP is still in common use, despite AOCS's action of officially removing it from the *Methods* manual. A small sample of oil, cast up on an aluminum plate with a hole drilled into it, is suspended between two layers of liquid in a test tube. The temperature is slowly raised. At some temperature, the pellet of oil starts changing shape and becomes elastic. Showing one the end point, or WMP, is easier than trying to describe it. This test is not likely to disappear until the shortcomings mentioned above for the MDP are rectified.

The melting point is important in predicting the effects of storage temperatures and establishing processing parameters, such as enrobing or moulding temperatures. Blocking of enrobed cookies made from a compound with a 95°F melt point is to be expected if unrefrigerated transport is used. If you have a fat with a melt point of 120°F, you have a better chance of avoiding blocking, but you obviously are going to trade off some other properties.

Regardless of what method is used, or what melting point is desired, a melting point specification for coating fats may need a narrow range compared to many other applications. On the other hand, a processing objective by those in the oil business may be to obtain a specific melt point through a process such as hydrogenation, but not always. For instance, refining, bleaching and deodorizing should not change the melting point of coconut oil. There is no way to adjust the parameter without some sort of label declaration.

A melting point specification for an oil such as refined, bleached and deodorized coconut oil, which is going to be what it is, is of no advantage. Secondly, there should be agreement between supplier and customer as to a single melting point method. A specification containing two methods only adds confusion. This is an ongoing issue as companies scramble to upgrade their internal specifications to fit their new quality or procedure programs. They may elect to have the Mettler as their official indicator of melt point without even contacting their suppliers to see if they can run collaborative tests for reproducibility results.

The flavor release and melting characteristics of cocoa butter are the target of alternative fats. A radical change in the solids of this fat is seen over a narrow temperature range. These properties and others can be predicted based on the level of solids the fat has at different temperatures.

Solids Profiles

Solids profiles are obtained primarily by two methods: dilatometry and nuclear magnetic resonance (NMR). In the early 1900s, a method was needed to describe butter solids so that a vegetable oil alternative could be developed. Important temperatures were selected: 50°F (10°C) was the internal temperature of the old iceboxes; the approximate temperature of the formal dining room was 70°F (21.1°C); kitchen temperature was 80°F (26.7°C); and mouth temperature was 92°F (33.3°C). Various higher temperatures have been used to help indicate the amount of residual solid oil that will be left in the mouth—typically 100°F (38.6°C), 104°F (40°C), or 108°F (43°C). Numerical values known as the solid fat index (SFI) were developed through a test that measures the volumetric difference between a liquid and a solid at the same temperature. It is important to note that SFIS are reported as an index number, not a percentage of the fat that is solid. SFIS tend to be reasonably close to a percentage at lower levels of solids, but the relationship disappears as solids increase. They are fairly inaccurate at 50 index units, and generally unrelated to percentage solids above 60 index units. With chocolate and compound coatings, the snap and heat resistance of the product is related to high levels of solids. This inability to significantly distinguish between different levels of solids in the range of these characteristics is particularly annoying, yet in the United States, many users of confectionery fats are used to seeing and are comfortable with SFI numbers.

Solid Fat Content

A truer, actual percentage of solids at a specific temperature can be determined by pulse nuclear magnetic resonance (pulse NMR). In the presence of a strong magnetic field, hydrogen nuclei (protons) are aligned with the magnetic field. When the magnetic field is removed, the protons then return (or decay) to a more random position. The rate at which this occurs in a solid is different than in a liquid. The NMR measures these differences, which are described as solid fat content (SFC).

A number of barriers exist to SFCS being generally accepted. Perhaps one of the major problems is a lack of a single, specific method. In addition to different tempering methods (AOCS or IUPAC), readings can be direct or indirect and samples can be tempered and measured in either a series or a parallel sequence. There are at least three different manufacturers whose equipment yields slightly different results. Temperature baths tend to take up a fair amount of bench space in the lab. At least seven baths are needed, and if there is demand for readings at both the even centigrade and at Fahrenheit points, an additional four or five baths may be required. AOCS Method Cd 16b-93 simply covers too many variables. The equipment is costly and demands on investment and space start to add up

Differential Scanning Calorimetry

A relatively new tool for the evaluation of oils is differential scanning calorimetry (DSC). As crystals are formed, energy is emitted; as crystals are melted, energy must be put into the system. If a sample is taken from one extreme of temperature to another, crystals may be formed, or melted. DSC takes a sample from one temperature extreme to the other at a set rate of temperature change, measuring the energy necessary to maintain this constant temperature change. This energy varies depending on changes in state of the sample—not just from a liquid to a solid, but from one polymorphic form to another. This not only provides an idea of what cooling capability is needed in a process, but it can also be used to look at the state of crystals in a finished product to see how stable the crystal structure is, or what the impact is of a change in a process condition. As with the other test mentioned, there is still no official procedure that has been accepted by the industry and many companies have developed their own procedure based on their specific needs.

Iodine Value

A commonly run test, which appears on virtually all specification sheets, is the iodine value (IV). This test provides a relative value for the number of double bonds in a triglyceride. It is not a percentage or absolute number, but rather the number of centigrams of iodine absorbed per gram of sample. Although this test does not tell you how many monounsaturated versus polyunsaturated bonds exist, or whether they are in the *cis-* or the *trans-*isomer, it is a valuable indicator of an oil's purity. It is a major process control test for fractionation and hydrogenation. Iodine values are often determined by wet chemistry methods (AOCS Method Cd 1-25), but can also be calculated from the fatty acid profile. New methods are being developed using FT-IR for both on-stream process control and sample analysis of the iodine value.

The actual fatty acid profile and triglyceride compositions of the oil can be determined in the lab by equipment like the high pressure liquid chromatograph (HPLC) and the gas liquid chromatograph (GLC). These tests provide information about source oils being used and processing, which may be necessary for verifying source oil labeling and nutritional characteristics.

SPECIFICATION SHEETS: WHAT SHOULD THEY INCLUDE?

A specification sheet should sufficiently describe a fat system to assure a consistent, quality product with the functional attributes needed. It may also provide other data or information unique to that fat. Proper label declarations or nutritional information may be appropriately included. A specification sheet, however, should be a reference sheet primarily for locating meaningful technical data.

As mentioned above, certain data reflects how well an oil is processed. Regardless of the source or application, free fatty acid, peroxide value, color, flavor and appearance are important parameters. Iodine value in confections may be more of an indicator of proper source oils, but it can also be an important indicator of both processing quality and functionality in some applications.

Melting point and solids profiles are usually important confection characteristics that should be in a specification. Dsc (or a similar test to reveal key crystalline characteristics) could easily find a prominence in the future, particularly in place of some tests such as the Jensen cooling curve.

Not every analysis that can be run needs to be in a specification sheet. There have been situations where a specification sheet including ranges for specific fatty acid content (FAC) has come back to haunt the owner. Prior to source oil labeling, a specification of this sort may have been necessary to assure only specific oils were used for functional purposes. Source oil labeling now assures this. A downstream customer, however, acquiring a copy of a specification, expects to see a specific fatty acid composition from the finished product made from that fat. Doing an extraction and analysis can easily present a different picture because of other sources of lipids—lecithin, emulsifiers, cocoa powder, etc. Now the uneducated have unwarranted concerns. In this particular case, the question of why a FAC was included in the specification was asked; I don't think a satisfactory answer rose to the surface.

In recent years there seems to have been a trend towards the inclusion of new items in product specifications. Allergen content is certainly a valid concern and perhaps has a place in a technical bulletin. However, some other trends are bothersome. Do references to Continuing Commodity Guarantees and California's Safe Drinking Water and Toxic Enforcement Act of 1986 belong in a specification sheet for an oil, or are they more appropriately reserved for a sales contract? If a technical person is asked to sign off on a specification, I wonder if there is any validity to that person's signature under a statement such as, "As changes in the formulation, the process, and/or the production location are anticipated…must be informed in writing and must approve these changes…" As smart as lawyers are, can't they find a more appropriate method of conveying this message than burying it in a technical specification? Sales contracts are handled by those responsible for terms and conditions of a sell. Technical specifications should relate to specific materials as opposed to general business requirements.

Many customer-generated specifications make reference to in-house test methods. An assumption may be made that an iodine value is going to be an iodine value, whether it is run by AOCS Method Cd 1-25, or by "ABC Company Method 327." Technically, when someone approves a specification referencing "Customer Test Procedure A33," rather than a specific IUPAC, AACC or AOCS method, they should have validated that the method used produces an appropriate result. Likewise, if "Customer Test Procedure A33" is modified, how often is that modification shared with suppliers? It's not surprising that individual companies modify internationally recognized methods for their own circumstances, but why a specific company expects all suppliers to keep up with that company's change is strange. If you want to see where your specifications might be improved, perhaps this is a place to start.

Questions & Answers

Q: You mentioned that there was poor correlation between testing laboratories when testing melt point with the Mettler drop point on the same samples, but better when using the Wiley melt point. Why?

A: There are probably a number of reasons, but we really don't know. Although the Mettler drop point is not as subjective, care must be taken in the preparation and handling of the sample. Details such as keeping the sample holder in a freezer and not handling it with bare hands have an impact. Without commercially available standards, the ability to validate the technique itself is difficult. The Mettler was relatively new to us at the time of that evaluation. Now that it is more widely used, the results may be different.

Q: For the confectionery industry, which solids profile testing method is more accurate, repeatable and meaningful, the dilatometry or NMR? Why?

A: The problem with the question is that it does not specify which NMR method is to be used. NMR ought to be the answer because it is far less subjective. A more meaningful question might be, With what tempering method, and at what temperatures, will the most meaningful results appear? Although the equipment is expensive, NMR is what future specifications ought to have, but not until there is agreement on which methodology will be standard. AOCS Method CD 16b-93 includes statistical data relating to accuracy and reproducibility.

Q: Are there standard ranges for some of the numerical attributes like iodine value or FFA content (for example, do numbers usually range in 0.1 units for FFA so the specification for a product could be 0.01–0.11) or are there mostly maximum specifications (like less than 0.05%)?

A: Although there may be reasons for exceptions to the following, in general, many parameters have greater accuracy available than is really meaningful in the commercial world. Iodine values, for instance, can be read with several different methods with good agreement at the 0.1 level of accuracy. But in what applications will the difference between xx.3 and xx.9 be of importance? Free fatty acids can be accurately read to 0.001 percent (and lower levels), but who cares? Parameters such as PV and FFA that reflect how well the processing was done should typically have a "Max." only. Those parameters that relate to functionality on the other hand, such as melting point, ought to have a range that is meaningful, and obtainable, for that characteristic. For confection applications, parameters such as iodine value are going to be a function of the base oils and their processing. In other applications (e.g., frying), iodine value may be of greater importance as an indication of actual functionality.

Q: Many companies do confirmatory testing on incoming raw materials. Are there times in the shelf life (or from shipping conditions) when results may show significant differences not due to testing but due to changes in the product? Do fat/oil manufacturers typically retest certain attributes before shipping stock items?

A: Factors such as time and temperature will have some impact on parameters like free fatty acid and peroxide value. Others such as melting point and solids profiles are not usually (or measurably) changed by storage and shipping conditions. Differences in iodine value, for instance, are more likely to be procedural; variations in FFA, flavor and peroxide, on the other hand, could be either a change in product quality or differences in methodology.

Whether or not a manufacturer retests certain attributes of stock items probably varies with the supplier. Distribution centers may not have lab facilities. The best answer is to refer you to your specific supplier.

Q: How useful is refractive index for quality measure in fats and oils?

A: Others may disagree, but I think it is a holdover from ages past, replaced long ago with better indicators.

Q: What is the surrounding liquid in the Wiley melt point method?

A: In this test, the "pellet" of oil floats at the interface between layers of water and alcohol. The test tube is in a water bath.

Q: Which fats (if any), other than cocoa butter or CBES, benefit from being tempered to give the required crystal form?

A: Although they function well without tempering, lauric-based confection fats do hold their gloss longer in most applications with tempering.

Q: What would be the critical analysis to perform to assess the quality of cocoa butter—the same as for specialty fats plus Blue value, for example?

A: Solids profile, melting point and other crystallization evaluations would be critical. Some other tests may be more important with cocoa butter than with other specialty fats—flavor for instance. Because of the difference in processing steps, when deodorized cocoa butter is being evaluated, there are a number of additional tests related to shelf life that may be of importance: OSI, tocopherol content, Totox value, etc.

Q: Please review again the barriers to acceptance of SFC by NMR and your opinion of industry preference.

A: Several barriers exist to acceptance of NMR:
- Cost of equipment and bench space needed.
- Understanding by customers (particularly small users who are used to SFI numbers).
- Most importantly, a standardized method of analysis.

I suspect the advantages of SFC are understood and recognized by many suppliers as well as buyers. Active participation in the process of modifying the method is needed by users.

Q: Based on customer spec, how are the Certificates of Analysis generated for a load of hydrogenated palm kernel oil? Controls? Lot system? Computer generated?

A: Whether the specification is established by the customer or by the supplier, the numbers on the Certificate of Analysis should be coming from actual analysis of the material being shipped.

Comparison of the analytical data with the prevailing specification, which will usually be the customer's specification if one exists, may be done automatically by a computer when data is entered, or manually. I'm sure both procedures are being done within the oil industry. At the end of the day, the supplier is responsible for providing material within the specifications of the purchasing agreement—or, as sometimes happens, obtaining a waver for the delivery of material that is out of specification. Different companies probably have different methods of control.

Lot numbering systems are interesting. Because a load of oil is different from individually packaged items, there is not a lot number stamped on the side of a box. Indeed, our company uses a system designed for the facilitation of our own, computerized recall/traceability system. Under this system, the lot number would automatically change if there is any oil (almost always the case) still in the tank at time of receipt. The supplier's lot number is only a reference point for the customer to identify part of the customer's lot. Is company A's lot number relevant if it tops off a tank that had 10,000 lbs of company B oil in the tank? Of course it is. But the customer is dealing with a lot number that is different from, but needs to include, both company A's and company B's material. Understanding the numbering system used by our company is not important. Having the number and knowing that it allows us to trace the material in the event of a recall is important.

Computer-generated Certificates of Analysis are certainly nice, but at the end of the day, accurate, legible, reliable data is more important.

Q: Wouldn't a Rancimat value be a better indication for the confectioner than the peroxide value?

A: This could certainly be argued. It is interesting that the Rancimat is so popular in much of the world, yet has not been widely accepted in the United States.

From a practical point of view, a peroxide

value can be run in a reasonably short period of time, with relatively low costs. Obtaining a PV on each and every batch is possible; that may not be feasible with the Rancimat. Time is a factor. Customers who want an AOM run on every shipment are asking a supplier to put aside and hold that oil for the 100 plus hours it may take an AOM to run. Few customers really want to pay for that. The PV can flag to the refiner (in combination with other analyses) a potential problem that the Rancimat wouldn't.

Q: Is there any method to detect flavor difference such as off-flavor by instruments instead of sensory test by mouth?

A: A number of companies have worked on this project—particularly with soft oils, which can have so many different flavor notes. Some have developed methodology they put much faith in. To my knowledge there is not presently a widely used test in the public domain.

Q: Would unsaponifiable matter determination not be relevant to specialty fats?

A: Unsaponifiable matter consists of compounds that are soluble in fats and oils, but will be converted to soaps by caustic. This group of, generally speaking, natural minor components of oils includes sterols, pigments, higher aliphatic alcohols and hydrocarbons.

What would such an analysis of an oil tell one in the confection industry? In the oleo-chemical industry purification of specific products made from oils may be affected by these components. With a confection fat from some specific source, do we want a high number of unsaponifiables or a low number?

If the analysis is going to be run, one would assume there is some specification to be met. What is the impact of being out of specification, and is there a return for whatever processing costs would be incurred in eliminating the problem?

If one is thinking this would be a nice value to monitor, I hope they will consider the hazards of the chemicals to which the analyst is being subjected (petroleum ether, 50% KOH).

If there is some specific concern that a customer feels should be addressed, that should be identified and, as appropriate, some method selected to evaluate that concern. I do not know what specific concern might have prompted the question. With the methods of processing specialty fats in common use in the United States, I am not aware of problems that might be monitored best by analyzing for unsaponifiable matter.

Oil and Fat Interactions

Theory, Problems and Solutions

Ralph E. Timms, PhD
Consultant to Britannia Food Ingredients Ltd.

Oils and fats (and the triglycerides that comprise them) have more than one melting point. Each different form of a triglyceride or fat that has a different melting point is called a *polymorph* and the phenomenon is called *polymorphism* (from the Greek meaning many forms). These polymorphs are different forms of the crystalline, solid state. Different solid and liquid forms, e.g., ice and water, are not different polymorphs but different phases.

For fats, the differences between polymorphs are often not very clear and special techniques are usually needed to identify polymorphs, especially when more than one are present. X-ray diffractometry is the only method that can unequivocally identify a polymorph, but differential scanning calorimetry (DSC) and microscopy are also useful. Sometimes, the presence of a particular polymorph can be inferred by its effect on the macroscopic properties of the fat or fat products, e.g., a shortening not in the β' polymorph will not cream well; chocolate not tempered to the β polymorph will not contract easily from the mould and will eventually bloom.

Fats and triglycerides occur in any one of three basic polymorph types which are designated α (alpha), β' (beta prime) and β (beta). (Other forms, γ and sub-α or sub-β, may also be seen). The least stable and lowest melting is α. The most stable and highest melting is β. Transformations from α to β' to β take place in that order and are irreversible. Most fats and triglycerides possess an α polymorph, although it is usually very unstable; some also possess both β' and β polymorphs; others only a stable β' polymorph and no β; or a stable β polymorph and no β'.

Studies of the crystal structures of triglycerides have shown that triglycerides pack side by side in separate layers and are arranged in pairs, head to tail. This is shown schematically in Figure 1. The zigzag refers to the structure of the fatty acid chain, where each C atom has its four bonds (C-C or C-H) arranged tetrahedrally.

In the α polymorph, the fatty acid chains are loosely packed and are considered to be oscillating with no fixed position in the crystal. In the β' polymorph, the chains tilt to accommodate the zigzag chains, but alternating chains are in different planes, perpendicular to each other. This configuration allows the β' polymorph to accommodate

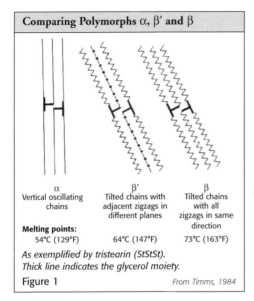

Comparing Polymorphs α, β′ and β

α	β′	β
Vertical oscillating chains	Tilted chains with adjacent zigzags in different planes	Tilted chains with all zigzags in same direction

Melting points:

54°C (129°F)	64°C (147°F)	73°C (163°F)

As exemplified by tristearin (StStSt).
Thick line indicates the glycerol moiety.

Figure 1 *From Timms, 1984*

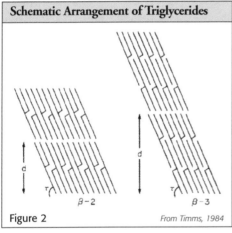

Schematic Arrangement of Triglycerides

β-2   β-3

Figure 2 *From Timms, 1984*

fatty acid chains of different types more easily than the β polymorph. In the β polymorph, the packing is the tightest and most stable possible, with the zigzags in the same plane. For a β polymorph to exist, the fatty acids in the adjacent planes must be identical or very similar to each other, e.g., all saturated and not more than four carbon atoms different in chain length.

Two triglyceride packing modes are possible, resulting in pairs of triglycerides two or three fatty acid chain lengths long, as shown in Figure 2. The packing is said to be double or triple chain length spacing and is indicated by adding -2 or -3 to the basic polymorph symbol, e.g., β′-2 or β-3. The packings shown in Figure 1 are thus α-2, β′-2 and β-2.

Triple chain length packing is favored when one fatty acid is different from the other two in the triglyceride molecule, e.g., if one fatty acid is unsaturated and the other two are saturated. The three major triglycerides in cocoa butter—POP, POSt and StOSt—are examples of triglycerides with stable β-3 polymorphs. In Figure 3 the β-3 polymorph of COC, which is of the same structure as these triglycerides, is depicted with the bent oleic acid chain (caused by the double bond in the middle of the chain) easily accommodated in the middle layer of the triple chain structure.

Polymorphism of Cocoa Butter

The definitive study of cocoa butter polymorphism was made by Wille & Lutton, who found six polymorphs as given in Figure 4. Their conclusions have been amply confirmed by many other workers since. They designated the polymorphs Forms I to VI, and this is still a convenient terminology, but the modern systematic nomencla-

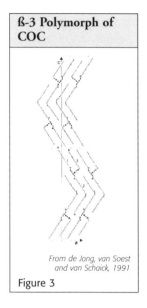

ß-3 Polymorph of COC

From de Jong, van Soest and van Schaick, 1991

Figure 3

ture is also given in the table. The subscripts indicate different polymorphs of the same type, with 1 being the highest melting point and most stable.

In practical, commercial chocolate making, only Forms IV to VI are important. Form V is the form found in correctly tempered chocolate, Form IV in untempered chocolate and Form VI in bloomed chocolate or chocolate stored for a long time (years).

Polymorphism of Other Confectionery Fats

Confectionery fats, often called cocoa butter alternative fats, can be divided into three types according to their chemistry and use:

Cocoa butter equivalents (CBE) based on palm oil and other tropical fats contain the same triglycerides as found in cocoa butter.

Cocoa butter substitutes (CBS) based on lauric oils contain mainly medium chain L and M fatty acids.

Cocoa butter replacers (CBR) based on hydrogenated liquid oils—soy, cotton, rape, palm olein—contain about 50 percent transunsaturated fatty acids.

CBES have very similar polymorphism to cocoa butter and all show a stable β-3 polymorph.

CBS and CBR are complex mixtures of triglycerides of varying fatty acid composition, molecular size and shape. The β' structure more easily accommodates such mixtures and both CBS and CBR show a stable β'-2 polymorph.

Milk fat, the other main fat used in confectionery, is also a complex mixture of triglycerides, with fatty acid chain lengths from 4 to 20. Unlike cocoa butter and

Polymorphs of Cocoa Butter			
Form	Melting Point (°C)	Systematic Nomenclature	Comments
I	17.3°C	β'_3 (sub-α)	Not found in practice.
II	23.3°C	α-2	Not found in practice.
III	25.5°C	β'_2-2	Not found in practice.
IV	27.5°C	β'_1-2	Characteristic of untempered chocolate.
V	33.8°C	β_2-3	Characteristic of tempered chocolate.
VI	36.2°C	β_1-3	Characteristic of bloomed chocolate.

Figure 4   From Wille & Lutton, 1966

cocoa butter alternative fats, milk fat is less homogeneous and three separate phases are easily distinguished (see next section). For our purpose we can consider milk fat to have a stable β′ polymorph, with a small amount of β and mainly double spacing, but some triple spacing.

PHASE BEHAVIOR

A phase is a state of matter that is homogeneous and is separated from other phases by a definite physical boundary. A phase is defined by its chemical composition, temperature and pressure. For most practical purposes, pressure can be ignored, but it could be important to consider in extruded confectionery products. Examples of phases follow:

- One solid and one liquid, e.g., ice and water, oil and fat.
- Two solid phases, e.g., cocoa and sugar in chocolate, two coexisting polymorphs such as Forms V and VI in bloomed chocolate.
- Two liquid phases, e.g., oil and water in a salad dressing, oil, solid fat and water in butter or margarine (a three-phase system).

All natural fats contain at least two phases, solid and liquid. There is always only one liquid phase, but there may be several solid phases although they are usually distinguishable only at the microscopic level.

Since a phase is defined by its temperature and composition, a diagram with temperature along one axis and composition along the other is sufficient to show all the phases in any two-component mixture. Such a diagram is called a phase diagram. The two important types of phase diagram found for confectionery fats are the monotectic and the eutectic type as shown in Figure 5.

The *liquidus* is the line above which the mixtures are completely melted. It is the complete melting point line. The *solidus* is the line below which the mixtures are completely solid and contain no liquid phase. In between the liquidus and solidus lines, the triglyceride mixtures contain both solid and liquid phases coexisting in equilibrium.

Monotectic phase diagrams are found when the two triglycerides, A and B, are very similar and mix completely to form a single solid phase or solid solution. A solid solution is a solid phase in which the two components are randomly mixed. Its properties vary continuously according to its composition, just like the more familiar liquid solutions. For example, as sugar is added to water the solution becomes more viscous, but there is no point at which sugar and water can be distinguished and the viscosity increases continuously as more sugar is added. Usually, however, the solubility of one solid in another is limited (just as with a solid dissolving in a liquid) and two solid phases are formed, each of which is usually a solid solution. This is the situation

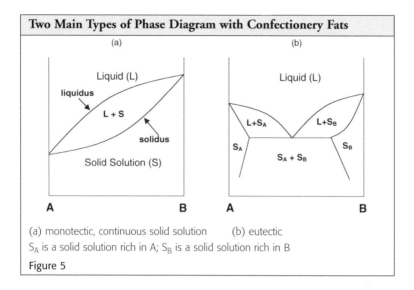

Two Main Types of Phase Diagram with Confectionery Fats

(a) monotectic, continuous solid solution   (b) eutectic
S_A is a solid solution rich in A; S_B is a solid solution rich in B

Figure 5

described by the eutectic phase diagram shown in Figure 5(b). The mixture of two incompatible triglycerides results in a eutectic mixture, with a melting point lower than the melting points of either of the two pure component triglycerides.

Mixtures of real fats, where many more than two triglycerides are involved, show similar types of phase diagram.

Phase diagrams may depict systems at equilibrium or at a given, metastable stage in a particular time-temperature storage history.

Crystallization and Melting of Fats

Crystallization is a complex process and a separate topic. For our purpose, we just need to note that a fat usually under- or super-cools 10°C (20°F) or more below its melting point before it starts to crystallize, and that crystallization usually starts in the α or other unstable polymorph, because the crystallization temperature is then below the α melting point. As crystallization proceeds, heat is evolved and the temperature may rise. The fat may then change to a stable β' or β polymorph.

Figure 6 shows a schematic phase diagram of the simplest fat, which is a mixture of two triglycerides, A and B. The vertical dashed line indicates the composition of the fat at about 35 percent B and 65 percent A.

If we heat the fat, it begins to melt at temperature T_4 and melts completely at T_2. Thus we note that, unlike pure A or B, the fat melts over a range of temperatures. At temperatures between T_4 and T_2, the fat is partly solid and partly liquid. If we consider temperature T_1, the fat consists of fraction *bc/ac* of liquid phase of the composition given at *a* and *ab/ac* of solid phase of the composition given at *c*. Thus another important conclusion is that as the temperature increases, not only does the amount of the liquid phase increase, but its composition changes as given by the upper, liquidus line. Furthermore, if we hold the fat at temperature T_1 until the system reaches equilibrium and then cool rapidly to a temperature below T_A, the two phases are frozen. Now when we heat the fat, melting will start at T_5, the point at which the liquid phase of composition a intersects the solidus line. Liquid phase of composition a melts over the range T_5 to T_1, solid phase of composition c melts over the range T_1 to T_3. Thus after holding (tempering) at temperature T_1, the fat melts over the temperature range T_5 to T_3, rather than the original T_4 to T_2.

In summary we can conclude the following:

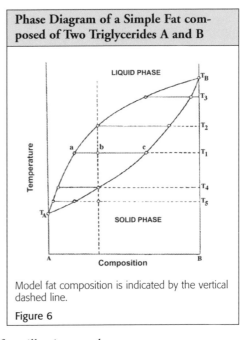

Phase Diagram of a Simple Fat composed of Two Triglycerides A and B

Model fat composition is indicated by the vertical dashed line.

Figure 6

- Fats melt over a melting range.

- At most temperatures solid and liquid fat will exist together.

- The amounts of solid and liquid fat, the final melting temperature and the compositions of the solid and liquid depend on the thermal history of the fat: how it was crystallized, tempered and stored.

For real fats, i.e., mixtures which consist of more than two triglycerides, all the above conclusions hold, except that we cannot deduce the amount of solid and liquid fat from theory/the phase diagram. We need an empirical, direct method of determination. Measurement of the solid fat index (SFI) by dilatometry is one such method, but measurement of the solid fat content (SFC) by NMR is now much more common and very much preferred for confectionery fats, which usually have high SFCS well above the 50 percent for which the SFI method is applicable.

In Figure 7 we see the SFC melting curves for a typical cocoa butter and milk fat. As predicted from theory, we see a wide melting range and even at 10°C (50°F) the apparently solid cocoa butter still contains about 15 percent liquid phase.

Figure 8 shows a DSC melting curve of cocoa butter which has been tempered to give the Form V found in normal production chocolate. A large, single, sharp peak shows that the cocoa butter triglycerides (POP, POSt, StOSt) form a single solid phase. (The few other smaller and lower-melting peaks correspond to the more-liquid minor triglycerides such as POO, StOO.) In contrast, Figure 9 shows a DSC melting curve of milk fat. Here, three solid phases can be distinguished corresponding to the high-, middle-melting and low-melting triglyceride groups in milk fat.

MIXTURES OF FATS

In chocolate and other confectionery we usually have mixtures of fats, e.g., cocoa butter and milk fat in milk chocolate, cocoa butter and CBS in compound chocolate. Fats interact in the same way as pure triglycerides interacted in our previous discussion.

Cocoa butter and milk fat mix to form a solid solution at up to 50 percent milk fat. The cocoa butter crystal structure accommodates the milk fat triglycerides, (which as we saw in Figure 5 are mostly liquid at normal-use temperatures) and steadily softens as more milk fat is added (but remains in the stable Form V if tempered correctly).

Solid Fat Melting Curves of Cocoa Butter and Milk Fat

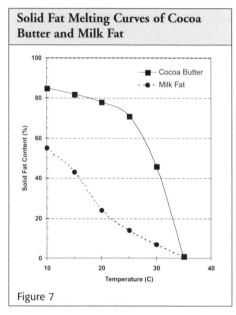

Figure 7

DSC Melting Curve of Cocoa Butter in Form V

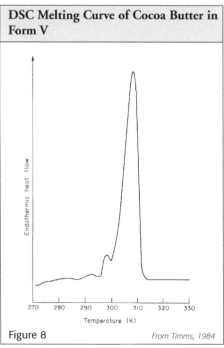

Figure 8   *From Timms, 1984*

DSC Melting Curve of Milk Fat after Tempering for 4 weeks at 13°C

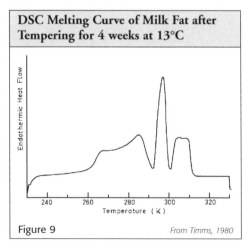

Figure 9   *From Timms, 1980*

Cocoa butter and CBE mix together with a phase diagram similar to Figure 5(a). A continuous solid solution forms. There is no softening of the cocoa butter and it is not possible to distinguish triglycerides from cocoa butter or CBE in the mixture.

Cocoa butter and CBS mix together to give a phase diagram similar to Figure 5(b). A so-called isosolid phase diagram, where the solidus and liquidus lines are replaced by lines of constant solid fat, is shown in Figure 10. The phase boundaries are indicated by the thick lines. The softening caused by the eutectic, the incompatibility between cocoa butter and CBS, is clearly shown by the dip in the isosolid lines. The phase boundaries show that no more than about 10 percent CBS can be added to cocoa butter while maintaining a single (β-3/Form V) solid solution. Beyond that, a two phase β-3 + β'-2 region exists. Similarly, if cocoa butter is added to CBS, only up to about 10 percent cocoa butter can dissolve to form a single (β'-2) solid solution. In practical terms, we can only make satisfactory chocolate in the single phase regions at the left and right of the diagram. If we try to make chocolate with fat compositions in the two-phase middle region of the diagram, the chocolate will be soft, difficult to temper and will bloom. These conclusions explain the facts that we must avoid contaminating cocoa butter chocolate with CBS compound chocolate in the factory; and when we make CBS compound chocolate we must use low-fat cocoa powder to ensure that the cocoa butter level remains well below 10 percent in the fat phase (usually about 5 percent).

Figure 11 shows the isosolid phase diagram of mixtures of cocoa butter and a CBR. Here, the single phase region on the right is much larger than for CB/CBS mixtures. In practice, we know that CBR can be used in recipes that contain cocoa liquor so that the amount of cocoa butter in the fat phase can be as high as 20 percent.

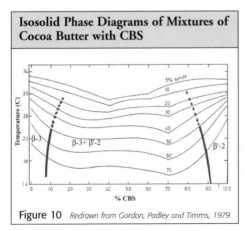

Isosolid Phase Diagrams of Mixtures of Cocoa Butter with CBS

Figure 10 *Redrawn from Gordon, Padley and Timms, 1979*

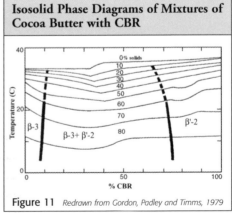

Isosolid Phase Diagrams of Mixtures of Cocoa Butter with CBR

Figure 11 *Redrawn from Gordon, Padley and Timms, 1979*

OIL MIGRATION

Food products, like everything else in the universe, tend towards chemical and thermodynamic equilibrium. For example, if we put ice in a martini, the ice and the martini move towards equilibrium: the ice melts, the gin and vermouth cool down and eventually the mixture becomes homogenous with uniform temperature and uniform composition. Similarly, if we take a biscuit, a center cream, praline/nougat or other filling (the center) and then enrobe it with chocolate (the shell), the center and shell try to come to thermodynamic and chemical equilibrium. The fat components of the center and the shell tend to become homogenous and identical.

We have seen that all fats, even apparently very solid and hard fats like cocoa butter, have some liquid oil at normal-use temperatures. The movement towards equilibrium is achieved mainly by the movement (migration) of the liquid phases. Figure 12 shows data on the center and shell composition of an enrobed biscuit stored at various temperatures. Notice that even at 21°C (70°F) substantial migration occurs. As the temperature rises and the amount of liquid fat increases, the rate and amount of migration increases. Migration is always a two-way process—from center to shell and from shell to center—and this is clearly seen by comparing the results at 21°C (70°F) and 38°C (100°F). At 21°C, net migration is from center to shell (the center is losing fat, the shell is gaining fat). At 38°C, net migration is from shell to center.

Chocolate is a fat-continuous product, as are pralines and many other centers. Biscuits are not fat-continuous, but fat can move to contact the shell by wicking. The biscuit base type affects the rate of migration, with denser biscuits showing higher rates of migration.

This two-way migration is further confirmed by model studies where cocoa butter/sugar mixtures were placed adjacent to sunflower oil/sugar mixtures. The results in Figure 13 show that the movement of cocoa butter into the sunflower oil is less than the movement of sunflower oil into the cocoa butter, but it is still substantial.

In a study of a chocolate-coated praline, the fatty acid and mass balance data shown in Figure 14 illustrate the

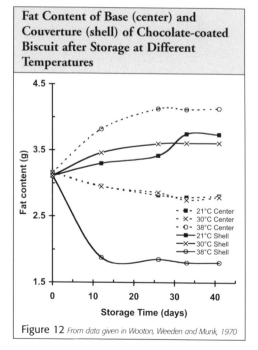

Fat Content of Base (center) and Couverture (shell) of Chocolate-coated Biscuit after Storage at Different Temperatures

Fat content (g)

Storage Time (days)

- 21°C Center
- 30°C Center
- 38°C Center
- 21°C Shell
- 30°C Shell
- 38°C Shell

Figure 12 *From data given in Wooton, Weeden and Munk, 1970*

full extent of the two-way migration.

The migration and mixing of the phases take place by diffusion and the rate of migration is initially proportional to the square root of the diffusion coefficient and the time.

Monitoring Migration

Migration can be observed and monitored by several methods:

- **Observation** The product will often soften, crack, bloom or otherwise change its appearance.

- **Weighing** The center and shell will change weight with time. The results given in Figure 12 were obtained by this method.

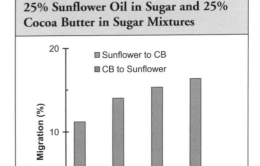

Migration between Adjacent Layers of 25% Sunflower Oil in Sugar and 25% Cocoa Butter in Sugar Mixtures

Storage at 25°C for 8 weeks

Figure 13   *Redrawn from Talbot, 1990*

- **Measuring the amount of liquid oil with time, using DSC or NMR methods** DSC was used to produce the results shown in Figure 15.

- **Measuring the fatty acid or triglyceride composition by gas liquid chromatograph or high pressure liquid chromatograph (HPLC)** HPLC was used to produce the results given in Figure 16.

- **Magnetic resonance imaging** MRI was used to produce the results shown in Figure 17. The steadily increasing movement of the hazelnut oil into the chocolate shell is clearly seen.

Migration in Enrobed Pralines

(after storage for 4 months at 20°C)

	Praline Center		Chocolate Shell	
	Before Storage	After Storage	Before Storage	After Storage
% of total product	49	42	51	58
% migrated	14.3		13.7	
% of fat migrated	34.3		32.9	
Fatty Acid Composition:				
16:0	7.4	9.5	25.0	17.6
18:0	5.2	6.4	34.2	22.6
18:1	74.8	71.2	36.5	52.2
18:2	12.6	12.9	4.2	7.6

Figure 14   *From Chaveron, Ollivon & Adenier, 1976*

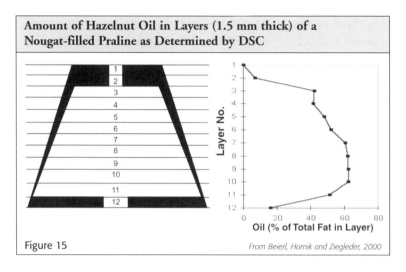

Amount of Hazelnut Oil in Layers (1.5 mm thick) of a Nougat-filled Praline as Determined by DSC

Figure 15
From Beierl, Hornik and Ziegleder, 2000

Preventing Migration

We have seen that migration depends on three factors:

• Temperature.

• Amount of liquid oil phase present in center and shell.

• Time.

Thus, we should expect migration to be prevented or minimized by these steps:

• Reducing the storage temperature and storage time of the product.

• Using harder fats in the center or shell to reduce the amount of liquid oil available for migration.

• Structuring the crystals of the fats so that they trap the liquid oil.

• Putting an oil-impermeable layer between the center and shell.

• Using a thicker chocolate shell so that the effect of migration into the shell may not be noticeable at the surface and not seen by the consumer.

• Using a fat for the center that is compatible with the fat in the shell.

Clearly if the SFC of the fat in the center is increased, the amount of liquid phase will decrease. In Figure 18 the

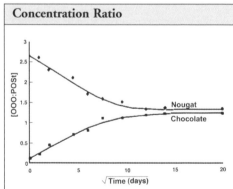

Concentration Ratio

Concentration ratio [OOO:POSt] of the fat in chocolate and nougat in nougat-filled milk chocolate as a function of the storage time at 26°C. Nougat fraction is 50 percent.

Figure 16 *From Ziegleder, Moser and Geier-Greguska, 1996*

amount of migration of various fats is shown to be strongly dependent on the SFC of the fats. It is also noticeable, however, that the correlation is not perfect. Fat CMF has a much lower rate of migration than HP1 or REF, but all have similar SFC. This is due to the structure or size and type of the crystals in the fat. Small β′ crystals form a large surface area and contain fissures which trap the liquid oil. Manufacturers sell so-called "structured fats" to minimize oil migration for a given SFC. The concept of a critical volume fraction, the concentration at which particles in a mixture are so crowded that mobility is virtually eliminated, has been developed to quantify and explain the phenomenon. On the other hand, adding lecithin tends to increase migration as it breaks up sugar aggregates, something which is often desirable because it may improve the flow properties of the filling.

If the fat in the center were 100 percent solid at normal-use temperatures, then migration could hardly occur. Such a solution to the problem is not really feasible, since the product would be rather unpalatable. A compromise solution is to use a barrier fat where a high-SFC fat is applied as a thin (<0.5 mm) layer between center and shell. The barrier fat must be applied so that it has no cracks which would allow oil to get through. Sugar may also be incorporated into the barrier layer.

An extension of the barrier fat concept is to use a nonfat barrier layer. Hydrocolloid layers have been proposed, but do not appear to have been used commercially.

In Figure 17 we see how the hazelnut oil from a center penetrates steadily into

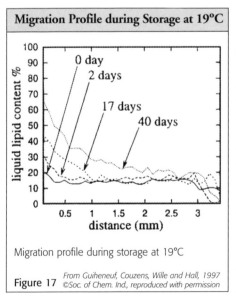

Migration Profile during Storage at 19°C

liquid lipid content %

0 day
2 days
17 days
40 days

distance (mm)

Migration profile during storage at 19°C

Figure 17 From Guiheneuf, Couzens, Wille and Hall, 1997
©Soc. of Chem. Ind., reproduced with permission

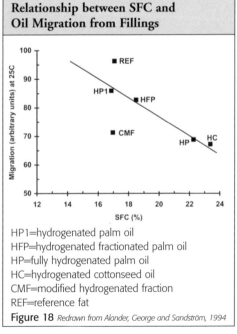

Relationship between SFC and Oil Migration from Fillings

Migration (arbitrary units) at 25C

REF
HP1
HFP
CMF
HP
HC

SFC (%)

HP1=hydrogenated palm oil
HFP=hydrogenated fractionated palm oil
HP=fully hydrogenated palm oil
HC=hydrogenated cottonseed oil
CMF=modified hydrogenated fraction
REF=reference fat

Figure 18 Redrawn from Alander, George and Sandström, 1994

the chocolate shell. In the experiment shown, the shell was about 3 mm thick and even after 40 days the oil had not quite reached the surface. If the shell had been only 1 mm thick, oil would have reached the surface by the 17th day. This shows the benefit of using a thicker shell to minimize the effects of migration.

Since it is impossible to prevent migration entirely, the final solution is to minimize the effects of the migration that does occur by using a fat in the center which is compatible with the fat in the shell. We saw in section 2 that CBS and CBR fats are incompatible with cocoa butter and CBE fats. If CBS from a filling migrates into a shell containing cocoa butter as the principal fat so that the level of CBS in the shell fat phase is more than 10 percent, then according to the isosolid phase diagram given in Figure 10, there will be solid solution disruption causing the shell to soften and bloom. Thus, if a chocolate shell based on cocoa butter or CBE is used, the center fat should preferably be cocoa butter, CBE or a palm-fraction-based filling fat. As second best, a CBR or other hydrogenated-oil-based filling fat could be used, because we saw in Figure 11 that cocoa butter can tolerate up to about 25 percent CBR before solid solution disruption occurs. On no account, though, should a CBS or other lauric-oil-based filling fat be used if significant migration is likely to occur.

If the chocolate shell is based on CBS, then the center fat should preferably also be based on a lauric oil. Similarly for CBR in the shell, the center fat should be a CBR or other hydrogenated-oil-based filling fat.

BLOOM

Sugar Bloom

Sugar bloom is caused by absorption of moisture so that the sugar in the chocolate is solubilized and then recrystallized at the surface as a thin film of sugar crystals. At low levels it has a greyish appearance and can resemble fat bloom, although when touched with the finger it is not removed and does not feel greasy. In a more severe form it appears crystalline and is then rough to the touch; small crystals can be seen using a microscope or even with the naked eye. Figure 19 shows a picture of sugar bloom compared with fat bloom. Seguine notes that you can often distinguish sugar and fat bloom by placing small drops of water on the surface. As shown in the figure, with sugar bloom the droplet quickly flattens and spreads as the water dissolves the microscopic sugar particles.

According to Minifie, sugar bloom is caused or exacerbated by the following:

• Storage of chocolate in damp conditions or against damp walls.

• Deposit of dew during manufacture from damp cooler air or allowing chocolates to enter a packing room at a temperature below the dew point of that room.

• Use of hygroscopic ingredients, e.g., low-grade or brown sugars.

- Removal of chocolate from cold storage without adequate wrapping protection.
- Use of damp packing materials.
- High-temperature storage conditions of chocolate-covered confectionery where centers have a high equilibrium relative humidity, e.g., fondants, and the water vapor given off is trapped in impervious wrappings.

Thus the only proper prevention is humidity control during all stages of production and storage of the products.

An investigation of the storage of chocolate at various temperatures and 60 percent relative humidity suggested that sugar bloom was prevented and the original quality of the product was maintained for 3 to 4 months at 17°C ± 1°C (63°F ± 2°F); 5 to 6 months at 2 to 4°C (36° to 39°F); and more than 12 months at -18°C (0°F).

When considering temperatures and storage times, it should be remembered that heating and cooling of the actual products can take many hours or even days before equilibrium is reached. This is especially so if the products are in boxes stacked on pallets, so that air circulation and opportunities for heat transfer are low. The warehouse temperature may not be the product temperature.

Fat Bloom—Causes

Fat bloom is the development of a new phase in a chocolate fat, where the new phase is manifested at the surface, often as clusters of large (5µ), frequently whitish crystals at several discrete points on the surface (Figure 20). Fat bloom is a bulk fat phenomenon, but is usually observed at the surface of chocolate.

A new phase may develop for three reasons:

- A polymorphic change.
- A transformation from a single solid phase to two phases, solid + liquid.
- A transformation from a single solid phase to two solid phases, a mixture of two solid solutions.

Each mechanism will now be considered in more detail.

Sugar Bloom versus Fat Bloom

Water droplets assist in distinguishing the two types of bloom.

Figure 19   *From Seguine, 2001*

Fat Bloom

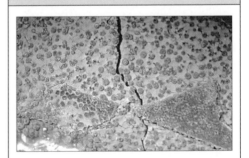

Figure 20   *From Hammond and Gedney, 2000*

Polymorphic Change

Pure cocoa butter itself, and chocolate containing it, may bloom because of a change from Form IV (β'-2) to Form V (β2-3) or Form VI (β1-3). This is what happens in poorly tempered chocolate. In well-tempered chocolate, the change from Form V to Form VI is also associated with bloom. Using electron microscopy, the large crystals on the surface of bloomed chocolate have been shown to be identical with crystals of cocoa butter in Form VI. Development of Form VI must eventually happen, because this is the most stable form of cocoa butter. It may, however, take several years, as shown by the results in Figure 21.

Polymorphic Changes in Chocolate		
(samples stored for several years)		
	After 3 Years Storage at:	
Sample	23°C	10°C
Dark chocolate	VI	V
Dark +2% milk fat	V	V
Dark +5% milk fat	V	V
Milk Chocolate	V	V
	After 4 Years Storage at:		
	23°C	18°C	-10°C
Dark chocolate	VI	V	V

Figure 21   *From Cebula & Ziegleder, 1993*

Solid to Solid + Liquid Phase Change

Consider Figure 6 and our model fat given by the vertical dashed line. If the fat (chocolate) is stored at temperature T_5 and then raised to T_1, we obtain a solid phase of composition c and a liquid phase of composition a, as discussed earlier. A drop in temperature back to T_5 will now cause the liquid to recrystallize. In theory, the solid and liquid phases should recombine to restore the original solid phase and equilibrium position at T_5. In practice, in chocolate, this does not happen. The liquid that forms when the temperature is raised occupies a greater volume than the solid, and the resulting overpressure forces the liquid out to the surface through fissures or pores in the chocolate. Thus solid and liquid phases become physically separated and are unable to recombine to give the original, equilibrium solid solution. As the temperature drops, some of the liquid recrystallizes where it is, with a composition completely different from that of the bulk fat. The recrystallized liquid shows as bloom at the surface, i.e., white fat crystals containing no brown cocoa particles.

Continuous cycling of the temperature up and down (as may happen in a warehouse or retail store between day and night) causes liquid to be pumped to the surface. Higher temperatures also encourage the change from Form V to Form VI, if cocoa butter or CBE is the chocolate fat, so that the bloom formation mechanisms are often associated.

Solid to Solid + Solid Phase Change

From Figure 10 and Figure 11 we see that if chocolate were made such that the fat phase contained 15 percent CB/85 percent CBS or 30 percent CB/70 percent CBR, a two-solid-phase system would result at equilibrium. As fats can take several weeks or months to reach equilibrium, it is quite possible to make compound chocolate with such potentially unstable compositions and to mould or enrobe it to give products with good appearance, snap and organoleptic properties. However, after several weeks the system moves inevitably to equilibrium, the initial single solid phase changes to two solid phases and bloom appears. This mechanism is clearly shown by phase diagrams determined by Paulicka. Figure 22a shows CB/CBR mixtures produced without tempering. Because both CB and CBR are in the β' polymorph, they mix easily and form a single solid solution. But after 7 months storage at 50°F (10°C), the cocoa butter transforms to the β-3 polymorph and two solid solutions form at most compositions. At this time, bloom was observed.

A clear case of this type of bloom, caused by migration and resulting in major structural change, is shown in Figure 23.

Fat Bloom — Prevention

Now that we understand the mechanism of the formation of fat bloom, several prevention strategies become apparent.

Control the storage temperature If the temperature is low, particularly less than 15°C (60°F), then polymorphic change and the movement to equilibrium are slowed considerably. Avoiding temperature cycling avoids the pumping of liquid oil to the surface and the further stimulation of polymorphic change. *Applicable to mechanisms (a) and (b).*

It should be noted that for filled products where migration is important, there is a temperature range at which

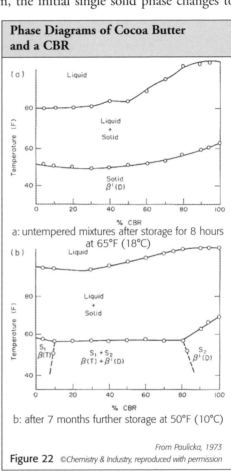

Phase Diagrams of Cocoa Butter and a CBR

a: untempered mixtures after storage for 8 hours at 65°F (18°C)

b: after 7 months further storage at 50°F (10°C)

From Paulicka, 1973
Figure 22   ©*Chemistry & Industry, reproduced with permission*

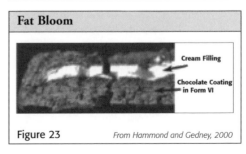

Fat Bloom

Cream Filling

Chocolate Coating in Form VI

Figure 23   *From Hammond and Gedney, 2000*

bloom formation is most likely. Bloom does not get steadily worse as the temperature rises. For milk chocolate, bloom formation is greatest between 18°C and 22°C (64°F and 72°F); for dark chocolate, between 18° to 26°C (64°F and 79°F), with a maximum at 20°C (68°F). This maximum at 20°C may be considered surprising since the tendency of dark chocolate to bloom increases over this temperature range, for reasons explained above. The difference results because migration is the mechanism of bloom formation in a

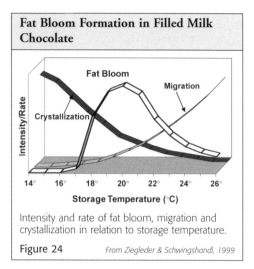

Fat Bloom Formation in Filled Milk Chocolate

Intensity and rate of fat bloom, migration and crystallization in relation to storage temperature.

Figure 24   *From Ziegleder & Schwingshandl, 1999*

praline, leading to mechanism (c) bloom. As the temperature rises, there is a balance between an increasing diffusion rate, and hence migration rate (positive for bloom formation), and a decreasing crystallization rate (negative for bloom formation) as illustrated in Figure 24. *Applicable to mechanism (c).*

Use an appropriate recipe for the fat For CBS and CBR chocolate, it is important to have a fat phase in which the amount of cocoa butter is limited to the maximum that can be tolerated by the fat in order to maintain a single solid solution at all storage temperatures and times. *Applicable to mechanism (c).*

Minimize migration Even when an appropriate recipe is used, migration of another fat from the center may move the system into a two-solid-phase area on the phase diagram. Thus all methods discussed earlier to minimize migration, or its effects, should be used. *Applicable to mechanism (c).*

Use a bloom inhibitor In dark chocolate 1 to 2 percent milk fat is effective in blocking the Form V to Form VI change, mechanism (a), as can be seen in Figure 21. This effect is believed to be due to the middle-melting triglycerides in milk fat, which contain medium chain length fatty acids (12:0 and 14:0) and longer chain fatty acids (16:0 and 18:0). Fats that contain similar triglycerides, obtained by interesterifying lauric and nonlauric oils, are also effective and are commercially sold as bloom inhibitors. Although currently used in the European Union, under the new Chocolate Directive they will not be permitted in real chocolate. Many other substances have been evaluated for their bloom-inhibiting effects and some are quite effective. For example, sucrose polyesters were recently shown to inhibit fat bloom development, and sorbitan tristearate and other sorbitan esters have often been shown to inhibit the

Form V to VI change and the bloom associated with it. *Applicable to mechanism (a).*

An effective bloom inhibitor for CBS compound chocolate is 1 to 3 percent sorbitan tristearate (STS). Laustsen showed that increasing the amount of cocoa butter in a compound chocolate formulation led to increasing incidence of fat bloom, especially when 10 percent CB was used. The composition of the bloom scraped from the surface was enriched in lauric acid, i.e., the solid solution rich in CBS had migrated to the surface. Exactly how STS works is not clear. It may retard the eventual formation of a β polymorph in CBS, but it may also improve the structure of the chocolate so that movement of triglycerides connected with bloom formation is minimized. During crystallization of the chocolate, its high melting point means it can act as potential seed crystals for the CBS, leading to a very uniform structure with STS cocrystallizing with the triglycerides and blocking any solid state changes.

Use a "permanent" seed The triglyceride BOB is a high-melting equivalent of StOSt. When added to chocolate at up to the 5 percent level, part of the BOB remains solid at temperatures up to about 40°C (104°F) and can then act as seed crystals when the liquid chocolate recrystallizes. Thus chocolate containing BOB always crystallizes in Form V and bloom does not occur, nor does the chocolate need the normal tempering process. BOB is unfortunately rather expensive and may not be permitted in real chocolate in many countries other than Japan. *Applicable to mechanisms (a) and (b).*

Temper chocolate to Form VI By special tempering, chocolate can be produced in Form VI. It is thus inherently stable to bloom and has a higher melting point than normal chocolate. *Applicable to mechanism (a).*

Use CBES CBES are deficient in the triglyceride POSt, which is often enriched in bloom compared to the composition of the bulk fat. Addition of CBES to cocoa butter chocolate does tend to reduce bloom, but the effect is relatively small at the low level of 5 percent (typically 15 to 17 percent of the fat phase) legally permitted in many countries. *Applicable to mechanisms (a) and (b).*

Post-tempering In this process, freshly enrobed products are warmed to 28° to 31°C (82° to 88°F) for 0.5 to 2 hours and then quickly cooled to normal storage temperature. This stimulates migration from the center to the shell and the shell becomes saturated with liquid oil triglycerides from the center. Since the warm chocolate shell is soft, no overpressure develops and the oil migration can be taken up without danger (provided the center and shell fats are compatible). After cooling down, a much more stable product results. However, there is a significant softening of the shell, which may limit the application of the technique. Figure 25 shows the example of a nougat-filled chocolate which was post-tempered at 29°C (84°F) for 30 minutes. It can be seen that both chocolate and filling have reached roughly the same point as after storage for 105 days at 23°C (73°F) without post-tempering.

REFERENCES AND FURTHER READING

Alander, J., P. George and L. Sandström. Prevention of Oil Migration in Confectionery Products. *International Food Ingredients* 4: 27–36, 1994.

Beierl, P., H. Hornik and G. Ziegleder. Indication of Fat Migration in Chocolate. *Zucker u. Süsswaren Wirtschaft* 53: 20–27, 2000.

Brake, N. C. and O.R. Fennema. Edible Coatings to Inhibit Lipid Migration in a Confectionery Product. *J. Food Science* 58: 1422–1425, 1993.

Cebula, D. J. and G. Ziegleder. Studies of Bloom Formation Using X-ray Diffraction from Chocolates After Long-Term Storage. *Fat Sc. Technol.* 95: 340–343, 1993.

Chapman, G.M., E.E. Akehurst and W.B. Wright. Cocoa Butter and Confectionery Fats. Studies using Programmed Temperature X-ray Diffraction and Differential Scanning Calorimetry. *J. Amer. Chem. Soc.* 48: 824–830, 1971.

Chaveron, H., M. Ollivon and H. Adenier. Fat Bloom: Migration of Fats in the Composite Products. *Chocolaterie Confiserie de France* 328: 3–11, 1976.

De Jong, S., T.C. van Soest and M.A. van Schaick. Crystal Structures and Melting Points of Unsaturated Triacylglycerols in the β Phase. *J. Amer. Chem. Soc.* 68(6): 371–378, 1991.

Gordon, M.H., F.B. Padley and R.E. Timms. Factors Influencing the use of Vegetable Fats in Chocolate. *Fette Seifen Anstrichmittel* 81: 116–121, 1979.

Guiheneuf, T.M., P.J. Couzens, H.J. Wille and L.D. Hall. Visualisation of Liquid Triacylglycerol Migration in Chocolate by Magnetic Resonance Imaging. *J. Sci. Food Agric.* 73: 265–273, 1997.

Hammond, E. and S. Gedney. *Fat Bloom*, on web site: www.britanniafood.com, United Biscuits (U.K.) Ltd. & Britannia Food Ingredients Ltd. 2000.

Hartel, R. W. Chocolate: Fat Bloom During Storage. *Manufacturing Confectioner* 79: 89–99, 1999.

Katsuragi, T. and K. Sato. Effects of Emulsifiers on Fat Bloom Stability of Cocoa Butter. *J. Oleo Science* 50:243–248, 2001.

Koyano, T., I. Hachiya and K. Sato. Fat Polymorphism and Crystal Seeding Effects on Fat Bloom Stability of Dark Chocolate. *Food Structure* 9: 231–240, 1990.

Laustsen, K. The Nature of Fat Bloom in Molded Coatings. *Manufacturing Confectioner* 71: 137–144, 1991.

McCarthy, M., J. Walton and K. McCarthy. Magnetic Resonance Imaging, *54th PMCA Production Conference* 69–77, 2000.

Minault, M.H. Low Temperature Storage of Chocolate and Confectionery Articles. *Revue Generale du Froid* 69: 91–93, 1978.

Minifie, B.W. *Chocolate, Cocoa and Confectionery: Science & Technology*, 3rd Ed. Chapman & Hall, New York. ISBN 0-442-26521-2. 1989.

Paulicka, F.R. Phase Behavior of Cocoa Butter Extenders. *Chemistry & Industry* 17: 835–839, 1973.

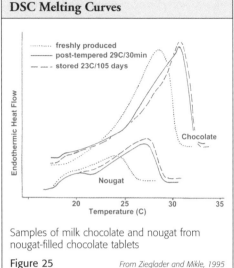

DSC Melting Curves

.... freshly produced
———— post-tempered 29C/30min
— – – stored 23C/105 days

Endothermic Heat Flow

Chocolate

Nougat

20   25   30   35
Temperature (C)

Samples of milk chocolate and nougat from nougat-filled chocolate tablets

Figure 25   *From Zieglader and Mikle, 1995*

Paulicka, F.R. Phase Behavior of Fats in Confectionery Coatings. *Manufacturing Confectioner* 50: 73–74, 76, 78, 1970.

Richardson, T. Back to Basics—Chocolate Tempering. *Proceedings of the 54th Production Conference*, Pennsylvania Manufacturing Confectioners' Association, Hershey, PA. pp. 30–41, 2000.

Schlichter-Aronhime, J. and N. Garti. Solidification and Polymorphism in Cocoa Butter and the Blooming Problems. *Crystallization and Polymorphism of Fats and Fatty Acids*, edited by N. Garti and K. Sato. Marcel Dekker Inc., New York, Chapter 9, pp. 363–393. ISBN 0-8247-7875-8, 1988.

Seguine, E.S. Tempering—The Inside Story. *Manufacturing Confectioner* 71: 117–125, 1991.

Seguine, E. Diagnosing Chocolate Bloom. *Manufacturing Confectioner* 81: 45–50, 2001.

Talbot, G. Chocolate Fat Bloom—The Cause and the Cure. *Intl. Food Ingredients* Jan/Feb, 1994.

Talbot, G. Fat Migration in Biscuits and Confectionery Systems. *Confectionery Production* 56: 265–272, 1990.

Timms, R.E. *Confectionery Fats Handbook,* The Oily Press, Bridgwater, England, 2003. ISBN 0-9531949-4-9

Timms, R.E. The Phase Behavior of Mixtures of Cocoa Butter and Milk Fat. *Lebensm. Wiss. Technol.* 13: 61–65, 1980.

Timms, R.E. Phase Behavior of Fats and Their Mixtures. *Progress Lipid Res.* 23: 1–38, 1984.

Wille, R.L. and E.S. Lutton. Polymorphism of Cocoa Butter. *J. Amer. Chem. Soc.* 43: 491–496, 1966.

Wootton, M., D. Weeden and N. Munk. Mechanism of Fat Migration in Chocolate Enrobed Goods. *Chemistry & Industry* 3(8 August): 1052–1053, 1970.

Wootton, M., D. Weeden and N. Munk. A Study of Fat Migration in Chocolate Enrobed Biscuits. *Gordian* 3: 95–100, 1972.

Ziegleder, G., and I. Schwingshandl. Kinetics of Fat Migration in Chocolate Products Part 3: Fat Bloom. *Fett/Lipid.* 100: 411–415, 1998.

Ziegleder, G. and I. Schwingshandl. Fat Bloom—A Question of the Storage Temperature. *Süsswaren* 43: 36–38, 1999.

Ziegleder, G. and H. Mikle. Fat Bloom (Part 1). Süsswaren Tech. *Wirtschaft* 39(9): 28–32, 1995.

Ziegleder, G. and H. Mikle. Fat Bloom (Part 2). Süsswaren Tech. *Wirtschaft* 39(10): 23–25, 1995.

Ziegleder, G. and H. Mikle, Fat Bloom (Part 3). Süsswaren Tech. *Wirtschaft* 39(11): 26-28 1995.

Ziegleder. G., C. Moser and J. Geier-Greguska. Kinetics of Fat Migration Within Chocolate Products. Part 1: Principles and Analytical Aspects. *Fett/Lipid* 98: 196–199, 1996.

Ziegleder. G., C. Moser and J. Geier-Greguska. Kinetics of Fat Migration Within Chocolate Products. Part 2: Influence of Storage Temperature, Diffusion Coefficient, Solid Fat Content. *Fett/Lipid* 98: 253–256,1996.

Questions & Answers

Q: How important is fat crystal size relative to migration and how do you control fat crystal size?

A: Migration will proceed more easily if the crystals are large because the liquid fat will not be trapped so easily by the crystals. Small, uniform crystals make migration more difficult. The fat crystal size and structure of chocolate are mostly controlled by the tempering and subsequent cooling.

Q: What happens when coating or shell-moulding fats are subjected to hot or cold center addition?

A: If the center is hot then there may be two effects: first, there will be more liquid fat in the center so that migration will proceed more and more quickly until the center is cooled (probably not a great effect as the center will usually be cooled in minutes); second, some of the shell will melt and this will allow the center to penetrate a little into the shell, giving a head start for migration.

Q: What method do you recommend for measuring fat migration in products?

A: Fatty acid or triglyceride compositional analysis is probably the best. Which one you use and what you measure may depend on the fats involved. For example, if the center is a lauric fat then measuring the lauric acid content by routine fatty acid analysis will be good. If the center is a CBE and the shell is real chocolate then triglyceride analysis by GLC or HPLC to monitor POP/POSt/StOSt will be required.

Q: What countries allow CBES and still call the product chocolate?

A: The following is not an exhaustive list and is to the best of my knowledge.
• Seven of the 15 countries in the European Union: Denmark, Sweden, Finland, Ireland, United Kingdom, Portugal, Austria
• Norway, Switzerland
• Japan (in quasi- or semi-chocolate)
• South Africa
• Australia, New Zealand

Q: When does the new Chocolate Directive come into effect in the European Union (as it relates to the allowed use of bloom inhibitors in real chocolate)?

A: The new Chocolate Directive must be ratified by all countries by August 2003. Bloom inhibitors containing enzyme-interesterified fats, e.g., BOB fat, or lauric fats, e.g., Prestine, will not be allowed.

Q: Can you suggest an oil-impermeable barrier to use between center and shell?

A: As mentioned in my paper, this needs to be a hard/high SFC fat. A fully hardened oil would do but can affect eating quality. I suggest you talk to your fat supplier.

Q: Milk fat often inhibits bloom in chocolate. Can you explain the mechanism of how this occurs?

A: It inhibits the Form V to VI polymorphic change in cocoa butter, perhaps by cocrystallizing with cocoa butter and preventing a change in the oleic acid configuration in the sos triglycerides, as has been suggested for the action of Prestine by Geoff Talbot of Loders-Croklaan.

Q: At 20°C where liquid fat is around 20 percent, can you describe how the liquid fat is dispersed in the solids, i.e., is it platelets of solid crystals with liquid layers between, or is it something else?

A: The liquid fat is a continuous phase with fat crystals and sugar and cocoa particles dispersed in it.

Q: If fat content and percent oil of a chocolate shell and center are identical at a given temperature, but differ in composition (i.e., fatty acids), what will be the equilibrium oil percent in the chocolate? How strong will the tendency for migration be? Is there a driving force for migration?

A: Probably no change in percent oil, but there will be a change in the triglyceride composition towards equilibrium. There will still be a strong tendency for migration to occur, provided there is plenty of liquid present. The driving force is the trend to equilibrium, both phase and composition equilibrium.

Q: Is triglyceride composition in Form VI bloom the same as in the cocoa butter it came from?

A: Usually there will be some difference in composition because the chocolate/cocoa butter has been equilibrated at a high temperature, or has been cycled up and down. In fact, this has been one of the enduring debates about Form VI (ß1): is it a new polymorph or a new phase? In a pure triglyceride like StOSt, there can be no doubt that it is a new polymorph.

Q: Could you discuss the mechanisms of bloom that occur in lauric compound coatings?

A: Bloom occurs by the transformation from a single solid to two solid phases as discussed in my paper. This sort of bloom will occur if the recipe is incorrect, i.e., too much cocoa butter. Even when the recipe is correct, there also seems to be bloom associated with a change to a ß polymorph when the bloom is enriched in 12:0 compared with the original fat. (See K. Laustsen, Manufacturing Confectioner 71: 137–144, 1991.)

Q: What is the physical cause of bloom in lauric/nonlauric mixtures? Some nonlaurics do contain C12. Does it become a factor of concentration, or are there other considerations?

A: Bloom occurs by the transformation from a single solid to two solid phases as discussed in my paper. If nonlaurics contain C12 it must be due to contamination in the factory and is not responsible for bloom.

Q: You said the main effect of milk fat in chocolate is simply to soften it as it does not really mix. If this is so, why does milk fat help retard bloom in dark chocolate (or give it tolerance), and does soybean oil not do an even better job?

A: The softening effect is caused mainly by the liquid triglycerides, the antibloom effect by the solid triglycerides, so soybean oil merely softens the chocolate.

Q: You said Form VI was associated with bloomed chocolate. I thought it was associated with the natural transition V to VI over long time regardless of whether bloom is present. Please comment. As a corollary, can you have bloomed chocolate without the presence of Form VI?

A: I do not clearly understand the first part of this question, but you can have chocolate in Form VI without bloom if it has been tempered to crystallize in Form VI. Regarding the second part, no for-real, i.e., not compound, chocolate bloom = Form VI assuming it was tempered properly to a good gloss in the first place. If it was not tempered properly, then the IV to V transition will also disrupt the surface/cause bloom.

Q: Is there any published data on the rate of the transition V to VI as a function of temperature?

A: Not that I know of.

Q: If the transition V to VI in dark chocolate (no milk fat) takes place in three to four years, why does the surface manifest a gray bloom? What is the surface and what is the surface mechanism since the center structure visually appears unchanged?

A: I do not understand the first question; the fact that bloom takes a long time does not seem to have a connection with the appearance or not of bloom. The center usually is changed, especially if you use a microscope to examine it.

Q: For bloom inhibition, will tempering of chocolate to Form VI work regardless of fat type?

A: Tempering to Form VI is only possible for real, cocoa-butter-containing chocolate.

Q: Are there any commercial applications of post-tempering?

A: Not that I know of, but I expect so in Europe.

Q: Why does the warming trick promote some resistance to bloom?

A: For more information you could refer to the paper by Ziegleder & Mikle that I quote, as I am not experienced in this technique. Essentially, the warming trick moves the system to equilibrium so that all the overpressure due to migration that would otherwise build up is released at a time when the shell can accept it, so that the surface is not disrupted. This technique is probably only applicable for a migrating oil which softens the cocoa butter but is not incompatible with it like a lauric fat. The migration of oil itself seems to stimulate bloom.

Q: What happens if chocolate is aerated—an increase or a decrease in oil migration?

A: I have no idea, but most likely it would slow down migration if the triglycerides have a longer route.

Q: Why does STS prevent bloom in CBS-type compound coatings?

A: It has a high melting point and a structure with some similarities to a triglyceride. Presumably it crystallizes in the CBS crystal lattice and prevents any transformation from ß' to ß that may be associated with bloom—see question 11 and also A.C. Noorden, *Süsswaren Technik Wirtschaft* 26:318–322, 1982. According to U. Petersen (*Malaysian Oil Science & Technology* 3:69–74, 1994) it also delays migration of C36 triglycerides to the surface where they appear as bloom.

Applications of Specialty Fats and Oils

Toshiharu Arishima, PhD, and Thomas McBrayer
Fuji Vegetable Oil, Inc.

In this paper we will introduce the characteristics of the physical chemistry of cocoa butter and its alternatives, and also briefly review fats and oils used for center filling and sandwich cream. In the second part, functional fats and oils that perform as seeding agents and antibloom agents will be summarized.

COCOA BUTTER

The annual production of chocolate reaches more than 4 million tons. Chocolate is a fat-based confection that consists of sugar, cocoa mass, milk solids and cocoa butter. As for the fats and oils which are used for chocolate products, cocoa butter is primarily used. Because it has characteristics which allow it to melt rapidly near body temperature, it gives strong cocoa aroma and it provides moderate snap when it is used in chocolate. Cocoa butter is obtained through the crushing and pressing of cocoa beans, yielding more than 70 percent of the 1,3-disaturated 2-oleoyl type triacylglycerols (Sat-O-Sat TAG), which are represented by the symmetrical POP, POS and SOS. Usually cocoa butter shows excellent oxidative stability. Another characteristic of cocoa butter which is related to its specific composition is polymorphism. Six polymorphic forms from I to VI have been identified in cocoa butter (Figure 1). The polymorphic form of cocoa butter in chocolate has been adjusted to Form V, which is the second most stable form.

Cacao beans are grown in regions near the equator, with the composition of triacylglycerol and the hardness changing with the producing country (Figure 2). There is a tendency for cocoa butter to become harder in order of South America (softer), Central Africa and Asia (harder).

This is related to the composition change of the Sat-O-Sat TAG, which is

Polymorphs of Cocoa Butter			
Polymorphic Form	Melting Point °C	°F	Systematic Nomenclature
I	17.3°	63.1°	beta'-3 (sub alpha, gamma)
II	23.3°	73.9°	alpha-2
III	25.5°	77.9°	$beta'_2$-2
IV	27.5°	81.5°	$beta'_1$-2
V	33.8°	92.8°	$beta_2$-3
VI	36.2°	97.2°	$beta_1$-3

Figure 1

Typical SFC Curves and Major Triacylglycerol Compositions of Origin Cocoa Butters

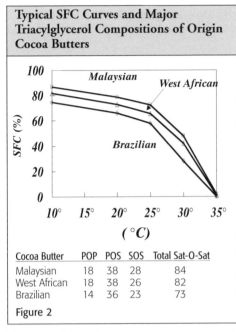

Cocoa Butter	POP	POS	SOS	Total Sat-O-Sat
Malaysian	18	38	28	84
West African	18	38	26	82
Brazilian	14	36	23	73

Figure 2

Points of Tempering

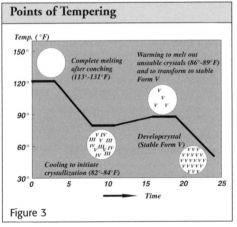

Figure 3

the main ingredient of cocoa butter. Basically, the harder cocoa butter shows a higher content in SOS and total Sat-O-Sat TAG.

Cocoa butter must be conditioned to Form V when producing chocolate products. This tempering process consists of four steps (Figure 3). In the first step, chocolate must be heated to around 45° to 50°C to preclude the development of any crystals; then it is cooled down to 28° to 29°C to initiate the crystallization of cocoa butter. At this point, the chocolate contains many unstable crystals as well as some in the desired stable crystal form. These unstable crystals are completely melted in the next step by heating up to 30° to 32°C. During step 2 to step 3, the melt-mediated transformation from unstable form to stable V form is also induced. Then the stable Form V crystals are developed by the last cooling process. The precise temperature adjustments in steps 2 and 3 can vary depending on the quality of cocoa butter.

COCOA BUTTER ALTERNATIVES

There is no doubt that cocoa butter is indispensable as a raw material of chocolate. There are, however, considerable fluctuations in the price, quality and suppliability. To address these issues, cocoa butter alternatives have been developed. Cocoa butter alternatives are classified in three types: cocoa butter equivalents (CBES), cocoa butter replacers (CBRS) and cocoa butter substitutes (CBSS). Cocoa butter alternatives are often referred to as hard butters because they exhibit varying degrees of similarity to cocoa butter in terms of percent solid fat at room temperature and rapid melting at body temperature. They are widely used in moulded products, centers for deposits like drops and inclusions and also in formulations of nonchocolate coating like pastels.

Cocoa Butter Equivalents

Cocoa butter equivalents (CBES) are vegetable fats with similar chemical and physical characteristics to cocoa butter and can thus blend with cocoa butter at any ratio. As sources of CBES, illipe, shea, sal, mango, kokum, palm, sunflower and safflower are generally available. CBES are prepared by the fractionation and enzymatic interesterification processes from those raw materials. Figure 4 shows Sat-O-Sat TAG compositions of typical CBE components. Cocoa butter usually includes a higher percentage of POS. However, most CBES show a high concentration of SOS, except fractionated palm oil, which has 68 percent of POP. Generally, CBES which have a higher SOS content are blended with fractionated palm oil to adjust the final melting profile.

Typical Sat-O-Sat Triacylglycerol Compositions of CBEs						
	Cocoa Butter	Frac. Palm	Illipe	Shea Stearin	Sal Stearin	Mango Stearin	I.E. Sun/Saf Stearin
POP	16	68	7	1	1	2	1
POS	39	14	35	11	11	19	16
SOS	26	2	45	68	59	58	66
SOA	2		4	3	18	5	2
Total Sat-O-Sat	83	84	91	83	89	84	85

Figure 4

Figure 5 shows solid fat content (SFC) curves of commercially available CBES. Although there are some differences in the Sat-O-Sat TAG of commercially available CBES, they are almost identical to cocoa butter in solid fat content. CBES require the tempering process as well as cocoa butter and also exhibit the same polymorphic behavior. CBES have good mouthfeel and flavor release properties, good gloss and shelf-life stability.

Cocoa Butter Replacers

Cocoa butter replacers (CBRS) are defined as nonlauric vegetable fats with similar physical, but not chemical, characteristics to cocoa butter, and when used as the major fat, only a limited amount of cocoa butter is allowed. Normally, cocoa butter can be compatible with CBRS up to 20 percent. CBRS are made through the partial hydro-

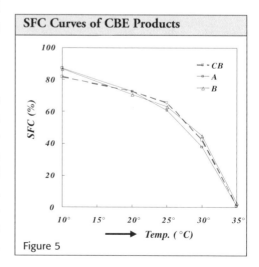

SFC Curves of CBE Products

Figure 5

genation and fractionation processes of the following raw materials: soybean, cottonseed, rice bran and palm olein. These source oils are essentially composed of triacylglycerols containing C16 and C18 fatty acids. One of the chemical characteristics of CBRS is that they have high *trans* fatty acids as a result of the hydrogenation process. Hydrogenation is the process of chemically adding hydrogen gas to liquid oil in the presence of a catalyst. This process converts some of the double bonds of unsaturated fatty acids in the fat molecule to single bonds. In the food industry it is an indispensable process to obtain the desired hardness, melting profile and stability in fats and oils. In general, the rate of hydrogenation is controlled by the reaction temperature and pressure of hydrogen gas. If there is some limitation of hydrogen supply, conversion of some *cis* double bonds to the *trans* configuration is easily synthesized. *Trans* fatty acid is a positional isomer of the *cis* double bond. The melting point of *trans* fatty acid is usually in between *cis*-unsaturated fatty acid and saturated fatty acid in the same chain length.

Figure 6 shows the typical triacylglycerol composition of a soybean-based CBR. *Trans* fatty acids give high-melting-point and hardness characteristics to the liquid oil. SFC curves of commercially available CBRS exhibit higher values than cocoa butter in the lower temperature range, and at higher temperature the melting profiles are almost the same as cocoa butter (Figure 7). However, actual compound chocolate products made by CBR and cocoa butter are slightly softer than that of pure chocolate due to the eutectic phenomena. Compound chocolate from CBRS can be solidified by simple cooling without the tempering process and it will solidify in the stable beta-prime form.

Cocoa Butter Substitutes

Cocoa butter substitutes (CBSS) are obtained from lauric fats such as coconut

Typical Composition of Soy-based CBR	
Triacylglycerols	%
OTT	10%
POT	6%
TTT	25%
PPO	2%
PTT	20%
PPT	2%
SOT	10%
STT	10%
O: Oleic acid; P: Palmitic acid; S: Stearic acid; T: *Trans* fatty acids	
Figure 6	

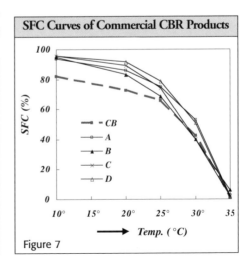

SFC Curves of Commercial CBR Products

Figure 7

oil (CNO) and palm kernel oil (PKO), and are processed by hydrogenation, fractionation and interesterification. Cocoa butter is only compatible with CBSS at a level of 5 percent maximum. The tempering process is also not required in CBS-based chocolate because it also stabilizes in the beta-prime form. CBS-based compound chocolate provides a light taste and quick melting behavior. CBSS with interesterified fats have better bloom stability as compared with CBSS which are only hydrogenated or fractionated. The SFCS of CBSS show higher values at lower temperature and lower values at higher temperature as compared with cocoa butter (Figure 8).

CRYSTALLINE PACKING ARRANGEMENT

From the previous studies by X-ray diffraction, it has been clarified that Form V of cocoa butter has formed a triple chain length structure, putting the oleoyl moiety between two lamellas of palmitic and stearic acid moieties (Figure 9). This configuration is peculiar to symmetric Sat-O-Sat TAG, so all CBES also take this type of structure. CBR and CBS consist of a double chain length structure with oleic acid and saturated acid moieties packed in the same lamella. These differences in chain length structure are related to the compatibility with cocoa butter. CBES are compatible with cocoa butter in any ratio, because the chain length structure and polymorphic form of CBES are identical to cocoa butter. CBRS and CBES are only compatible with cocoa butter in a limited ratio, because their chain length structures and polymorphic forms are completely different from cocoa butter.

CHOCOLATE STANDARDS

In the United States, the FDA adopted the original standards of identity for chocolate in 1944, and they have changed only slightly over the years. The Codex standards for Chocolate (Codex Stan 87-1981) define 14 products (Figure 10). U.S.

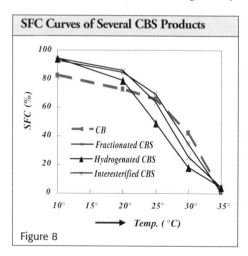

SFC Curves of Several CBS Products

Figure 8

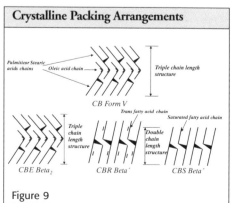

Crystalline Packing Arrangements

Figure 9

Composition of the Chocolate Products Defined by Codex Standard 87-1981						
Product	Cocoa Butter	Fatfree Cocoa Solids	Total Cocoa Solids	Milk Fat	Fatfree Milk Solids	Total Fat	Sugar
Chocolate	>18	>14	>35				
Unsweetened chocolate	>50–<58						
Couverture chocolate	>31	>2.5	>35				
Sweet (plain) chocolate	>18	>12	>30				
Milk chocolate		>2.5	>25	>3.5	>10.5	>25	<55
Milk couverture chocolate		>2.5	>25	>3.5	>10.5	>31	<55
Milk chocolate with high milk content		>2.5	>20	>5	>15	>25	<55
Skimmed milk chocolate		>2.5	>25	<0.5	>14	>25	>55
Skimmed milk couverture chocolate		>2.5	>25	<0.5	>14	>31	>55
Cream chocolate		>2.5	>25	>7	3–14	>25	<55
Chocolate vermicelli	>12	>14	>32				
Chocolate flakes	>12	>14	>32				
Milk chocolate vermicelli		>2.5	>20	>3.5	>10.5	>12	<66
Milk chocolate flake		>2.5	>20	>3.5	>10.5	>12	<66

Source: from Codex Standards for Chocolate (World Standard) formerly CAC/RS 87-1976.

Figure 10

Standards in 21 CFR Part 163 also define 14 cocoa products, but 6 of those, like chocolate liquor, sweet chocolate, buttermilk chocolate, skim milk chocolate, etc., have similar, but not identical, counterparts in the Codex standard.

In the year 2000, the European Union permitted the use of up to 5 percent of six vegetable fats in chocolate, milk chocolate, family milk chocolate, white chocolate, chocolate a la taza and chocolate-familiar a la taza products. The allowed fats are illipe, palm, sal, shea, kokum and mango. To improve the labeling discrepancy in the European market, the Codex committee is continuously considering the chocolate standard, with emphasis on the 5 percent addition rule of vegetable fat into chocolate.

FATS AND OILS FOR CENTER FILLING AND SANDWICH CREAM

The typical fat used for center filling and sandwich cream is a continuous matrix of fat with dispersed particles of sugar, milk powder, nut paste and cocoa solids. The nature of the fat will play a crucial role in determining the consistency and the character of the filling. In center filling and sandwich cream applications, fats and oils have an effect on the production process, texture, mouthfeel and shelf life.

When choosing oils and fats for use in center filling and sandwich cream confectionery, manufacturers should consider the ingredients which address hardness, process and melt profiles (Figure 11). For example, in a sandwich cream, when the center filling combines with the biscuit or wafer and provides a desired slow melt in the mouth, the partially hydrogenated fat that shows some tailing in SFC around 35°C is more suitable for this application than a sharper melting fat (Figure 12). The cream made with a sharper fat melts away quickly while the biscuit still remains in the mouth, giving an uneven sensation.

It is interesting to use various fat systems for center creams which are combined with chocolate. Because chocolate quickly melts at body temperature, it is possible to enjoy the differences in texture, melting profile and flavor release (Figure 13).

Various fat systems are used for center filling and sandwich cream in the United States, Europe and Japan. The fat sources vary, but generally fractionated palm and palm kernel and partially hydrogenated oil, having a lower melting point, are used in

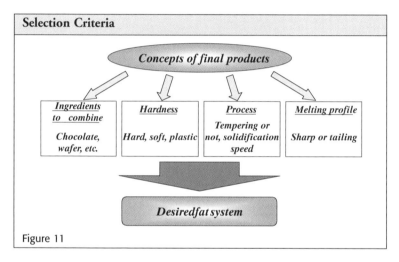

Figure 11

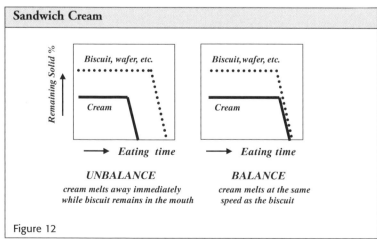

Figure 12

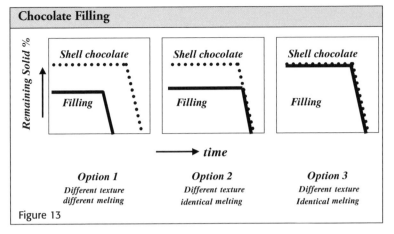

Figure 13

center fillings. Figure 14 shows a melt profile comparison of the fats for center filling and sandwich cream. Fats for center filling are rather sharper than those for sandwich cream. Typically, fractionated lauric and palm oil are used in center filling, and hydrogenated soybean and hydrogenated palm oil are used in sandwich cream.

FUNCTIONAL FATS AND OILS

In recent studies it was found that some specific triacylglycerols have some interesting functions in chocolate applications. Several specific triacylglycerols, such as seeding agents and antibloom agents, are introduced in this section.

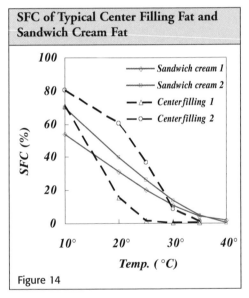

Figure 14

Seeding Agents

Hydrogenated fat (HPO and HSBO) for lauric fat Usually lauric hard butters representing fractionated palm kernel oil are recognized as nontempering fats which can be solidified by simply cooling from the melted condition. However, compound chocolates made from lauric hard butter have some problems in appearance, demoulding and bloom stability in most cases. This is basically caused by the slow rate of crystallization at constant cooling. The initial solidification speed of fractionated palm kernel oil is improved by adding a couple of percent of fully hydrogenated palm oil (HPO). This seeding material causes the base fat to crystallize quickly in fine crystals. Figure 15 summarizes the effect of various seeding agents for compound chocolate made from fractionated PKO. As described before, unseeded compound shows bloom, insufficient demould or wrinkle on the surface due to slow crystallization. However, the tendency for bloom formation in an unseeded compound sample is diminished by changing the cooling condition to a much cooler temperature. This indicates that solidification speed is the key factor. In the actual manufacturing process, this rapid cooling is not realistic and, generally, seeding material such as fully hydrogenated soybean, rapeseed and palm oil is used in the manufacturing process. As far as the amount of seeding material, it depends on the fatty acid chain length and melt point. The seeding agent having longer chain fatty acids and a higher melting point shows good effect with minimum addition. On the other hand, monoacylglycerol, which has a higher melting point than the typical seeding material, has no effect. This suggests that the crystal structure of the seeding agent should be the same as the base fat.

Beta-2 crystal of symmetric TAGs (SOS, AOA and BOB) for cocoa butter The same theory is true for traditional chocolate made with cocoa butter. In a small-scale production facility, they have adopted a seeding method instead of tempering by adding powdered chocolate which has been stored for a long period. If we compare this with the conventional tempering method there are some advantages, such as omission of the tempering machine, saving of space and reduction of production costs. Recent advances in the powdering techniques and studies on the polymorphism of fats and oils have led to the industrial use of seeding agents.

Koyano et al. systematically studied the seeding materials for cocoa butter. The beta-2 crystal of 1,3-distearoyl 2-oleoyl glycerol (SOS) and 1,3-dibenyl 2-oleoyl glycerol (BOB), which has a higher melting point than cocoa butter, is only effective in dark chocolate (Figure 16). In contrast, pseudo beta prime of bob and beta of

Seeding Effects on the Fractionated Palm Kernel Stearin				
Seeding Agent	Solidified Temperature	Bloom	Appearance (Surface)	Demoulding
No seed	5°C	Yes	Uneven	Poor
No seed	-5°C	No	Even	Good
1% HPO	5°C	Slight	Uneven	Acceptable
3% HPO	5°C	No	Even	Good
2% HSBO	5°C	No	Even	Good
1% HRSO	5°C	No	Even	Good
1% MG (C18)	5°C	No	Uneven	Acceptable

Figure 15

Demoulding and Fat Bloom Occurrence of Seeded Dark Chocolate (@15°C for 15 Min.)									
Percent seed	0.001	0.005	0.01	0.05	0.1	0.5	1.0	2.5	5.0
SOS (Beta₁)									
Demoulding	**Good**	**Good**	**Good**	**Good**	**Good**	**Good**	**Good**	**Good**	**Good**
Fat Bloom	Slight	Slight	**No**	**No**	**No**	**No**	**No**	**No**	**No**
BOB (Beta₁)									
Demoulding	Bad	**Good**	**Good**	**Good**	**Good**	**Good**	**Good**	**Good**	**Good**
Fat Bloom	Yes	Slight	**No**	**No**	**No**	**No**	**No**	**No**	**No**
BOB (Pseudo-Beta')									
Demoulding				Very bad		Bad		**Good**	**Good**
Fat Bloom				Yes		Slight		Slight	Slight
SSS (Beta)									
Demoulding				Very bad		Very bad		Very bad	Very bad
Fat Bloom				Yes		Yes		Yes	Yes

Figure 16

tristearin (SSS) have no effect on dark chocolate because the crystal structure, especially the chain length structures of these, are completely different from Form V of cocoa butter. As stated before, the chain length structure of Form V in cocoa butter is a triple chain length structure. The pseudo beta prime of bob and beta of SSS are double chain length structures. As far as the amount of seeding material, 0.01 percent is sufficient at 30°C. We have, however, to consider the solubility of these seeding agents in cocoa butter above 31°C. Figure 17 shows the solubility data of each beta-2 crystal of SOS, 1,3-diarachidoyl 2-oleoyl glycerol (AOA) and bob into cocoa butter. Basically the seeding agent having the shorter chain length shows higher solubility, but SOS has lower solubility below 36°C. This is because SOS is working as a seeding agent around these temperatures. AOA should be added at more than 5 percent at 34°C, but 2 to 3 percent additions are sufficient for SOS and bob at the same temperature.

Compound formation by cocoa butter and OSO Normally cocoa butter solidifies as Form V when it is tempered. If not tempered it will crystallize in the unstable beta-prime form such as Form I, II, III and IV, and therefore cause

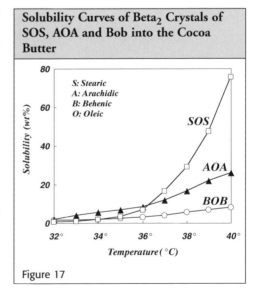

Solubility Curves of Beta₂ Crystals of SOS, AOA and Bob into the Cocoa Butter

S: Stearic
A: Arachidic
B: Behenic
O: Oleic

Figure 17

bloom in most cases. Koyano et al. studied the symmetric-type triacylglycerol, 1, 3-oleoyl 2-stearoyl glycerol (OSO), and found that OSO forms a compound beta crystal (or solid solution) with cocoa butter when they are blended in a 50/50 ratio (Figure 18). The interesting thing is that this blended fat does not require any tempering and solidifies in the beta form by simple cooling from 45°C to 5°C. It is suggested that the compound beta crystal of CB/OSO forms a double chain length structure which divides saturated fatty acid and oleic acid moieties, respectively.

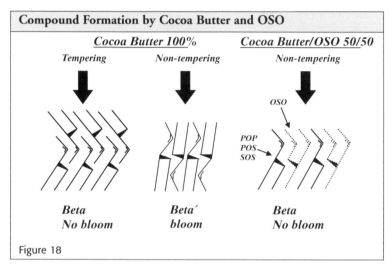

Figure 18

Bloom Inhibitors

Fat bloom of chocolate is mainly caused by crystal growth and phase segregation of fats and oils. Its appearance changes from showing a good gloss to a light gray moth-eaten appearance on the surface. The texture also changes from the original smooth melting to tasteless.

Classification of bloom Chocolate has to be completely tempered to prevent bloom. If tempering is not proper, chocolate will show some bloom due to the solidification of unstable forms. In this part of the paper, the focus will be to describe the bloom which occurs during the storage period and the bloom inhibitors used in the prevention of this type of bloom. The type of bloom and the mechanism of the occurrence are roughly classified into the following four kinds depending on the storage temperature and type of products.

In the first one, bloom is caused by the crystal growth. Most of the bloom which occurs at room temperature is this type of bloom. The chocolate surface becomes uniformly white and the whiteness increases as the bloom progresses. The polymorphic form of the bloom portion itself is not the normal Form V but has changed to Form

VI, which is the most stable form of cocoa butter. As for the mechanism, it is understood that the partial melting or partial dissolving into the liquid oil of Form V occurs due to the fluctuation of storage temperature even under the conditions below the melting point. The molten triacylglycerol molecules reach the surface through small capillary holes inside the chocolate. Then Form VI, which was formed by a solid state transformation from Form V, starts to grow by taking in the melted triacylglycerols such as POP, POS and SOS at the chocolate surface (Figure 19).

Bloom also occurs when the chocolate is exposed to a higher temperature than the melting point of the cocoa butter chocolate. This type of bloom is often observed in the summer season. Appearance of this bloom differs from that caused by crystal growth as an uneven surface is formed. The internal structure also changes and spherical lumps are observed. The mechanism is that the cocoa butter in chocolate completely melts at a temperature higher than the melting point and then solidifies as unstable Form III and IV followed by transformation into the stable form (Figure 20). The actual appearance of bloom is quite similar to that occurring by insufficient tempering.

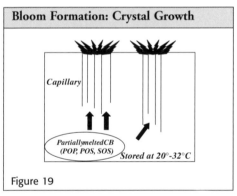

Figure 19

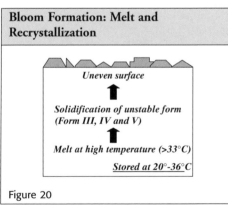

Figure 20

A third type of bloom occurs when there is a difference in storage conditions such as between a chilled temperature and room temperature. It is well observed in chocolate products that include a center cream or are coated on baked goods such as biscuits and cookies that include some liquid oil. Oil migration from the center cream or biscuit into the chocolate triggers this type of bloom. Liquid oil that migrates into the chocolate at room temperature dissolves the Form V crystal of cocoa butter. The solubility of cocoa butter into the liquid oil is dependent on the ambient temperature. When this chocolate product is chilled, the dissolved cocoa butter immediately crystallizes due to the supersaturation (Figure 21). It is interesting that this bloom disappears when we increase the storage temperature to the room temperature. Another characteristic of bloomed products is that they are rich in the POP triacylglycerol and this is quite reasonable because the solubility of the POP molecule into the liquid oil is higher than that of POS and SOS.

The above three types of bloom are mainly induced by thermal factors, but bloom also occurs because of the low miscibility between cocoa butter and cocoa butter alternatives such as CBR and CBS. In most cases, cocoa butter can be blended at only 20 and 5 percent into CBR and CBS recipes respectively, and above this ratio it will bloom due to the phase segregation in cocoa butter and others (Figure 22).

Figure 23 shows scanning electron microscopic (SEM) photographs of bloom caused by each typical condition. Each photograph well reflects each occurrence mechanism. For example, in bloom A, which was caused by the crystal growth, the partial crystal growth of Form VI was observed. Photograph D shows the typical phase segregation of cocoa butter from CBR.

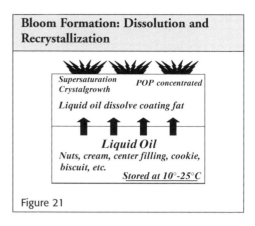

Bloom Formation: Dissolution and Recrystallization

Supersaturation Crystalgrowth   POP concentrated

Liquid oil dissolve coating fat

Liquid Oil
Nuts, cream, center filling, cookie, biscuit, etc.
    Stored at 10°-25°C

Figure 21

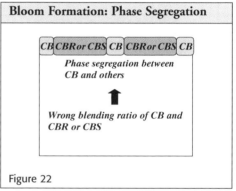

Bloom Formation: Phase Segregation

CB | CBR or CBS | CB | CBR or CBS | CB

Phase segregation between CB and others

Wrong blending ratio of CB and CBR or CBS

Figure 22

Preventing bloom As described above, bloom of chocolate products is mainly classified into four types based on the occurrence mechanism and appearance. The methods for preventing bloom will therefore also be different for each case. Figure 24 summarizes types, storage conditions, preventative measures and typical inhibitors of bloom.

Asymmetric triacylglycerols for bloom caused by crystal growth A key point of prevention is to retard the formation of Form VI, which is a seeding material of the bloom crystal. In many prior studies it is clear that asymmetric triacylglycerols are effective in the retardation of the form V–VI transformation. There is a short spacing spectrum of X-ray diffraction between cocoa butter Form V and transformation rates of V to VI at 17° to 32.5°C. The spectrum of 4.00A decreases in the transformation from Form V to Form VI and the spectrum of 3.65A increases simultaneously. When asymmetric 1, 2-distearoyl 3-oleoylglycerol (SSO) was added to cocoa

Scanning Electron Microscopic Photographs of Bloom

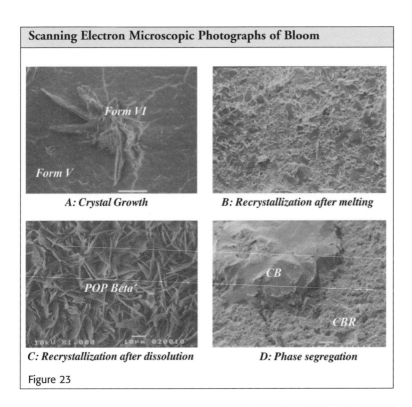

A: Crystal Growth

B: Recrystallization after melting

C: Recrystallization after dissolution

D: Phase segregation

Figure 23

Prevention of Bloom

Types of Bloom	Storage Conditions	Key Points of Prevention	Bloom Inhibitors
Crystal growth of Form VI	20°–32°C	Retardation of a) transformation V–VI b) crystal growth of Form VI	Asymmetric TAG (MF, SSO, BBO)
Recrystallization after melting	20°–36°C	Increase heat resistance Remaining seed crystal	Symmetric TAG (SOS, BOB)
Recrystallization Fat after dissolution	10°–25°C	Retardation of crystal growth Equilibrate liquid oil conc.	Interesterified (H_2M/M_2H) SOS/Liquid oil
Phase segregation	20°–36°C	Keep proper blend ratio	—

Figure 24

butter, the transformation rate was significantly retarded. And SSO also shows an effect against crystal growth of Form V. Under the presence of 10 percent SSO in cocoa butter, crystal growth of cocoa butter Form VI was prevented remarkably. The effects of other asymmetric triacylglycerols on bloom stability are shown in Figure 25. Milk fat contains various asymmetric triacylglycerol molecules such as OPM, OP4

Retardation of the Transformation from Form V to Form VI			
Antibloom agents (asymmetric triacylglycerols): milk fat, SSO, BBO			
Fat System	Stored @ 28°C	Stored @ 20°–28°C	Stored @ 20°–30°C
CB (100)	1 month	2 months	5 days
CB/milk fat (84/16)	3 months	4 months	–
CB/SSO fat (90/10)*	>7 months	>7 months	–
CB/BBO fat (90/10)**	–	–	46 days

* Patent US 5424090
** Patent JP 1-21734

Figure 25

and PPO. These asymmetric triacylglycerols may be adopting a different conformation from symmetric triacylglycerol, like POP, POS and SOS, and thus preventing the transformation and the crystal growth of cocoa butter.

Symmetric triacylglycerols for the bloom caused by melt-recrystallization The rate of polymorphic transformation in melt-mediation is normally higher than that of solid-state transformation and liquid oil is indispensable for the crystal growth. So, the addition of symmetric triacylglycerol into cocoa butter and the reduction of liquid oil simultaneously are reasonable measures towards bloom prevention. Bloom which is caused by melt-recrystallization is improved by adding symmetric triacylglycerols such as SOS and bob which have a higher melting point than cocoa butter. However, the working mechanisms are somewhat different from each other. Figure 26 shows symmetric triacylglycerol compositions of cocoa butter and a typical CBE which has some heat resistance.

We can increase the melting point, SFC and bloom resistance by blending SOS parts from shea stearin, sal stearin, mango stearin and enzymatic interesterified sunflower/safflower stearin. The melting point cannot be raised too high, however, because it affects the mouthfeel of chocolate. Actually, about a 1°C increase is the limit.

The main cause of bloom occurring at the temperature above the melting point is due to the disappearance of the seed crystal. This indicates that if the seeding crystal can still exist at a higher temperature, this type of bloom will be prevented. The bob beta-2 crystal with a melt point of 52°C satisfies this requirement because the bob beta-2 crystal is a symmetric triacylglycerol the same as cocoa butter. First, BOB beta-2 crystal is added into melted chocolate around 30° to 33°C, and chocolate is simply cooled without the tempering process and solidified as normal in Form V, because the bob beta-2 is identical to cocoa butter Form V. If normal chocolate is exposed to a temperature of 37°C, it is completely melted and will have a bloom problem after cooling down. However, when chocolate includes some bob beta-2 crystals, bloom will not occur because the bob beta-2 crystals do not melt in the chocolate at 37°C and while cooling this work as a seeding agent. Normal chocolate had bloom after just one cycle. Chocolate containing 3 percent bob beta-2 crystals, however, is bloom free up to 37 cycles.

Interesterified fat for the bloom of dissolution-recrystallization When the bloom is caused by oil migration in combination products such as baked goods/coating chocolate and center filling/shell chocolate, the method of prevention is to retard the crystal growth. The H2M/M2H mixture, which is prepared by the interesterification between hydrogenated palm oil and hydrogenated palm kernel oil, was developed as the crystal growth inhibitor. (H means saturated fatty acid, >C16, M means saturated fatty acid with C8-C14). It is characteristic that this H2M/M2H mixture can be used in baked goods as shortening. It is speculated that the H2M/M2H mixture easily migrates to

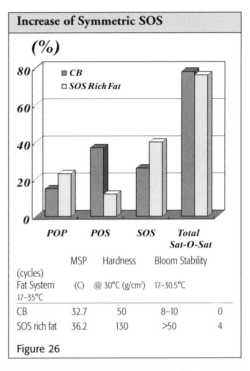

Increase of Symmetric SOS

(cycles) Fat System 17–35°C	MSP (C)	Hardness @ 30°C (g/cm²)	Bloom Stability 17–30.5°C	
CB	32.7	50	8–10	0
SOS rich fat	36.2	130	>50	4

Figure 26

Bloom Stability of Coating Fat

Fat System of Dough			Bloom Stability of Coating			
H₂M/M₂H	PL	HPL	13°C	20°C	25°C	30°C
—	70	30	5	4/5	2	3
10	70	20	5	5	4	4
20	70	10	5	5	5	4
25	70	5	5	5	5	5

5 (good) ⟷ (bloom) 1

Figure 27

the coating chocolate or shell chocolate with some liquid oil and works as an inhibitor of crystal growth of symmetric triacylglycerols such as POP, POS and SOS. According to the patent, it is able to prevent bloom if the shortening includes more than 10 percent of this inhibitor (Figure 27).

Sat-O-Sat TAG with liquid oil for the bloom of dissolution-recrystallization Another way to prevent this type of bloom is to equilibrate the liquid oil content between two phases, in particular by increasing the liquid oil in the shell or coating chocolate. It is possible to minimize the oil migration from shortening or center-filling cream to outside chocolate when the initial liquid oil content is almost identical in the two phase.s However, if cocoa butter is simply blended with liquid oil, the compound chocolate will be rather soft and could be sticky. In this case, the base fat, which is blended with liquid oil, should have high heat resistance at around 30° to 35°C and should contain much more SOS TAG than POP and POS.

CONCLUSION

In closing, as confectioners seek to develop new and interesting (and hopefully tasty) products, care must be taken in the selection of the appropriate fat system. When questions or problems arise, contact your fats and oils supplier to accompany you on your search to create new products or rejuvenate existing ones. It is believed that vegetable fats will play an important role in improving and developing the new and innovative chocolate products of the future.

REFERENCES

Cain, F.W. et al. Bloom-Inhibiting Fat Blends: U.S. Patent, U.S. 5,431,948, July 11, 1995.
Dimick, P.S. *Manufact. Confect.* 72(5): 109, 1991.
Johnston, G.M. *J. Am. Oil Chem. Soc.* 49:462, 1972.
Koyano, T. et al., *J. Jpn. Oil Chem. Soc.* 48(3): 184–189, 1993.
Koyano, T. et al. *Food Structure* 9:231–240, 1990.
Nomura, M. et al. Bloom Inhibitor: Japanese Patent, JP01-021734.
Okawauchi T. et al. Japanese Patent U.S. 5,424,090.
Wille, R.L. and E.S. Lutton. *J. Am. Oil Chem. Soc.* 43: 491, 1966.

Questions & Answers

Q: Are chocolates based on harder (Malaysian) cocoa butter more or less susceptible to liquid oil fat migration bloom compared to softer (Brazilian) cocoa-butter-based chocolate?

A: Chocolate containing harder cocoa butter will be much more susceptible to oil migration because the driving force of oil migration is the difference of liquid oil concentration between two phases. Also, harder cocoa butter will make more capillary holes in chocolate due to its high contraction rate caused by polymorphic transition. These capillary holes may promote the liquid oil migration.

Q: In an enrobed nut product, will different levels of milk fat in the milk chocolate have an effect on retarding migration of liquid oil fat bloom?

A: Yes, higher content of milk fat in shell chocolate will give better stability against oil migration from the center filling up to certain levels. However, you should find a good balance between bloom stability and hardness of shell chocolate.

Q: What is the melting point of cocoa butter OSO compound?

A: The melting point of cocoa butter (West African) and its compound with OSO is 28.6°C and 27.9°C by DSC, respectively. Generally, the melting point of cocoa butter/OSO compound is dependent on the melting point of the cocoa butter with which it is blended and is slightly lower than that of the cocoa butter.

Q: You mentioned a small chocolate company that uses as seed powdered chocolate that has been stored a long time. Could you give the details of this?

A: They first prepare the shavings of chocolate by using a knife and then pulverize them by grind mill to disperse easily into chocolate. Adding temperature is usually around 30° to 31°C. Then it is simply cooled down after good agitation.

Q: If a seeding agent (AOA, bob) is used in chocolate, does its presence increase the V to VI transition rate in storage?

A: No, it does not. If considering both AOA and bob, these seeding agents having longer fatty acid chains act as inhibitors of the V-VI transition. It is understood that dissolved AOA and bob molecules form a matrix which traps the liquid oil.

Q: How could you accelerate the transition in dark chocolate V to VI?

A: You can accelerate the transition by just simply storing the chocolate under the cyclic condition such as 20° to 32°C (one cycle/day).

Q: A number of years ago, John Clapperton (Mars, UK) did work on the Bal Estate to improve the flavor of Malaysian cacao. The work showed major flavor improvement with pod storage and slow drying. How would (or did) this regimen affect cocoa butter hardness?

A: We have no idea on the relationship between flavor improvement and cocoa butter hardness, but we believe that, basically, hardness is determined by the triacylglycerol composition. And triacylglycerol composition is dependent on the ripening temperature of cocoa fruit before harvesting.

Q: In one of your figures you show that rewarming melts the lower forms. Why don't they primarily transform, preserving the number of seeds?

A: The unstable form does not completely melt away in the reheating process. Some of the unstable crystals will transform to stable Form V during the reheating process. This is called melt-mediated transformation.

Q: You indicated a reason for the inclusion of 5 percent CBE in Europe in new products. Can you give us examples of products in both Europe and Japan that offer greater functionality at the permitted 5 percent than real chocolate alone can provide?

A: There are several products having a greater functionality in regard to bloom resistance, heat resistance, aeration and texture change.

Q: When adding bob to give thermal stability to chocolate, how high in temperature can you go? You used the example of 37°C (98.6°F). Does the crystal size of the bob make a difference? To what extent is the benefit lost by dissolving rather than melting the bob?

A: Melting point of bob beta-2 crystal is 52°C. Theoretically, chocolate containing bob can keep seed crystals up to this temperature. Of course, you have to add the bob beta-2 crystal at more than the amount of solubility. For example, the solubility of bob beta-2 crystal into chocolate at 40°C is about 7 percent. If you want heat resistance at 40°C, you should add the bob at more than 7 percent. Crystal size of the bob may be getting smaller due to the partial dissolution.

Q: How do you propose to introduce seeding agents in a continuous tempering operation?

A: It will require a blending tank of bob instead of a tempering machine. After blending at around 30° to 33°C, chocolate will be sent directly to the cooling tunnel.

Q: *How do you know what type of bloom you are going to get, i.e., which one to prevent?*

A: Probably you can judge the type of bloom from the appearance, storage condition and product recipe.

Q: *As a mixed triglyceride is heated, the proportion of liquid increases and solid crystals decrease. Is this due strictly to the solid crystals melting, or is there some component of the solids dissolving into the liquid? If so, any idea how much?*

A: Triacylglycerols having shorter chain, unsaturated fatty acid and unstable polymorphic form show higher solubility than others. The solubility at 30°C will be a couple of percent in total fats and oils content.

Q: *Why does seeding not help phase segregation?*

A: Basically, seeding agents such as SOS and bob work for Sat-O-Sat TAG in cocoa butter. As indicated in the paper, CBR and CBS were packed in a double chain length structure which is completely different from the triple chain length structures of cocoa butter and CBE. To prevent the phase segregation, transition of double chain length structure to triple chain length structure in the cocoa butter component must be prevented.

Q: *We periodically hear about off-flavors that can arise when using a lauric fat. When using a lauric-fat-based compound coating, what other ingredients should be avoided (in the compound coating and in the filling) to prevent the generation of off-flavors?*

A: In most cases, off-flavor means soapy flavor in the product containing lauric fat. Soapy flavor is normally generated by the hydrolysis of lauric fat. Usually hydrolysis is promoted by the existence of moisture and lipase, so other ingredients containing both moisture and lipase should be avoided. Also, there is a tendency that the larger crystal has much more off-flavor. Lauric fat which is rearranged is more suitable than hydrogenated or fractionated lauric fats.

Q: *Will the addition of 3 percent bob as seed crystal affect the viscosity of the tempered coating?*

A: No, it will not. Bob has a function to prevent the chocolate viscosity from increasing.

Q: *What would be the result of not fully melting out crystals prior to tempering?*

A: It depends on the previous storage condition of chocolate and the temperature to melt.

In some specific conditions, such as proper amount and proper crystal form remaining, it may give a good result (no bloom), but this condition is very narrow and it is difficult to control.

Q: *Omega-3 fatty acids are getting a lot of attention currently due to their health benefits. How can fish oil be used to create a healthier confection?*

A: We believe the keys are oxidative stability and flavor. If these issues are solved, it may be used in some confections as the liquid oil component.

Q: *Is bob allowed in chocolates in the United States?*

A: Bob (bohenin) has already been approved as GRAS for use as a tempering aid and as an antiblooming agent in the United States. It could be used for compound chocolate products except pure chocolate because there is no change in regulation regarding the chocolate standard in the United States or Canada. Japan has been using bob for many years in chocolate. In Mexico and South American countries, bob can be used for compound chocolate products except "pure chocolate." As far as other countries, currently the application for use in chocolate has been made to the proper agencies in each country.

Caramel

Caramel – Introduction and Definitions

Maurice Jeffery
Jeffery Associates

Next to chocolate, caramel is probably the confection used in more types of candy than any other, and one (like chocolate) which has worldwide appeal.

It covers a wide range of textures and physical characteristics, from a soft, free-flowing liquid, suitable for an ice cream or dessert sauce, to a more viscous center for moulded chocolate units, or from a firm, chewy texture, suitable for cut-and-wrap units, to hard English toffee.

Caramels are technically more complex than most other confections and the objective of this paper is to try to simplify their technology, from raw materials and formulation to finished products.

Figure 1 shows some liquid caramel products used for ice cream and dessert toppings.

The caramel in these has to be free flowing with a good flavor and rich caramel color. It must also have a long shelf life for normal use in the home, which is often intermittent.

Figure 2 shows some well-known brands of moulded chocolate products with a soft caramel center, made by shell moulding or single-shot depositing.

The caramel in these products is soft and strong in flavor to blend with the chocolate, which generally makes up 50 to 60 percent of the final product. It must also have the correct depositing characteristics to minimize tailing, particularly in single-shot depositors.

Figure 3 shows major brands in which caramel is used as a soft, chewy layer in bar products, generally made by sheet-and-cut or extrusion methods.

Figure 4 shows firmer caramel with good standup properties used for cut-and-wrap products.

Figure 5 shows which caramel is used

Liquid Caramel Products

Figure 1

Moulded Chocolate Products with Soft Caramel Centers

Figure 2

as a binder to stick nuts, cereals, etc., together, either by depositing or extrusion methods.

In these products the caramel must be a good glue or binder to hold the confection together, to make sure nuts or other solid pieces stick firmly to the caramel, particularly as the product passes through an enrober.

Formulations and processing conditions must be tailored to suit a wide variety of functional properties, including final texture, taste, flowability, depositing characteristics, etc. A review of formulations in recipe books often presents a confusing picture because there are so many variables that affect these products. An understanding of the nature of caramel and the function of the ingredients in it is far more valuable than a book full of recipes. Once this understanding is attained, the logic of the recipe changes and possibilities become clearer.

THE STRUCTURE OF CARAMEL

Caramel is physically a glass, consisting of a viscous syrup with milk solids dissolved or dispersed in it, and fat emulsified into it.

Caramel used as a Soft, Chewy Layer in Bar Products

Figure 3

Firmer Caramel used for Cut-and-Wrap Products

Figure 4

Caramel used as a Binder for Keeping Nuts, Cereals, etc., Together

Figure 5

The viscosity of the syrup binding the whole structure together depends on many variable factors (particularly water content) that affect texture, taste and other characteristics.

Sometimes sugar crystals, particularly lactose crystals, are dispersed in the syrup. These have a significant effect on the flow properties of the caramel and its stand-up character and heat stability. In the extreme situation where the syrup is made to partially crystallize, the texture is changed dramatically to produce fudge products, which will not be dealt with in this paper.

Despite the wide range of caramels used in our industry, they each have the following things in common:

- A syrup structure binding the whole confection together—they are syrup phase confections and essentially contain water.
- Milk solids, particularly milk protein, are dissolved or dispersed in the syrup.
- A characteristic flavor, produced by the Maillard reaction between the milk protein and reducing sugars in the recipe.
- Fat emulsified into the syrup.

Because there is water in caramels, they all have a water activity (a_w) which affects their microbiological stability, as in all syrup phase confections. For most caramels this is low and well below the 0.65 a_w maximum required for stability. Very liquid caramels, if they have not been properly formulated, can, however, have a higher than desirable a_w.

Here is a general recipe for sugar-based products, covering a wide range of possibilities:

Sugar (carbohydrate) solids	60%–75%
Water content	5%–20%
Fat	5%–20%
Total milk solids	5%–20%
Milk protein content	0.5%–4%

This does not apply to sugarfree caramels, which will not be discussed in this paper.

This year's Back to Basics papers will explain the functional properties and variables which make up these ingredients, and how they affect the following:

- The flavor of caramels through the Maillard reaction.
- Their texture and, particularly, controlling the water content of the finished caramel products, which is critical to this.
- Their flow properties and depositing or forming character.

The papers discuss how caramels are made, and how recipe, raw materials and cooking conditions affect their color, taste and texture.

Caramel – Raw Materials and Formulations

Mark Heim
Hershey Foods Corporation

Previous chapters have covered high boils, fondants and cremes. In them was described how to make both grained and ungrained confections, and how their ingredients and processes would control the finished product form. The basics given for mixing carbohydrates (usually sucrose and a corn syrup) and the effects of their ratio and final moisture on the syrup phase for texture, water activity and graining also apply in making a caramel (as well as any sugar confection).

Making a caramel uses your knowledge of carbohydrates and then adds milk to develop a confection with its own unique properties in flavor, color and texture, so we need to similarly understand the effects of adding milk. When adding milk, you are actually introducing three new components to your recipe: milk proteins, milk fat and milk sugar.

Milk proteins can be broken down to casein and whey proteins, roughly at a ratio of 80 to 20. The casein has most of its effect on texture, making the confection chewier, adding more body and giving it some elasticity. The whey proteins most affect the color and flavor that we are so familiar with.

The milk fat helps in flavor and also in texture by reducing stickiness and softening the bite. The fat in the amount of milk we add is not enough to do a good job, so additional fat is added, either as more milk fat or more commonly as hydrogenated vegetable fats. The melting curve of the fat used will have a significant effect on the finished caramel texture, flavor and product standup. Milk fat provides the rich, flavorful profile but will result in a soft piece due to its low melt point and a shorter shelf life due to its unstable fatty acids. The higher-melt hydrogenated fats will help firm up the caramel without making it much chewier or tougher and help it have a longer shelf life as they are more stable, but will not contribute as much to the rich flavor.

The milk sugar is lactose. It provides a low-intensity sweetness, but keep in mind that it is not very soluble and its low solubility can be a concern in how it processes and its effect on the finished piece.

MAILLARD REACTION

As just mentioned, the uniqueness of caramel is due in part to the milk proteins. The reaction of these proteins with the reducing sugars in a recipe is called a Maillard reaction. This reaction produces brown nitrogenous polymers or melanoidins, which contribute to the flavor, color and texture. The reaction itself goes through too many steps to cover here so just remember the basics:

- It is a reaction between amino acids and reducing sugars.
- It is affected by the type and levels of amino acids and reducing sugars.
- It is affected by temperature (slow below 100°F, fast above 200°F).
- It is affected by time, the thermal profile at each stage of the process.
- It is affected by pH, faster at higher pH.
- It is affected by moisture level throughout the process.

A TWO-PHASE CONFECTION

Caramel is often a two-phase confection, continuous and dispersed. To visualize this, imagine wet sand. The sand is the dispersed phase, the water the continuous phase. With the sand, using water gives you a texture for forming your desired shapes. In our caramel, the sand is the crystallized sugars and the water is the syrup. As in the wet sand, the ratio of dispersed and continuous phase will affect the texture, from something you can pour, to something you can shape, to something that is dry and crumbly.

The syrup or continuous phase is made up of the water and all ingredients that can remain dissolved in the water. What cannot stay in solution will crystallize or precipitate out to form the dispersed phase. This syrup affects texture and controls shelf life. The water level has the greatest influence in controlling texture, primarily hardness. The dissolved-sugars ratio controls stickiness, chewiness and toughness. The level of water and types of sugars together will control water activity, determining shelf life and what kind of protection the product will need, from moisture pickup or loss to cold flow. The proteins affect the body or elasticity. This continuous phase can be like a lubricant that allows the dispersed particles to flow or even pour as in a syrup, or it can be like a binder or glue to hold them in a given shape to the extent of a hard candy. The key is knowing what you want that continuous phase to do for your particular product, how you want it to behave and its effect on texture, flavor and shelf life.

The dispersed phase is not only made up of the sugars that crystallize out, but also oil, fat, precipitates and any inclusions such as nutmeats. What makes up the dispersed particles will affect texture differently. Their overall quantity or ratio of dispersed to continuous will affect how long or short the texture will be (go back to the wet sand and compare the pourable to the crumbly). The particle size affects surface area, affecting the amount of syrup that is needed just to coat the particles, like comparing wet sand to wet clay and similarly the possible range of textures of your confection. Their hardness also has an effect on texture. Is it a hard sugar crystal or a deformable oil globule? Even particulate shape has its effect.

The characteristics of your finished product will then be the result of the properties of each phase and how both phases complement each other.

Once you figure all this out, you then have to know what characteristics you need at each phase of your process. Is it a small kettle batch cook of a few pounds or a large-scale continuous process of more than 1,000 lbs an hour? How long will it take to cook or cool to temperature? How much shear is involved? Are you depositing or extruding? How much graining, if any, do you need when forming? Is it to be held and used later as a component to a more elaborate confection? Then, what do you want to happen after packaging so it's perfect when the consumer eats it? These are some of the questions you have to ask, and whose answers you need to understand.

A CARAMEL RECIPE

First, let's describe caramel. Depending on who you ask, you can get a variety of answers. You'll even get different pronunciations. Answers will range from a flowable ice cream topping to a glassy hard candy. It can be part of a candy bar as a layer to add texture and flavor, something that is sticky to hold peanuts or other inclusions in place, or one of the favorite fillings in a box chocolate, where it can be shaped with good standup for enrobing or flowable enough at cooler temperatures for shell-moulded candy. The most recognizable form may be the brown cube-shaped, soft and creamy confection. But even this last description can vary; is it a chewy, long-textured, ungrained piece or is it a tender, short-grained one? Is it fudge? Once you've decided exactly what it is that you want to make and how it is to function, you can then begin to determine what your recipe will be and which raw materials to use.

There are hundreds of recipes and such a wide range of raw materials available that it can become very confusing as to where to begin, let alone how to modify your recipe to get the exact product you want. There are some basic parameters often given, such as ratio of sucrose to corn syrup, level of milk proteins and so on, but to me that just limits your possibilities and creativity. After all, if you want to make something different, you have to do it differently. It first comes down to knowing exactly what you want to make. You can start by looking at the variety of books and articles (e.g., as in the *Manufacturing Confectioner*) that are available and select a recipe that comes closest to what you want in a caramel. You can even start with the label of an existing product.

Understanding the Recipe

Following the old adage that it is better to teach a person how to fish than to give him a fish, we will show you how to get a better understanding of your recipe and the raw materials and how to use that understanding to modify your recipe to best fit your process and give you that *perfect* caramel you want to make. So, rather than give parameters that may limit you, we'll just start with a recipe we've found and learn what to do to understand it so you can meaningfully change it as necessary.

This recipe (Figure 1) looks fine and is written just as you need it for batching in production. But it really doesn't tell us what is in there. To better understand a recipe, change it into a formula. Break it down so you know exactly what it is you're working with.

Let's start going through the recipe ingredients and break them down where

Caramel Recipe
Water . . . . 170.0 g
Sugar, granulated . . . . 454.0 g
Corn Syrup, 42DE/A . . . . 369.0 g
Sweetened condensed whole milk . . . . . 312.0 g
Partially hydrogenated vegetable fat . . . . 184.0 g
Salt . . . . 14.0 g
Soy lecithin . . . . 2.5 g

Figure 1

we can. Then we can discuss their purpose and see how together they make that particular caramel. For this paper, the numbers used are simplified to help you understand things easier. For your use, talk to your supplier and find out exactly what is in the raw material you are using.

Ingredients

Water—170.0 g No, we're not going to break down the water but just make a few comments. Its level before, after and at each stage of the process can have a lot of influence. With other ingredients, you may be off a percent or two and it will modify the product some if it does anything at all. If you are off a percent or two on water, the following could happen:

- The caramel could grain when you don't want it to or not grain when you do.

- It could be too hard or too soft.

- It could be less stable due to the water activity being too high, where you have problems with micro if sealed or its tendency to dry out if not; or too low, with problems of it picking up moisture and requiring more expensive packaging.

As an ingredient before cook, a starting point for how much water to add is about one-third the level of sugar, to help make sure all the sugar is dissolved. This, of course, will change due to the process you use, because, after cook, it's the final texture you want that determines how much water is left. For each of the processing stages, it's how fast or slow you want to develop the color and flavor or the when and how it will or will not grain.

Don't forget about the water quality—it should not be overlooked. You write specifications and have quality control checks for all of your ingredients; make sure you also do so for water. The best example is if it's too acidic you may need to use a buffer salt to prevent the milk proteins from denaturing or precipitating out.

Sugar, granulated—454.0 g Although for this exercise you can assume no moisture, you can also assume there will be some inversion. We'll keep the numbers simple and assume 1 percent inversion. So now our recipe looks like Figure 2.

Some confectioners prefer using brown sugar to partially replace the sucrose, developing a very nice change to the overall flavor. When you do, be sure to get its breakdown. It will contain some invert sugar and ash, with the invert sugar affecting texture, solids of the syrup phase and water activity, while the ash affects processing (foaming) and both affect the Maillard reaction.

Corn syrup, 42 DE/A—369.0 g For the sake of simplicity, we'll break it down only to DP1, 2, 3+ (DP1–dextrose, DP2–maltose, DP3+–higher saccharides) and its water level. The breakdown percentages are simplified to demonstrate the idea (Figure 3).

Again, check with your supplier for exact numbers. There are many corn syrups available, with different ranges of the components and even with different components.

Sweetened condensed whole milk—312.0 g To keep this part simple we'll break it down to the sugar, fat, lactose, total protein and water levels. The numbers again are examples (Figure 4).

Look at the sugar in the scwm; it's almost a quarter of all the sucrose in the caramel recipe and most of the solids of the ingredient. Remember to check with your supplier for exact numbers.

There are many other forms of milk that can be used or even different components from milk such as casein or whey that may be added. The casein

Breakdown of Sugar, Granulated	
Sugar	454.00 g
Sucrose (99%)	449.50 g
Invert (1%)	4.50 g
Dextrose (50%)	2.25 g
Fructose (50%)	2.25 g

Figure 2

Breakdown of Corn Syrup 42 DE/A	
Corn syrup	369.0 g
Dextrose (18% dry, 14.5% wet)	53.5 g
Maltose (14% dry, 11.0% wet)	40.6 g
Polysaccharides (68% dry, 54.5% wet)	201.1 g
Water (20% wet)	73.8 g

Figure 3

Breakdown of Sweetened Condensed Whole Milk	
Scwm	312.0 g
Sucrose (61.1% dry, 44.0% wet)	137.3 g
Butterfat (11.8% dry, 8.5% wet)	26.5 g
Lactose (14.6% dry, 10.5% wet)	32.8 g
Protein (12.5% dry, 9.0% wet)	28.1 g
Water (28% wet)	87.3 g

Figure 4

mostly affects texture by adding body and the whey proteins add color and flavor. They could be used to cut costs or modify your texture or flavor. Again, break them down, for example, for the lactose usually found in the whey. If adding more casein or whey, break down the protein above so you know how much you're starting with.

So many things about the milk can have an effect. The differences in the raw milk itself, how it was processed, stored and reconstituted all have their effect, mostly due to protein quality. You need to find which of the differences will affect your caramel and then you need to control them.

Partially hydrogenated vegetable fat—184.0 g We won't break the fat down, but here are the critical numbers of the fat:

- The melt point—the higher the melt point, the better the standup, but be careful going above 92° to 95°F as it can start to give it a waxy texture and flavor.
- The solid fat index (SFI)—this will let you know how sharp a melt curve you will have. This can influence the flavor release.

Other factors in deciding are resistance to oxidation and even how the fats are added. Blending several fats before emulsification can yield overall softer fats due to eutectic effect.

Salt—14.0 g The salt is used primarily to enhance flavor.

Soy lecithin—2.5 g The soy lecithin is an emulsifier, ensuring a good dispersion and homogenization of the fat. Other emulsifiers can be used to help with specific needs of your caramel. For example, GMS can be used to help with standup or to help with cutting a caramel that is sticky. Talk to your suppliers to determine which are best for your needs. Don't forget that the milk proteins also help in emulsification and in some cases may be all you need. Just make sure you have the level and type of emulsifier correct. If too much, you're wasting money and it could even contribute to off flavor or texture and if too little, it could oil out.

Other ingredients It is common to use carbonates, phosphates or other buffers to adjust the pH of your caramel. If the pH is too low—below the isoelectric point of the milk proteins (~4.6)—the proteins will precipitate. As the pH rises, you affect the rate of the Maillard reaction, but if it is too high your flavor quality decreases. A good starting point is a pH between 6 and 6.5.

You can use other ingredients to modify texture and flavor, such as various nut-meats and vanilla or vanillin. Starches or other thickeners can be used to modify product texture and your process.

Putting it all Together

Now rewrite your recipe and turn it into a formula. Our recipe turns into Figure 5.

Simplify It

Combine similar ingredients. Now you have your formula (Figure 6).

A next step would be to add another column with water at your finished moisture level and recalculate the percentage of your dries accordingly. If you go to available data on how much sugar your final corn syrup and moisture levels will hold, you can tell how much sucrose, if any, will potentially grain, but remember that viscosity also affects graining. You can set this process up in a spreadsheet program, tie it all together and then with just a few keystrokes know exactly how your recipe changes will affect your formulation. You can combine the components into their type (sugars, fats) or functions (texture/flavor), etc., for whatever works for the purpose of your doing this. How far you pull apart and rearrange is up to you and what you want to get out of it.

If you want to change your recipe, look at its formula, look at which components will make the changes you're looking for and look at which raw materials provide those components.

Now you can make better-informed decisions. You know exactly what has changed in your formula and then can look at the product made before and after the changes to see their effects in your process.

UNDERSTAND YOUR COMPONENTS

Take the time to learn more about what your components will and will not do. See

Revised Caramel Recipe
Water . . . . 170.00 g
Sugar
Sucrose . . . . 449.50 g
Dextrose . . . . 2.25 g
Fructose . . . . 2.25 g
Corn Syrup
Dextrose . . . . 53.50 g
Maltose . . . . 40.60 g
Polysaccharides . . . . 201.10 g
Water . . . . 73.80 g
Sweetened Condensed Whole Milk
Sucrose . . . . 137.30 g
Butterfat . . . . 26.50 g
Lactose . . . . 32.80 g
Protein . . . . 28.10 g
Water . . . . 87.30 g
Partially hydrogenated vegetable fat . . . 184.00 g
Salt . . . . 14.00 g
Soy lecithin . . . . 2.50 g
Figure 5

Simplified Caramel Recipe			
Ingredient	Weight	% Wet	% Dry
Dextrose	55.75g	3.72%	4.77%
Fructose	2.25g	0.17%	0.21%
Sucrose	586.80g	38.98%	49.97%
Maltose	40.60g	2.70%	3.46%
Lactose	32.80g	2.18%	2.79%
Polysaccharides	201.10g	13.36%	17.12%
Protein	28.10g	1.87%	2.39%
Fats	210.50g	13.98%	17.92%
Soy lecithin	2.50g	0.17%	0.21%
Salt	14.00g	0.93%	1.19%
Water	331.20g	22.00%	—
Total	1,505.50g	100.06%	100.04%
Figure 6			

how their combinations affect texture, flavor, color, shelf life and behavior in processing.

General affects you should know are shown in Figure 7. You can find further effects of your raw materials in literature or from your supplier; this is only to get you started.

REVIEW OF STAGES

- Get your starting recipe from books, articles, wrappers, etc., or one you currently use.
- Break it down, change it to a formula.
- Try it, evaluate it and decide where to take it.

General Effects of Ingredients

Dextrose and Fructose
Monosaccharides.
Reduce water activity.
React strongly with the milk proteins in Maillard reaction (fructose > dextrose).
Higher levels soften the product and increase stickiness.
Help more sucrose stay in solution, increasing finished solids of the syrup phase.

Sucrose
Disaccharide.
Bulk filler.
Provides most of the sweetness.
Does not react with milk proteins in the Maillard reaction; it is not a reducing sugar.
Higher levels make harder or can grain.
How much stays in solution depends on level of moisture and the ratio with other sugars present. Also rework, shear and its thermal history after cook.

Maltose
Disaccharide.
Texturally similar to sucrose in syrup phase.
Reacts with the milk proteins in the Maillard reaction, but much less than the monosaccharides.

Lactose
Disaccharide.
Very low solubility, tendency to grain.
Reacts with the milk proteins in Maillard reaction, but much less than the monosaccharides.

Polysaccharides
Provide texture, chewier, firmer, tougher, less cold flow.
Help control graining by increasing viscosity.
No significant reaction with the milk proteins in the Maillard reaction.

Protein
Know how much casein versus whey proteins.
Casein gives it texture, body.
Whey gives it color, flavor.
Know quality of proteins, how effective.

Fats/Emulsifiers
Reduce stickiness.
Give standup (differs by melt point).
Modify bite.
Control processing.
Flavor — quality, release, rancidity (add antioxidant).
If blending fats, emulsify before (firmer) or after blending (softer).
How well emulsified
  — Color
  — Surface oiling
Emulsifier type
  — e.g., GMS, use less, more standup.

Figure 7

- Decide what to change, components or process.

If you reformulate the recipe, do the following:

- Decide which components will affect your change and how much you need.
- Look at the source of those components.
- Make the appropriate recipe changes.
- Confirm all the changes made by ingredients on your formula.
- Test the changes.
- Compare formula changes to finished-product changes.

Once you have this set up on your spreadsheet to give you the information you're most comfortable using, you can make changes quickly and easily. Even doing it long-hand can save you time over guessing. The more you understand, the more you can figure it out and the more effective your work will be, in formulating or troubleshooting.

When comparing samples, don't just look at the ingredients and finished product. Follow your changes through your process so you know where they start to affect the caramel and by how much.

As confectioners you are artists, combining selected materials into a form with an appearance, aroma, flavor, texture and even sound that delivers an experience to your customer. How many art forms affect all five senses? Any true artist understands his materials and tools, what they will and will not do and how they can be altered and formed to deliver that experience to your customer.

So don't just know, understand. Knowing gives you specifics and can only take you so far; understanding gives you possibilities and will take you anywhere.

REFERENCES

Lees, and Jackson. *Sugar Confectionery & Chocolate Manufacture.*
Minifie, Bernard. *Chocolate, Cocoa and Confectionery.*

Questions & Answers

Q: Is the caramel formula that you presented a grained or ungrained finished caramel?

A: This recipe is one that was used in the demonstrations and not my own. Looking at the recipe after the ingredients have been broken down to their components, you can see that on a dry weight basis, sucrose makes up half of your solids. With this high level and having enough moisture to keep the product soft (viscosity influence), graining can be expected.

Q: At what level does lactose become a problem from a crystallization standpoint in finished caramel with a moisture of 10 to 18 percent?

A: Lactose is not very soluble, and much of the crystal form you start with in your cooking will remain throughout the process. When the product cools to ambient temperatures, additional lactose will crystallize out. The key with recipes for typical caramels is not so much lactose level but control of its crystallization. It only takes a few large crystals in a piece to be a problem. Some milk products, such as dulce de leche, have much more lactose, but a smooth product can still be made. You want the lactose to crystallize out quickly with a very fine seed. Large crystals form when it slowly crystallizes without any or enough seed, or the seed is already larger crystals. So make sure that the lactose has not formed larger crystals in the sweetened condensed milk, and if you are using milk or whey powder, that it has been properly reconstituted.

Q: You mention the impact of ingredients on the flavor and texture of caramel, but what role, if any, does the process (e.g., order of ingredient additions) or processing equipment (e.g., copper versus stainless steel vessels) have on these attributes?

A: The presentation was not meant to cover processing or equipment, but the process and equipment have a definite impact on flavor and texture of caramel. A good caramel will be one where the formulation and process match. A formula that works well on one processing line

may have to be changed to get the same finished product when using a different process.

Regarding order of ingredient additions, examples follow:
- Is your sucrose in solution before the cook? You may have to dissolve it in your water before adding other ingredients to control the crystallization in your finished product.
- Are you adding different fats, such as partially hydrogenated vegetable fat and butter? You will get a softer product if the fats are blended before emulsifying due to eutectic effect.
- Are you adding your milk source later in the process, for example, after first increasing your sugar and corn syrup solids? Here the lactose in the milk can initiate sucrose graining. Also, if the milk is not properly warmed when added to the hot sugar mass you can denature some of your milk proteins and lose the ability to make a smooth piece.

Regarding copper versus stainless steel vessels, the copper will react with your ingredients and give you a different flavor profile than using stainless. With copper, the resulting flavor is usually preferred, and copper will heat more evenly, but copper vessels cannot handle the same pressures as stainless in modern processing systems.

Q: Starting with a basic caramel recipe and considering doing an ingredient substitution (i.e., low fat, low calorie), are there any ingredients to look out for in terms of detrimental ingredient interactions?

A: When considering substitutions, break down the recipes to their components and then group them. Look at which ingredients will be in the continuous phase and which will be dispersed.

Compare solubilities of your new ingredients and determine doctor effects. If you have an ungrained caramel you don't want anything to crystallize out, and if you do want a grained product, you want to look at controlling crystal size and level so you still have an acceptable continuous to dispersed phase ratio.

Look at which components are replaced by new components. Compare the effects of old and new with texture, sweetness, solubility and their role, if any, in the Maillard reaction.

If you are reducing fat levels, expect textural changes. The fat helps reduce stickiness in eating as well as processing, such as slitting or cutting. Use of different emulsifiers can help reduce the fat level and still yield an acceptable texture and processable product, but then look at their effect on flavor. Also look at how you emulsify your product. A proper emulsion will allow you to use a minimal level of fat to get the functionality you need.

Q: What happens if you use butter instead of vegetable fat?

A: You get a softer, more flavorful product that could lose its smoothness and have reduced shelf life. Butter brings with it a lot of flavor, but be sure to look at the stability of the butter over the shelf life of your product; you may need to use antioxidants. The reason for using the partially hydrogenated vegetable fat is not to just help get a longer shelf life, but to change the texture of the caramel. The globules of any fat are part of the dispersed phase of your caramel. The hydrogenated fat is more solid and will be less likely to deform, resulting in better standup.

Q: What is the optimal size of fat globules in well-emulsified caramel?

A: I don't know of an optimal size. The fat globules are part of the dispersed phase. Like any dispersion, the smaller they are, the more consistent or smooth your product will be. Smaller globules also increase the surface area for the continuous phase to coat, and so help with standup. Poorly emulsified fat can reduce the smoothness of your caramel and can also work itself toward the surface where you will get a greasy texture and the exposed oil can oxidize faster. An optimal size would be one where you get the smoothness, standup, color and stability you want.

Q: Would you please explain briefly about the caramel formulations that use/contain carrageenan gum or maltodextrin in the product? What would be different?

A: Your starting formula may give you the exact color and flavor that you want, but you may want more body to your confection. Adding more corn syrup or casein would do that, but increasing either would change color, flavor and texture. You can also cook to a higher solids but that makes the product harder rather than just adding body. Carrageenan and maltodextrin are just two of the ingredients that can be added to primarily only affect texture. The carrageenan reacts with the milk's calcium to help form a gel network. The maltodextrins are like adding the polysaccharides from corn syrup without all the dextrose and maltose and will make a tougher product.

Q: What can be done to reduce the opportunity for lactose to grain or crystallize out, protecting it from making "gritty" texture in a hard (1–2 percent moisture) caramel?

A: At normal milk levels, the lactose will crystallize out and you will notice a powder-like gritty texture. In chocolate or fondant, a particle size of under 15 to 20 microns will feel smooth to the tongue, but in a hard candy your continuous phase is a glass and the particles are immobilized, like sandpaper. This is more a problem with deposited high boils than stamped. It is better to replace the milk with components in milk that you need to develop your Maillard reaction, such as cream or whey (lactose free).

When making a caramel high boiling, also watch for the following:
- The milk proteins easily burning in a cooker.
- Changes in the rheology of your finished product in forming.
- Stamped pieces changing shape due to elasticity of the rope.
- Deposited pieces having more of a tendency to tail.

Q: Please briefly comment on the effects of other emulsifiers.

A: There are many emulsifiers used and each has its own effect. Contact your supplier to learn what they may be since they don't all work as you want them to. Soy lecithin is commonly used because it works well and is low cost. High-melt emulsifiers, such as GMS, are used at a much lower level and have to be completely melted before you emulsify and the cost is higher.

Q: How is caramel pH measured?

A: Dilute the caramel in hot deionized water at a ratio of one part caramel to nine parts water. Measure pH with a standard probe. Because of the dilution and pH being inversely proportional to the concentration of hydrogen ions, report the results as a dilution.

Q: Does caramel used as a coloring agent contain milk?

A: Caramel color is caramelized sugars and is not from a Maillard reaction. It is formed by heating the sugars and does not use milk.

Q: What is the best vegetable fat to use to maximize shelf life and minimize saturated and trans fatty acids?

A: To maximize shelf life, use a vegetable fat, preferably a nonlauric fat. Common sources of fats and oils are unsaturated, and thus less stable, and low in melt point so they will not contribute to standup and will tend to have many of the same issues when using just milk fat. To raise the melt point, the fat is hydrogenated, adding hydrogen to the unsaturated points of the fatty acids, saturating them and improving stability and hardness, but a side reaction of this process makes *trans* fatty acids. Discuss with your supplier what is currently available; a lot of new work is being done to reduce or eliminate the *trans* fatty acids.

Q: When I eat a caramel, I experience throat burn in the back of my mouth. What causes this?

A: There are several thoughts on this. I have noticed that caramels higher in monosaccharides, particularly fructose, have more of this throat burn. Some of the resulting compounds from the Maillard reaction may also contribute. The milk proteins cling more to the throat, holding these aldehydes and ketones against the tissues of the throat.

Q: What effect does hardness of water have on caramels? At what point would it begin to affect the caramel?

A: Water hardness is the level of salts and minerals in the water. They can increase the tendency to foam, affect pH and form undesirable reactions with your components.

Q: Are preservatives needed in free-flow caramel? How does water activity determine need for preservatives?

A: For bacteria, mold or yeast to grow, the product water activity (a_w) and pH have to be able to support them. Just the texture alone does not determine if you need a preservative or not. In fact, a grained product will have a higher a_w and be more likely to have problems. Also, be careful with grained products to measure a_w after graining is completed and the syrup phase is no longer supersaturated, since the a_w will rise as the product grains. Bacteria usually require higher a_w but molds and particularly yeasts can grow at much lower levels. If your product a_w and pH can support micro growth, you will need to add a preservative. The other need for a preservative would be to help prevent oxidation of your fats, particularly butterfat. For this, you would use an antioxidant.

Q: How do you make sugarfree caramel?

A: To have the Maillard reaction take place, you need reducing sugars. But for a product to be sugarfree, the sugars level in the product is very limited. You can just add color and flavor to a sugarfree product, but the quality of the product will be very different in flavor, as well as texture. If you have good control of your process, you can start with just enough reducing sugars so that after the Maillard reaction is done, you have little to none left. This can be confirmed through analytical testing.

Milk – The Essential Ingredient in Caramel

Tim Galloway
Galloway Co.

Milk has been called nature's most perfect food. It is also the essential ingredient of one of the most common forms of confection—caramel. Whether the caramel is cut and wrapped, enrobed with chocolate, a layer in a candy bar or combined with nuts or other inclusions, it is one of the most popular confectionery ingredients.

In this paper we will explore basic milk composition, various milk products and components, the function of various milk products used in caramel and the price relationship of various milk products in caramel. By understanding these elements you can select the right milk product given the desired ease of use, functionality and price point.

BASIC COMPOSITION AND FUNCTION OF MILK

The milk processor generally considers milk as composed of water, milk solids nonfat and milk fat. These components vary by breed of cattle, feed and climate. Typically, milk in the United States contains the following:

- 87% to 88% water
- 8.4% to 8.7% milk solids nonfat (MSNF)
- 3.5% to 3.8% milk fat (BF = butterfat)

The milk solids nonfat is typically composed of the following:

- 4.7% to 4.9% lactose
- 2.8% to 3.0% true protein (non-nitrogen)
- 0.5% to 0.9% ash, vitamins, salts

Water

The amount of water in milk makes the product very perishable due to the high water activity. Therefore, it must be converted to another milk product soon after production, or pasteurized and refrigerated prior to being converted. The water could be used to hydrate dry ingredients in a caramel recipe. However, unconcentrated milk is rarely used for reasons that will be described below.

Lactose

The lactose in milk is a naturally occurring disaccharide sugar. When subjected to heat, it contributes to the distinctive caramel color via the Maillard reaction by interaction with amino acids found in the protein. It is often used as a bulking agent as it does not provide much sweetness, and can positively carry and enhance flavors. However, it can also cause grittiness, as it is relatively insoluble. The lactose content of milk can be reduced by enzymatic reactions, crystallization or filtration.

Milk Protein

The protein in milk is the most important component of milk as it relates to caramel production. It is also an incredibly complex molecule and there is still much that is unknown about how all of its subcomponents interact in the process of making caramel. There are two types of protein in milk—casein and whey. Approximately 80 percent of the total protein is casein and 20 percent is whey. Note the distinction between whey protein (sometimes known as serum protein) and whey (the liquid left after the cheese-making process that contains whey protein, ash and lactose). The casein and whey proteins can be separated in the following ways:

• The cheese-making process (enzymatic, with rennet), by acidification or by reactions with sodium, potassium or calcium.

• Casein proteins are very heat stable, whereas the whey proteins are easily denatured with heat above 70°C.

• Denaturation causes proteins to unfold. This unfolding allows bonds to form that create heat-induced irreversible gels.

These gels hold water and fat, stabilize emulsions and provide the structural support to a caramel. If a formula can hold more water and provide the proper firmness it will be more economical. The casein protein is mostly responsible for the body of a caramel, whereas the whey is more responsible for the color and flavor of a caramel.

Ash

The ash in milk is primarily made up of minerals and vitamins. The balance of minerals can be affected by heat treatment, age and quality of the milk and other factors. When the minerals are out of balance it can cause sensory and shelf-life defects in the caramel. Membrane filtration can be used to remove selected minerals. Stabilizing salts are often added to long-shelf-life concentrated fluid milk products to prevent problems over time.

Milk Fat

Milk fat provides lubricity, taste and mouthfeel to caramel. Milk fat contains lecithin, a naturally occurring emulsifier, which contributes to mouthfeel and shelf life. Milk fat used in caramel comes from milk or cream (fluid or dry), butter, concentrated milk fat (CMF) or anhydrous milk fat (AMF, also known as butter oil). Although the function of the fat is relatively similar regardless of whether it is in liquid or solid form, the flavor can be different due to reactions caused when manufacturing the different forms.

Raw Milk

The confectioner should be concerned with the quality of the raw milk used to make the milk product. Raw milk is full of bacteria and needs to be effectively pasteurized shortly after production in order to assure the best flavor and functionality from the milk ingredient. Typically raw milk should have a somatic cell count of less than 200,000. Higher somatic cell counts may be indicative of milk from diseased animals, which can cause detrimental flavor and functional reactions even after pasteurization. Although pasteurization eliminates all pathogens, some spoilage bacteria survive. Higher initial bacteria loads will lead to higher ending spoilage bacteria counts.

Many dairy manufacturers have faced the issue of whether milk produced from cows that have been treated with bovine growth hormone, or fed genetically modified feed, is "all natural" or "GMO-free." The recombinant bovine growth hormone is genetically identical to the naturally occurring hormone. There is the same amount of hormone present in milk obtained from treated and untreated cows. The milk has not been altered although the cow has. Similarly, even though the cow consumes GMO feed, none of the genetic material ends up in the milk. The milk has not been modified even if the feed has been altered. Therefore, most milk manufacturers consider milk to be GMO-free and natural.

TYPES AND FUNCTIONALITY OF MILK PRODUCTS

There are many different types of milk products used in the manufacture of caramel. The following is a brief discussion of various types, forms, packaging and functionality of the most common milk ingredients. The confectioner should select the most effective (in terms of cost, functionality or flavor) source of dairy protein and fat for the desired caramel. Traditionally, concentrated milk and concentrated blended fluid ingredients have been preferred because they deliver the necessary dairy components in a cost-effective manner, are easy to work with in processing, have an extended shelf life and provide some moisture for hydrating dry ingredients but not so much that it unduly extends cooking times.

Nonconcentrated Milk

Whole milk and skim milk are nonconcentrated milk products. Even after conventional pasteurization they have a very short shelf life (7 to 10 days) due to their high water activity. These products must be kept refrigerated. They are costly to transport and package relative to other dairy ingredients due to their high water and low solids content. They must be added slowly in the cooking process to avoid scorching and curdling, and need to be cooked longer to remove excessive moisture. Therefore, nonconcentrated products are rarely used as they fall short on cost and functional criteria.

Concentrated Milk Products

Concentrated milk products take several forms. If whole milk is concentrated to at least 6.5 percent butterfat (BF), 16.5 percent milk solids nonfat (MSNF) and 23 percent total solids (TS); is hermetically sealed and processed for extended shelf life; and has vitamin D added, it can be called evaporated milk. This product may also contain other vitamins, stabilizers and emulsifiers. Extended shelf-life processing usually means retorting; however, sterile processing and filling can be done, albeit at greater cost. The hermetically sealed products have a shelf life of over one year. The package is either a can or pouch containing from 8 to 96 oz.

If whole milk is concentrated to at least 7.5 percent BF, 17.5 percent MSNF and 25 percent TS, it can be called concentrated milk. There are no requirements for packing for extended shelf life and all additional ingredients are optional. In dairy circles, this product is known as evap and is most commonly shipped bulk at up to 44 percent TS. It must be refrigerated and agitated, and has a shelf life of about 10 to 14 days.

Skim milk may also be concentrated. If it is packed for extended shelf life and vitamin A is added in the same concentration as in whole milk (vitamin A is removed with the butterfat), the product can be called evaporated skim milk. There are no minimum standards of identity for composition of evaporated skim milk. Dairies often use a bulk skim product at 33 percent TS known simply as "condensed." It must be kept refrigerated and agitated and has a shelf life of 10 to 14 days.

Evaporated and condensed whole and skim milk products are made using reverse osmosis (RO) membrane filtration or evaporation. Membrane filtration uses pressure and membrane size to selectively remove water. Evaporators remove water by boiling under vacuum. Membrane filtration is less costly but cannot produce the highly concentrated bulk industrial product.

Separating milk fat from milk via centrifugation produces cream, another concentrated milk product. It must be at least 18 percent BF to be considered light cream and 36 percent BF to be heavy cream. There is a small amount of MSNF remaining in all cream products. It is sold as a bulk or packaged refrigerated product having a shelf life of 10 to 14 days. Some cream is frozen in order to have extended shelf life but care must be taken to properly temper the product as it thaws to avoid functional problems. Cream can also be dried for extended shelf life, though this product imparts a different flavor than fresh product.

Packaged concentrated milk products have the advantage of having a long shelf life and a convenient size for small batch operations. There are fewer concerns about running out of product or spoiled product due to age. There is less risk of settling due to their lower concentration and use of stabilizers. Due to their lower solids content, freight and packaging costs per pound of milk solids are higher than some other dairy ingredients. The ingredients must be added slowly during cooking to prevent scorching and curdling. Bulk concentrated milk products have the advantage of more cost-effective shipping and packaging due to their higher solids content. They must be kept refrigerated and agitated to prevent spoilage and settling. Bulk products have a higher initial capital cost for the tank and associated equipment. There is also a greater risk of loss due to out-of-date product.

Concentrated, Blended Milk Products

There are a variety of concentrated, blended milk products that are generally referred to as sweetened condensed milk (SCM) products. Various liquid dairy and/or nondairy components are blended with a nutritive carbohydrate sweetener. The sweetener is used at a concentration high enough to create sufficient osmotic pressure to retard bacterial growth. Usually, SCM is produced on an evaporator, shipped in bulk or large packages and has a shelf life of several months at room temperature. If the product is hermetically sealed in pouches or cans, it can have a shelf life of several years.

The sweetener of choice is usually sugar. It makes no difference whether the sugar source is beet or cane. Other sweeteners can be used in conjunction with sugar. Corn syrup, dextrose and fructose have all been used. High concentrations of these other sweeteners can create too much viscosity for practical use. The sugar to sugar-in-water ratio should be between 60 and 65 percent in order to have sufficient osmotic pressure to retard spoilage without the mixture becoming supersaturated, leading to precipitation. Products made with SCM are seeded at the proper time and temperature with a small quantity of finely milled lactose in order to control crystallization of the naturally occurring lactose.

The current standards of identity for SCM call for the partial removal of water only from a mixture of milk and sweetener. Recombined products made from nonfat dry milk, dry milk proteins and the like cannot be labeled as SCM. Concentrated milk products like evaporated milk, condensed skim milk and cream can be used to make s c m. Other milk components may be added to the mixture so long as the minimum standards are met and the additional ingredients are properly labeled. Recommendations made at the latest round of Codex may change the standards of identity to allow s c m to be made out of a variety of wet and dry dairy ingredients.

The current standard of identity only lists sweetened condensed milk, which is commonly referred to as sweetened condensed whole milk. It proscribes a minimum b f of 8 percent and total milk solids (t m s) of 28 percent. A typical packaged product meets those minimum criteria and adds 45 percent or more sugar to get the greatest preservative power for extended shelf life. Usually, packaged s c m is manufactured at close to the minimum standards as it is a price-competitive industry and no manufacturer can afford to give away solids. Industrial product is often designed to have the greatest amount of dairy solids and total solids possible while still pumpable. A typical industrial formula may contain 8.5 percent b f, 24 percent m s n f and 43.5 percent sugar for 76 percent t s. This formula provides a higher percentage of the needed dairy solids. It also has a lower percentage of sugar, which isn't needed for shelf life given the shorter use cycle time and can be added by the caramel manufacturer. Freight and packaging costs per pound of dairy solids also go down with a more highly concentrated product. There are a number of variations on the typical s c m formula whereby additional fat, milk protein or sweetener is added.

Sweetened condensed skim milk (s c s) had a standard of identity until the enforcement of the Nutritional Labeling and Education Act (NLEA) regulation pertaining to dairy. The manufacturer can still make a product labeled s c s but he must add the proper amount of vitamin A to make it nutritionally equivalent to whole milk. If vitamin A is added, there can be variations of reduced fat and low fat s c m if the fat percentages are consistent with NLEA guidelines. If vitamin A is not added, the manufacturer must give the product a fanciful name such as sweetened skim milk blend. As with s c m, the packaged skim product usually has lower total solids to prevent settling and more sugar to increase shelf life than the industrial product—typically at least 24 percent m s n f and 47 percent sugar. The industrial product may have 28 percent m s n f and 42 percent sugar. Again, there can be custom formulations of the skim product. In no-fat caramels and those where the manufacturer adds the diary or nondairy fat, s c s is used.

Filled milk is another common name for a variant of s c m. In this product, the milk fat is replaced by vegetable fat, which reduces the cost of the caramel. The standard of identity for this product also no longer exists. Sweetened condensed cream (s c c) is another concentrated, blended milk product. It is similar to cream but preserved with sugar. A typical formula may have 35 percent BF, 8 percent MSNF, 35 percent sugar for 78 percent TS. Unlike fresh cream, this product does not need refrigeration and has a shelf life similar to SCM. Due to the low water content, SCC can be used very late in the cook process in order to retain the most cream flavor. There are any number of caramel blends that include, in a liquid form, most (if not all) of the ingredients in the final caramel. These products are ideal where the manufacturer has limited blending and processing equipment but can remove the last bit of moisture and complete the Maillard reaction.

Products with SCM are desirable ingredients, as they provide fresh dairy components in a shelf-stable form. There is little water for the caramel manufacturer to remove, saving time and energy. In addition, industrial products have cost savings in that they can be shipped in bulk or with low-cost packaging. There are some potential negative attributes. Over time, SCM is susceptible to thickening, settling and discoloration. In addition, customers pay for processing sugar along with the milk, which does not happen with other milk products.

Long-shelf-life Milk Products

Whole milk powder (WMP) and nonfat dried milk powder (NFDM) are the two most common long-shelf-life milk products used to make caramel. Conventionally packed, WMP has a shelf life of three months, or nine months if the bag is gas flushed to prevent oxidative rancidity of the fat. In sealed bags, NFDM has a shelf life of up to two years. Both powders can be shipped bulk or in totes. Milk powders are classified by the heat treatment given during processing. The heat treatment affects the amount of protein denaturation. Low-heat powders are most soluble but have little denaturation so are not as good in forming bonds. Higher heat powders form better bonds but must be carefully hydrated for optimum functionality. Most powders can be hydrated cold overnight with agitation. Much quicker hydration can be achieved with higher temperatures but then the blend must be immediately processed to avoid bacterial growth. The confectioner must recognize the 2 to 4 percent moisture in the product when formulating and costing.

Milk fat can also be processed and stored for extended periods and then used to make caramel. The most common product is butter, which is milk fat in the form of cream that has been churned to yield 80 to 82 percent BF. Salt, flavor and color are often added. The fat is subject to oxidation over time so the product is refrigerated for up to six months or frozen for up to two years. Due to physical changes and additions in the butter-making process, butter and milk fat or cream are not interchangeable as to flavor and functionality. Concentrated milk fat (CMF) also has a long shelf life. It is basically unflavored, uncolored, unsalted butter. The product must be refrigerated or frozen. Anhydrous milk fat (AMF), often called butter oil, is another long-shelf-life milk fat. With the repeated separation of cream or butter, AMF is made. The product contains more than 99 percent fat. It is shelf stable and pumpable at room temperature but must be properly packaged to avoid flavor degradation.

The dried long-shelf-life products don't need any costly storage conditions or packaging. They are very price effective in shipping solids long distances. Given the high solids content, they are the most cost-effective product to pack, ship and store per pound of dairy solids. Many of the products can be imported in order to obtain favorable pricing due to currency exchange rates or lower production costs in other countries. There is less waste due to out-of-date product; however, there is shrink in the hydration process. In addition, care must be taken to allow the proper time and temperature for complete hydration so the proteins can have full functionality. Frozen and refrigerated long-shelf-life products offer similar cost advantages in packing and shipping per pound of dairy solids. There is also less risk of lost product due to code date issues. The disadvantages include care in proper tempering of refrigerated and frozen products, cost of storing refrigerated and frozen products, and shrink factors.

MILK COMPONENTS

There are a number of milk components and by-products that may be used in the manufacture of caramel. Many of these items are by-products of some part of the dairy manufacturing industry and therefore enjoy a price advantage against other milk proteins, fats or bulking agents. Below are several of the most common.

The lactose found in liquid whey can be crystallized, recovered and dried. It is packed in bags or totes and has a long shelf life. It is often used as a low-cost bulking agent in caramels that also provides a little sweetness, carries flavor and adds color. Sweet cream buttermilk is the by-product of the butter-making process. It does not have the distinctive taste of cultured buttermilk but it is not as bland as skim milk. The product has a nonfat milk solids content similar to skim milk but also contains some residual butterfat. Buttermilk is available in unconcentrated, condensed and dry forms or can be included in a concentrated blended milk product. As a by-product, buttermilk is a less expensive source for milk protein than skim or whole milk and provides a little fat at skim solids prices, which are usually cheaper. Whey is another by-product that can be used to make caramel. Whey proteins can bind water at a lower cost than casein protein, although additional lactose in whey makes a darker caramel and the ash in whey can provide off-flavors. Demineralized and delactated whey are available to help mitigate some of these problems. Whey is available in unconcentrated, condensed and dry forms or can be included in a concentrated, blended product. Cost advantages outlined above for other dried dairy ingredients apply to these by-products, as do the disadvantages.

Protein concentrates are beginning to be used in more foods. These products are made from ultrafiltered (UF) milk or whey by recovering the desired protein and eliminating most of the water, minerals and lactose. The resulting product is then dried. Protein levels up to 85 percent total solids can be achieved in the case of milk protein concentrate (MPC) and whey protein concentrate (WPC), and up to 95 percent in the case of milk or whey protein isolates (MPI, WPI). These products can be used to replace milk or whey proteins from other dairy sources. Currently there are limited domestic sources of MPC due to our relatively higher cost of production and subsidized floor price for milk. Much of the MPC comes from Australia and New Zealand, which are low-cost milk producers, major dairy exporters and currently have favorable currency exchange rates. WPC is readily available domestically, but is a more expensive source of whey protein than the alternatives. Caseinates are dried casein proteins created through enzymatic reactions. Although they have a relatively high concentration of the desired casein protein, they are not manufactured domestically and are rather expensive compared to alternative casein sources. The concentrated protein forms are advantageous to those who are creating specialty products, or to those who can combine them with other less expensive by-products to create blends with similar composition to traditional milk sources at a lower cost. Care must be taken in selecting protein sources as some of the imported products are merely combinations of NFDM and caseinate, come from countries with poor sanitary conditions or are combinations of out-of-date or out-of-spec product.

PRICES OF MILK PRODUCTS USED IN CARAMEL

The USDA uses a classified pricing system to determine the minimum price producers are paid for Grade A milk. Fluid milk is in Class I, soft products like ice cream and SCM are in Class II, cheese is in Class III and butter and powder are in Class IV. Butter and powder are subsidized products so they set a floor for milk pricing. The Class IV milk price is based on prices of butter and NFDM. Class III prices are based on the price of cheddar cheese. The Class II price uses Class IV as a base and adds a set differential. Class I milk uses the higher of Class IV or III prices and then adds an even greater differential. The minimum producer price for a geographical area, known as a Federal Order, is set by determining the weighted average price of all milk used in each class in that area. In many parts of the country where there is competition for procurement of his milk, the farmer will get paid an additional premium to attract his milk. In setting the class prices the government also determines

Average Milk Product Prices in Chicago Region (2003)				
Product	Package	Price	Unit	Notes
Class II milk	Bulk	$12.04	cwt	Includes $1.50 cwt premium
Condensed skim milk	Tank	$0.90	lb solid	33% solids
WMP	Bag	$1.14	lb	96% solids
NFDM	Bag	$0.83	lb	96% solids
Butter	68# block	$1.09	lb	82% BF
Cream	Tank	$1.42	lb fat	42% BF
Buttermilk	Powder	$0.70	lb	96% solids
Whey	Powder	$0.17	lb	96% solids
Lactose	Powder	$0.50	lb	96% solids

Figure 1

values for protein, skim milk solids, butterfat and whey that can be used as a basis to price commercial products. As of March 31, 2003, the average prices in Figure 1 were reported by the USDA in the Chicago region, FOB manufacturer.

SUMMARY

A number of constituents of milk provide functional benefits in the production of caramel. Proteins provide body and texture. Fat provides flavor and mouthfeel. Lactose provides body and flavor. In combination, they provide the essential color of caramel. Traditionally, concentrated milk products and concentrated blended milk products have been the ingredients of choice. They provide the right combination of ease of use, adequate shelf life, flavor development, protein quality and favorable cost of packaging and shipping dairy solids to make high-quality caramels. Modern processing techniques are allowing confectioners more variety in their dairy solids choices. Regardless of the ingredient selected, the goal should be to make a great tasting and performing product at a reasonable cost so that more caramel is consumed more often.

Questions & Answers

Q: Can you please explain the difference between anhydrous milk fat (AMF) and concentrated milk fat (CMF)? From your description, they sound practically the same.

A: Anhydrous milk fat (AMF) is more than 99 percent milk fat. Concentrated milk fat (CMF) is only 80 to 82 percent milk fat. Essentially, CMF is butter without any coloring or flavor while AMF is much more concentrated.

Q: From a functionality view, why would a confectioner choose AMF over CMF?

A: As AMF has less water, it is more cost effective to package, ship and store per pound of fat. CMF has more milk solids nonfat (protein), so it can contribute to standup and body. AMF only provides fat.

Q: How can milk products be evaluated for initial bacterial load or for enzymatic activity resulting from "dead bodies?"

A: Once a product is pasteurized, it is difficult to tell what was the initial microbial load of the raw milk. However, the intermediate milk product and the finished confection may be more susceptible to spoilage or off-flavor and odor if the initial milk product had a high microbial load.

Q: What happens if I use cheese to substitute or use partly for milk protein and fat? Will I cut down the cooking time to achieve the same result of caramel processing?

A: I have not encountered cheese as a substitute for part of the milk requirements. Depending on the milk product used, the cheese may provide more or less moisture. In addition, most cheese has distinct flavor and color, which would affect the confection.

Q: What are the optimum cooking conditions (temperature, time) to give optimum denaturation of milk protein in caramel? What will happen if cooking temperature is too low, or the time is too long in terms of protein denaturation?

A: Protein denaturation is affected by heat and time and processing conditions (atmospheric or vacuum). Other ingredients present when cooked also influence it. For instance, sugar tends to protect the protein, causing the product to be cooked at a higher temperature than if the milk alone was present. It is usually preferable to have a higher temperature than a longer hold, as time will affect color and flavor more than heat alone.

Q: For SCWM, how long can you store it at 65°F before protein or lactose grit appears in finished high-boil caramel?

A: The storage temperature has less to do with lactose or protein precipitation than processing conditions. If the product was not seeded correctly or the sugar-in-water ratio is too large there will be lactose and/or sucrose precipitation regardless of the storage temperature. Protein can be precipitated by variations in acidity, enzymatic reactions and other causes. If properly produced from good milk, SCWM can be stored at room temperature for at least one month packed in pails, drums or totes, and over a year if hermetically packed in a can.

Q: Please elaborate on the challenges of using frozen or dried cream in a caramel formulation.

A: Frozen cream must be carefully thawed to prevent separation or spoilage. Often, frozen cream has up to 10 percent sugar to make sure the fat does not crack when tempered. Dried cream must be hydrated with enough water and with enough time given the water temperature to insure complete hydration. If high temperature/short time is used, the resulting liquid cream must be either used immediately or cooled back down for storage.

Q: Is there any way to determine a somatic cell count in a finished caramel when at a loss to determine what is causing an off-flavor, after eliminating lipase, fat rancidity, etc.? What would the taste be – cheesy, sour, tart?

A: Once pasteurized, the intermediate milk product resulting from high-somatic-cell-count milk will contain a higher than normal standard plate count as the process will only kill 99 percent of the original load. The intermediate product would probably have a higher titratable acidity. The end product could have a variety of off-notes from cheesy to sour depending on the characteristics of the particular spoilage bacteria present.

Q: How do the prices of milk protein concentrate (MPC) and whey protein concentrate (WPC) compare?

A: Per percent of protein, the WPC is much less costly than the comparable percent of MPC. It is very similar to the cost difference between liquid skim milk and liquid whey at the same total solids. Whey solids usually are 15 to 20 percent the cost of skim solids.

Q: Can caramel be made without homogenizing the premix?

A: Most caramel, I believe, is not made by passing the premix through a homogenizer. However, all good caramel is thoroughly blended before cooking in order to get a homogeneous end product.

Q: What is the milk fat content for the three formulations: SCM, WMP, evaporated?

A: The SCM formula contained about 1.8 percent milk fat, as did the WMP formula. The evaporated milk formula contained about 1.4 percent milk fat.

Q: In using soy protein, what differences would there be? What are some of the concerns and what percentage would you use in a formulation? The only concern I know is that milk protein and fat separate at a higher pH, while soy protein and fat separate at a lower pH.

A: I am not very familiar with the functionality of soy protein in confections. Generally, soy proteins are much harder to hydrate and keep in solution than milk proteins, so they may be more difficult to process. They typically provide a distinct flavor, which some consumers find objectionable.

Q: What is the optimal time/temperature relationship to hydrate powdered milk?

A: Milk powders may be hydrated cold over 24 hours. This temperature would allow hydration and storage without need for additional heat transfer equipment. They can also be hydrated in half an hour at 150°F but then must be cooled down to prevent spoilage or used immediately.

Q: Must acidulated fruit-flavored cream candy be buffered? For instance, citric acid?

A: Most of the fruit-flavored cream candies of which I am aware are manufactured at neutral pH, avoiding the need for any buffering.

Q: What is block milk and what are its uses?

A: Block milk is a concentrated milk product that has sugar added to increase shelf life. Typically it has 12 percent fat, 38 percent milk solids nonfat, 40 percent sucrose and 10 percent water. The milk is first evaporated, then sugar is added while further evaporating and the product is hermetically sealed. When it cools it achieves a thick and pasty consistency, hence the name. I am not aware of any block milk produced in the United States. Although it has a shelf life up to 12 months, the cost of processing and packaging are greater per pound of total milk solids than alternative milk sources.

Caramel Processing Batch to Continuous

Arthur Rittenberg
Humko Oil Products

This paper is about caramel processing, including both batch and continuous methods. The first discussion will be making the caramel premix using a typical formula. From there, we will discuss the mixing of these ingredients, and then cover the various cooking processes including lab batch, production batch and automatic cookers. Finally, we will cover two methods of cooling the cooked caramel and several forming processes.

Figure 1 is a picture of a lab-sized batch caramel cooker—a copper kettle, typically heated on a gas-fired burner.

Figure 2 shows a premix kettle. For optimal accuracy, the weigh vessel can be placed on weigh cells or loss-in-weight feeders can be used. The weigh vessel is the tank at the top of the unit. All connections to this unit are flexible so that there is no interference with the weigh cells.

Lab-sized Batch Caramel Cooker

Figure 1

Figure 3 illustrates a typical caramel formula. The liquids are usually added first and solids last. Intermediate mix times are usually used, with a final mix time that lasts 10 to 15 minutes. The fats as well as the emulsifiers need to be completely melted. Note that the formula contains sodium bicarbonate to adjust the pH of the mix. It is important that the pH is approximately 6.5. If the

Batch Caramel Cooker

Figure 2

Caramel Formula	
Ingredients	%
Water	10.0%
Sugar, granulated	21.0%
Corn syrup, 42 DE	24.5%
Sweetened condensed whole milk	20.7%
(Partially hydrogenated soybean oil)	15.2%
Butter	6.0%
Salt	1.0%
Mono- and Diglycerides	1.0%
Sodium bicarbonate	0.3%
Soy lecithin	0.2%
Total	100.0%

Cook to 236°F for approximate 15 percent moisture in the finished caramel.

Corn syrup: use 42 DE for chewy texture and less sweet product, or 63 DE for softer texture but increased sweetness.

Figure 3

premix is too acidic, then the milk protein will coagulate when heated and cause the final caramel to be grainy.

One of the problem areas encountered involves the proper melting of the ingredients. Ingredients that need to be melted (such as fats and emulsifiers) must be heated above their melting point. A good rule of thumb is 10°F above the melting point. If the ingredients are not melted to the proper temperature, then they will affect the final texture. Solid emulsifiers, such as mono- and diglycerides, must also be melted completely. A good process involves mixing the emulsifier with a portion of the melted fat and then storing the blend at the temperature of the melted fat. As an example, melt mono- and diglycerides (with a 140°F melting point) completely and mix them with a portion of the 95° to 100°F fat. This mixture can then be stored at 110°F until it is needed for addition to the mixture. This process is very effective since the emulsifier is completely melted. If the emulsifier is not completely melted, it will be ineffective as an emulsifier and oil separation can occur when the premix is cooked.

Mixing of the ingredients is important because a thorough mixture must be achieved. High-sheer mixers are commonly used. The ingredients are usually mixed for 10 to 15 minutes. Another process that can be used is to mix the ingredients and then pump the premix through a two-stage homogenizer. Examining a drop of the blended premix under a microscope can be useful in evaluating how well the mix has been homogenized. Comparing a sample of well-mixed ingredients against a sample that is barely blended will give you a good point of reference when evaluating how well your mixing process is working.

Figure 4 is a cut-away diagram illustrating how the weigh vessel operates. The ingredient valves above can control both solid and liquid ingredients. The order of addition of these ingredients (as well as mix times) is controlled by the computer. Both the weigh mixer and holding tank are held at a temperature between 120°F and 130°F. The holding tank should have vigorous mixing to maintain the well-mixed ingredients.

The next step up in size can also be used in production (Figure 5). The caramel kettle sits on a gas-fired burner and has a mechanical agitator stirring the premix from above. For those energetic folks, the mix can also be hand-stirred. Batch cooking will be discussed later since the starting point in either process is to weigh each ingredient accu-

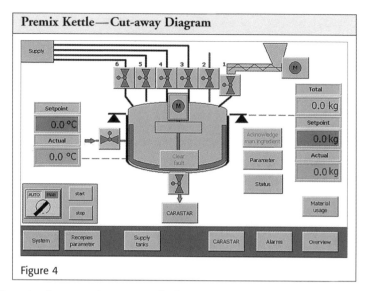

Premix Kettle — Cut-away Diagram

Figure 4

rately and thoroughly mix the ingredients specified in your formula. The methods used to weigh the ingredients have to be done accurately since any variation at this point will carry through to variations in the cooked caramel. Accurate scales that are calibrated on a routine schedule are commonly used. For continuous operations, it is common to use weigh cells on the mix tank.

BATCH COOKING

Small batch cookers can be used for development or R&D projects. Typically they are small benchtop units. Larger units can also be used and in some cases make samples that more closely approximate the flavor and texture of caramel products while in the development stage when made in large-scale production.

Figure 5 illustrates a batch production unit that has a copper or stainless steel kettle with mechanical agitators fitted with spring-loaded scrapers. The unit has the electrical control box on the right and the agitator in the raised position. The heat source in this case is gas-fired. It typically has temperature readouts, which are combined with the electrical controls. Some units have a feature that allows adjustment of a set point that will shut the flame off when the finished temperature is reached. This is important so that the product stops cooking at the proper end temperature. Years ago, the cook would put a metal rod in the cooked caramel, place the

Batch Cooker

Figure 5

Batch Caramel Cooking
cooker above reservoir

Figure 6

caramel-coated rod in a bucket of water and then manually feel the caramel to see if it was the texture that he was expecting. One of the more amazing things that we have seen in this regard involved the cook operator holding a bucket of water in one hand, placing the other hand in the cold water, very quickly reaching into the boiling caramel, grabbing a handful of caramel and putting it into the bucket of water. The operator would then fold the caramel with both hands in the water and judge the caramel texture. This, of course, is not recommended.

Batch cookers have become more sophisticated. Figure 6 shows a unit that has the cooker positioned above a reservoir or buffer tank. The cut-away diagram in Figure 7 illustrates the basic concept used in the cooker in Figure 2. Starting from the left is the mix tank, which then feeds a holding or buffer tank. The premix is then pumped to the top of the cooker, which is fitted with a scraped-surface agitator. After cooking, the caramel is dropped into the agitated reservoir tank. The finished caramel is then pumped to cooling units that will be described later. Figure 8 shows another type of batch cooker. The lower part of the cooker is steel-jacketed, which allows for steam cooking. The agitator has Teflon blades. The top cover or dome has a lid that allows for the manual feeding of ingredients. This cooker can also be equipped to provide vacuum to the cooker. This setup would allow for cooking products like jellies.

Batch Caramel Cooking: Cut-away Diagram

Manual:	Manuell:
sugar	Zucker
glucose	Glucose
water	Wasser
milk	Milch
fat	Fett

vapor
Bruden

mixing tank
Mischbehalter

buffer tank
Pufferbehalter

Reservoir

caramel pump
Karamell pumpe

Figure 7

These cookers typically are stainless steel and are heated by pressurized steam. The cook temperature is automatically controlled by PLC or chart-type units controlling and recording the temperature. An important feature is a steam relief valve, which has to be activated as soon as the caramel reaches the proper cook temperature. The steam must be blown down through the relief valve after the cook temperature is reached and the cooking steam valve is shut off, or the caramel will continue to cook. Another important factor in these batch cookers is the condition of the scrapers. Worn scrapers can easily lead to burned caramel since they are not efficiently moving the partially cooked premix off the hot cooking surface. This is likely to lead to black specks or chunks in the caramel.

AUTOMATIC COOKING

Figure 9 illustrates a generic schematic of a typical automatic caramel processing system. This figure is meant to give you an idea graphically of what the general systems look like. It does not represent a specific actual system. The temperatures are also meant to give approximate numbers. Note that at the top there is a premix weigh tank sitting on weigh cells. Ingredients are weighed as they are pumped to this vessel. This operation is controlled by computer. Also, the diagram shows high-shear mixers which are needed to produce a well-homogenized premix. After all the ingredients are added, they are blended by these high-shear mixers for 10 to 20 minutes. The mixing vessel is heated in the 130°F range. The mixed slurry is then transferred to a 130°F holding tank that is fitted with strong mixers.

The premix is now ready for cooking. In this schematic it is pumped to a predissolver or precooker. Temperature of the premix will reach the 190° to 200°F range. As an alternative, this precooker can be replaced by a sealed caramelizing reactor, which will be discussed later. From the precooker, the premix is then heated in swept surface heat exchangers, which are set up in series or parallel. Note on the diagram that they are drawn in series. The final product temperature (approximately 230° to 250°F) is reached at the exit of the heat exchanger. This final cook temperature is critical to the texture of the caramel. Variations in cook temperature affect the caramel texture. The cook temperature is controlled by a computer, which should be able to control this temperature within ±0.5°F.

Another Type of Batch Cooker

Figure 8

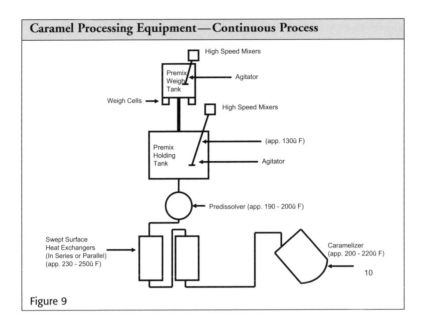

Caramel Processing Equipment—Continuous Process

High Speed Mixers

Premix Weigh Tank

Agitator

Weigh Cells

High Speed Mixers

Premix Holding Tank

(app. 130û F)

Agitator

Predissolver (app. 190 - 200û F)

Swept Surface Heat Exchangers (In Series or Parallel) (app. 230 - 250û F)

Caramelizer (app. 200 - 220û F)

10

Figure 9

As the cooked product exits the heat exchanger, the moisture is removed through a flash-off box. Flavors can be added automatically at this point. The caramel is a blond color and needs to be caramelized. The caramelizer is agitated and heated to approximately 200° to 220°F. The speed of the agitator and jacket temperature influence the color and flavor of the caramel. Note that the caramelizer vessel is slanted. This aids the caramelization reaction, keeping the cooked caramel stratified, preventing mixing from the bottom and top (which would produce quite a bit of variation of the finished caramelized product). This caramelization is based on the Maillard reaction between the carbohydrates and protein. This develops the typical caramel color and flavor. Figure 10 illustrates this type of cooking process, called post-caramelization, which means that the product is caramelized after cooking.

As indicated earlier, there is another technology which uses the principle of pre-caramelizing the premix first in a sealed reactor. This precaramelized material is then pumped through a horizontal swept surface thin film cooker to remove the moisture. In Figure 11, note that the pressurized caramelizing reactor vessel is followed by the horizontal thin film cooker. This approach, according to the equipment manufacturer, results in a more consistent product. This is due to the fact that the sealed, pressurized reactor can accurately control temperature, residence time, water activity, pressure and mixing, all factors that will result in uniform and consistent caramel color, flavor and moisture.

There are numerous other manufacturers that supply continuous caramel cookers.

**Automatic Cooker—
Postcaramelization**

Figure 10

**Automatic Cooker—
Precaramelization**

Figure 11

Since time limits a discussion of all these cookers, the last two cookers will be described in order to give an idea of the various cooking principles available. Figure 12 illustrates a continuous cooker with inner and outer stirrers. The caramel premix enters the unit from the predissolver. The preheated mix is pumped into the cooker from below and exits near the top of the cooker. The adjustable outlet weir controls residence time in the cooker. Figure 13 is a cutout of this cooker. Note the product inlet from the dissolver, the adjustable outlet weir and the product outlet.

The next continuous caramel cooker (Figure 14) uses the principle of thin film cooking using a vertical heat exchange unit. This cooker has a large rotor fitted with Teflon blades. Figure 15 shows a good view of this rotor lifted out of the cooker.

COOLING AND FORMING

The next step in the process involves the cooling of the caramel. If it is not cooled,

Continuous Caramel Cooker

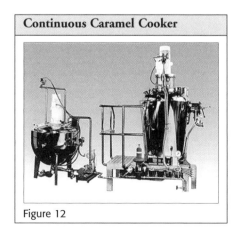

Figure 12

Continuous Caramel Cooker (*cut-away*)

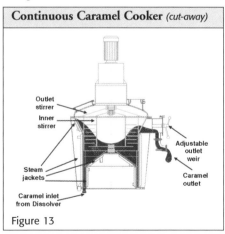

Figure 13

Continuous Caramel Cooker	Continuous Caramel Cooking *showing rotor blades*

Figure 14	Figure 15

then the caramel will continue to get darker in color and the flavor will continue to develop. In other words, the reason for cooling the caramel is to stop the Maillard reaction. There are some processes where you would not cool the caramel immediately. They would include using the caramel to enrobe the candy, for baked centers and for depositing into moulds. In these cases, the coated or deposited caramel pieces would then be immediately cooled.

In most candy processes—such as cut and wrapping, forming into various shapes and center fillings—the finished caramel would be cooled immediately after cooking. As the next figures indicate, there are a number of processes to cool the caramel to the proper temperature needed. A method which lends itself more to a batch process involves pouring the caramel onto water-cooled tables that are coated with a release agent. In this case, the caramel is folded onto itself in an attempt to get a uniform temperature of the caramel mass. This is necessary since the bottom of the caramel is in direct contact with the cold table surface and can become very hard if not folded into the hot caramel on the surface.

Cooling units intended to handle continuous cooking include cooling belts and wheels. In the case of the cooling belts (Figure 16), they usually have a metal belt that has a heated hopper that spreads a caramel slab onto the surface of the belt. The belt is first coated with a release agent that can be sprayed onto the metal belt and spread with a squeegee or dripped onto the belt with orbiting pads used to spread the release agent. These cooling belts have a series of plows along them that scrape the caramel from the belt and fold it onto itself. This helps to get a uniform temperature of the caramel that is scraped off the end of the cooling belt. Note the slab release agent applicator in the upper left picture.

As Figure 17 indicates, an alternative way to cool the caramel is to pump the caramel to a cooling wheel. Most of these systems are stainless steel and have internal cooling water. The layer of caramel is continuously placed on the wheel by the hopper as the wheel rotates. Thickness of the caramel can thus be controlled. Other control features are cooling water temperature and rotational speed of the wheel. The cooled caramel is finally scraped off as the wheel turns.

Cooling Conveyor

Figure 16

CONCLUSION

You have been given a brief description of the caramel-manufacturing process. As you saw, the equipment available varies from relatively simple to sophisticated batch mixing, cooking and cooling. The continuous systems that we looked at give you an idea of the various techniques that are available.

Keep in mind that no matter how sophisticated the equipment is, attention to details is critical for caramel with consistent flavor and color. These details include accuracy of the blended ingredients, proper agitation of the ingredient mixer, accurate cook temperature, proper operation of the cooker and good cooling-equipment control. The ingredients must meet the required specifications. These can be checked by internal labs or with certificates of analysis based on tests done by the supplier.

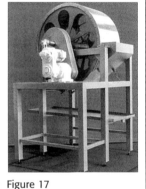

Cooling Wheel

Figure 17

Questions & Answers

Q: Can you easily scale up caramel production from a small batch lab cooker to a continuous caramel cooking operation. What are the major considerations to take into account?

A: The small batch lab cookers are very good for doing R&D projects. They can give you direction when changing ingredients or cook temperatures, for example. I always preferred to do larger batches or, in many cases, run the tests on the full-scale equipment. This approach gives you a product close to what to expect when changes are made. Of course, a use for the rework created in the test has to be dealt with.

Q: You included photographs of both copper and stainless steel cookers. Caramel made in copper vessels has a very distinctive flavor profile due to the reaction between copper and butter. Do you know of a simple way to get the same flavor in a cooking system that you discussed?

A: A lot of the difference seen between cooking with copper kettles versus stainless steel cookers has to do with heat transfer. I would suggest that when using a stainless steel cooking system that you ensure that there is adequate steam pressure to approximate the heat transfer seen in copper systems. You might look at adding flavors to the cooked caramel as well.

Q: Can continuous caramel cookers use in-line refractometers to more accurately determine the solids content of the cooked caramel instead of the simple temperature probe that you discussed?

A: This might be a possibility, but refractometers are best suited for measuring the premix solids. In addition to continuous temperature readings, quick moisture lab methods are available, and you might also look into doing texture analysis of the caramel as the process is running. This approach can give you a look at what the texture is really going to be, although these texture results are obtained after the fact, so to speak.

Q: During the ingredient mixing stage, what is the impact, if any, of ingredient inaccuracy on the finished product?

A: Accuracy of ingredient addition is the key to the whole operation, including how the product processes and what the finished product temperature, flavor and texture will be. I always strongly advise designing a premix system that is very accurate. For the optimum premix ingredient accuracy, companies will use weigh cells on the premix vessel and loss-in-weight ingredient feeders.

Q: You mention that final cook temperature impacts caramel texture. What is the relationship between cook temperature and caramel texture?

A: There is a direct relationship between final cook temperature and caramel texture for almost all caramels. The higher the cook temperature, the lower the moisture and the harder the texture. The lower the cook temperature, the higher the moisture and the softer the texture.

Q: Are there any advantages in using one system over the other (batch versus continuous) in terms of caramel quality, i.e., flavor, texture?

A: Basically, one should be able to get the same caramel quality in terms of flavor and texture using either batch or continuous systems. In practice, though, continuous systems that are well controlled generally will make a more consistent product in terms of flavor, color, moisture and texture.

Q: You say short and long cook to same temperature will have the same texture. When you caramelize, you form new polymers. Does this mean the new polymers have little effect on texture, chewiness, etc.?

A: Varying cook times to the same temperature will result in different textures. You may have the same moisture content, but the texture, flavor and color will vary.

Q: I have a steam-jacketed stainless steel kettle fitted with a "lightning mixer" and want to produce caramel with this setup. Any suggestions, since no scraped-surface agitation is available.

A: I definitely don't recommend this setup. The lightning mixer may be able to move the mix around the kettle, but the lack of a scraped- or swept-surface agitator will cause the mix to burn on the cooking surface with numerous burnt particles formed.

Q: What types of pumps need to be used to convey cooked caramel that will prevent in-process crystallization?

A: It is best to use positive displacement

pumps. If you are having crystallization problems, I would suggest that you review your caramel formula to primarily see if the formula is correct. One example would be the ratio of sugar to corn syrup. With the proper formula, I have seen caramel pumped, folded, stretched, heated, cooled and formed under intense pressure into various shapes without any crystallization.

Q: Can the premix homogenization process be eliminated by adding all ingredients into a cooking kettle (batch cooking)? What are the advantages and disadvantages?

A: This practice of adding all the ingredients into a cooking kettle is still done by some manufacturers. The advantage is less equipment, such as the mix tank and blending system. The disadvantage is that the ingredients tend to not mix well. An example would be the milk settling down to the bottom of the cooker and either getting burnt or being denatured. To get the proper Maillard reaction, the premix must be mixed well before heating so that the mix is homogenous and therefore the individual ingredients are in a position to react more readily and consistently.

Q: How long does it take to vent moisture after heating in a swept surface heat exchanger before going to a caramelizer?

A: As the superheated mixture exits the swept surface heat exchanger, the moisture literally flashes off from the cooked product. That is why most equipment manufacturers build a flash-off box at the exit of the heat exchanger. This box is attached to a strong blower that extracts the moisture. If there is more than one cooker, the flash boxes are typically joined together with a manifold. It is important that the blower extracting the moisture is sized properly; otherwise, the moisture can condense and drip into the caramelizer.

Q: What is the significance of shear rate (agitation) during caramel cooking and caramelizing with respect to the finished product standup?

A: In looking at the process, the premix agitation and the shear rate during cooking do not affect the final texture as much as the agitation applied during the caramelizing step. Over- or undermixing affects the caramel texture, flavor and color depending on the agitator rpm and amount of heat applied to the caramelizing vessel. Therefore, the texture or standup can be affected at this caramelization step, especially in a postcaramelization process.

Q: If you are making caramel with sweetened condensed milk, vegetable fat, butter, sugar, corn syrup and water, when should you add the butter and vegetable fat? How long to melt and mix before adding other ingredients?

A: There seem to be various schemes used in adding the ingredients to the mixer. I prefer to add the water, sugar and corn syrup, then mix until dissolved. Next add the sweetened condensed milk and mix. Then add the melted fats, followed by the emulsifiers, and mix until a good homogenous mixture is formed. Incidentally, the fats, including the butter, should be completely melted before adding them to the mixer. Final mix times should be 15 to 20 minutes.

Q: Please provide a point of view on precaramelization versus postcaramelization.

A: Most of my experience has been with caramelizing during cooking as in open batch cookers and postcaramelization in continuous cookers. In the case of postcaramelization, variability can be controlled well if the process is properly under control. In the case of precaramelization, the premix is first caramelized under very close conditions. The advantage to this approach, according to the equipment manufacturer, is a more consistent product as opposed to postcaramelization. This is due to the fact that the sealed, pressurized reactor can accurately control temperature, residence time, water activity, pressure and mixing, all factors that will result in uniform and consistent caramel color, flavor and moisture.

Caramel Quality Assurance and Troubleshooting

John I. Cooke
Morley Candy Makers

In the production of caramel, things go wrong no matter what equipment or ingredients you may use or how well your cooks are trained. There are always good opportunities to use your troubleshooting skills. This will be our focus for this paper and, hopefully, you will gain a better understanding about what to do or how to correct batches that just don't turn out the way you expected.

The list of problems that may occur in the manufacture of caramel is substantial (this list is not all-inclusive and there probably are additional causes other than what we will explore):

- Graining
- Stickiness
- No body
- Clumpy (not smooth)
- Color either too dark or too light
- Off taste
- Too hard
- Too soft
- Poor machinability

Now let's take a brief look at each one of these issues by examining the most frequent causes and some possible solutions to correct the problems.

Graining

Graining is defined as when sugar crystals re-form in a product that, by design, is supposed to be smooth and creamy. A good example is the two types of marshmallow. There is a smooth "eating" marshmallow that you would find in a high-quality chocolate-enrobed Easter product and there is grained marshmallow, such as the banana-flavored, orange-colored circus peanut. One product is smooth and one product is grainy. Each is designed to be just as it is. However, when the enrobed product's marshmallow turns into the same texture as the circus peanut, it is considered a quality issue. It's the same way with caramels. Some are designed to be smooth and flowing while others are designed to be short in texture with a mouthfeel somewhat similar to a hard cheese.

When the flowing caramel stops flowing and sugar crystals are evident either visually or when eating, the graining (which is not designed into the product image) is a fault. Following are the common causes and solutions for this fault:

Too much sugar Increase the ratio of corn syrup in the next batch.

Excessive agitation after the batch has finished cooking Stop the agitators and remove the batch from the cooking vessel immediately after reaching the correct temperature and/or stop the agitation and cool the batch in the kettle.

Addition of milk too late in the cooking cycle Milk should be added at the start of the boil. If added too late or after the cook is complete, the lactose will seed the graining process.

Batch is too small Whatever your cooking vessel, the batch should be large enough to be above the steam jacket.

Addition of scrap Scrap, also called seconds, can seed the sugar in the batch if there is crystallized sugar present in the product. This is similar to seeding chocolate to encourage temper by adding already seeded or tempered shavings to a melter.

Stickiness

Nothing is worse than throwing a batch of caramel into an extruder, only to have it slide around the rollers, drip through the dies and puddle out onto the belt into a shapeless mass heading relentlessly toward the enrober. This is what we describe as sticky caramel. What causes it and what can you do about it?

Not enough fat Increase the percentage of fat and/or the amount of milk being used in the recipe. It's difficult to say how much to add since each end user has a different final use and specification for their product.

Excessive inversion Check the pH. A good starting point is between 6.0 and 6.5, then adjust according to your own preferences. Remember that inversion is a result of time, temperature and pH. Keep this in the back of your mind at all times.

Seconds As stated earlier, just as scrap with graining can cause graining, scrap with a low pH can cause stickiness. Check pH of scrap and make adjustments as necessary with something like sodium bicarbonate.

Not enough milk Increase the amount of milk used.

Low cook Increase final cooking temperature ever so slightly until you reach the product you desire. One or two degrees increase in the final cook could make a significant difference.

Too much corn syrup Too much corn syrup has the exact opposite effect on the caramel as the excessive sugar discussed during the graining section. Just change the ratio of sugar to corn syrup (reduce the corn syrup).

Humidity This is very difficult for someone in Salt Lake City to understand, but confectioners cooking caramel in southeast Louisiana know exactly what effect high humidity can have. Not only is the product sticky but it may also seem to have a layer of scum on the surface. Cooked caramel should be stored away from the steam kettles and in reasonable temperature and humidity conditions.

No Body

No body may seem to be the same as sticky; however, this is not the case. Lacking body would indicate an ingredient or cooking temperature problem. The product is not necessarily gooey or slimy but will definitely flatten or puddle out due to extreme cold flow characteristics.

Wrong fat used in formula Typically this is an issue with the melting-point issue rather than the type of fat being used. If you are using a fat that melts at 72°F, the body will be less than if using a fat with a melting point of 102°F. This is just common sense.

Low cook Increase final cook one to two degrees at a time until the desired end product is reached.

Clumpiness or Not Smooth in Texture

Clumpiness or a texture that is not smooth may not affect some final products. The issue here is similar to buttermilk versus whole milk. You expect buttermilk to be lumpy because it was designed that way. Whole milk with lumps may cause a spectrum of involuntary reactions when swallowed. Usually, clumpy, not-smooth or gritty caramel is unacceptable, however. Here are a few of the reasons for less than smooth and creamy caramel.

Fats are not dispersed Premelt the hard fats, then add to your batch; if not using an emulsifier, start using one. Lecithin is the most common.

Lecithin not added correctly It may be that the lecithin needs to be premixed with the melted fat.

Milk variations Check with your supplier to ensure you are receiving a consistent ingredient, or add a stabilizer such as sodium carbonate to the batch.

Poor premixing Mix the ingredients of your batch for approximately 10 minutes before beginning the cook.

Grit If using powdered milk, reconstitute prior to adding to the batch. Also, there is a slight possibility that you have kept your condensed milk for too long or under improper conditions. The sugar may have grained off. You should check.

Too Light

Not long ago, while developing a sugarfree caramel, we had the experience of actually developing no color whatsoever. Due to the constraints of the formula and the final product for which it was to be used, the recipe contained only small amounts of the ingredients necessary to provide the normal brown caramel color while cooking. In this extreme case, we had to stay with the original formula and had a caramel that tasted good and looked good after it had been layered in a bar with other ingredients, but one that would not be appealing as a wrapped piece standing on its own.

To develop enough color so that the product looks like caramel you should include enough milk fat in the recipe to allow for browning and not rush the cook; it takes time for natural color development. You could add a commercial caramel color or replace some of the white sugar with brown sugar.

Too dark

Burnt milk You may be burning the milk. Add the milk after the rest of the mix has reached 250°F, then boil to end temperature.

High temperature You may be cooking to too high a temperature. This may be causing other problems as well.

Burnt candy You may have some burnt candy in the bottom of your cooking vessel. If this is the case, the burnt candy will continue to darken the batches until you clean it out of the vessel.

Scorching You may not be scraping the sides of the kettle enough to avoid scorching the milk and butter.

Bad-tasting Product

At some point we have all tasted our competitors' products and thought they tasted bad. This is not about your competitors, however; this is about developing a bad taste in a product that you have cooked and used successfully day after day. What can cause your product to taste bad?

Rancid nuts! If you are adding nuts to your product while still in the cooking vessel and there is a bad taste and/or smell, check the peanuts or pecans you are using. If you don't notice anything by smelling and/or tasting, you can check the peroxide values of the nuts and the free fatty acid percentage of the oil in which the nuts were roasted. The level of rancidity that is undesirable is a personal opinion and unless the nuts are really far gone, you will get different opinions from different individuals.

Fat issues The fat could be rancid; someone may have added too much fat to this particular batch; your purchasing agent may have saved a few cents per pound and changed the fat altogether, so your taste may not be bad, just different.

Milk issues The milk could be going bad. When using powdered or evaporated or sweetened condensed milk, this may not be much of an issue. When using fresh whole milk, half & half or full cream, this can become an issue if the product is out of date or has not been stored properly.

Commercial flavorings A true-blue caramel person would ask why you were using flavor in the first place. In reality, many caramel producers do use flavors to enhance their products. If off-flavors exist, you may have added too much flavor.

Salt This is usually a matter of personal taste. However, in my opinion, you can't get enough salt into caramel or butterscotch. If the taste just doesn't seem to be great after all of your efforts, add a little salt.

Too Hard
- Overcooked
- Too much corn syrup
- Fat has too high a melting point
- Dextrose equivalent (DE) is too low in corn syrup

Too Soft
- Undercooked
- Fat is too soft or has a melting point too low
- Corn syrup DE is too high
- Too much invert sugar

Poor Machining Characteristics

Although the ultimate consumer is more interested in how the finished candy tastes, manufacturers would typically be interested in how easy or difficult it may be to form the caramel into that finished product. The areas of concern, previously discussed, that will affect your production efficiencies and scrap levels are stickiness, lack of body, clumpiness, too hard or soft. It's just a fact that when trying to process caramel with these five defects you will run into trouble with your extruder, hot depositor, moulding equipment and starch-casting operation.

The main concern is that your product be consistent. In an effort to control your operation so that this consistency is achieved, you should take the necessary steps and spend the money to ensure the following:

- Accurately weigh your materials. Be sure you have a foolproof method of ensuring that the correct weight of each ingredient is added to each batch.
- Check your ingredients, especially the milk products, upon receipt and monitor the length of storage, as well as the temperature of the room in which the products are stored.
- Take the time to train your personnel in the proper methods of mixing, cooking and handling each material and finished product.
- Invest in the best temperature controllers possible.

Also, every once in a while, you will find that even after having cooked the same formula in the same kettles with the same personnel day after day, there is a batch that suddenly turns out substandard. Rather than going on a witch-hunt or blaming the full moon, there are a few areas that should be examined first. These checks should be carried out in an analytical method and really need to be checked one at a time so you will be able to determine if any of the individual factors have affected your batch:

Corn syrup meter Is it malfunctioning or set improperly? Just a bit too much or too little corn syrup can produce a completely different product than you are accustomed to.

Scales and load cells Have the scales and load cells been zeroed correctly? Check the tare on your scales each morning and you will save yourself a lot of grief.

Thermometers and probes These instruments are continually the brunt of large chunks of fondant, butter, scrap, etc., and have the tendency to be misaligned or broken. Even the most expensive and well-installed probes can be damaged and become inaccurate.

Steam pressure There could be that one time when everything is operating so well in your plant that the boiler is just not large enough to handle the need for steam. This could cause the batch to sit in the kettle for too long. Browning may occur if not adequately agitated, or your cook may have gotten impatient and called it complete when it wasn't. Have your maintenance crew check it out to make sure it is functioning properly and check the cook's log sheet to see if there is anything unusual.

Holding times If the batch has hit the prescribed cooking temperature and was not cooled quickly enough or perhaps it finished cooking just as the lunch buzzer went off, that particular batch may have a timing problem. Just remember, dextrose equivalent is dependent on time, temperature and pH. If you leave a batch of caramel under heat for too long, you have three out of three of these factors.

Sanitation

Sanitation is so important when dealing with milk products in your facility. Even though caramels themselves are cooked to a high enough temperature to take care of most microbiological issues, the equipment, floors, walls and any other nonheated surfaces, if allowed to sit with traces of these ingredients, can cause a microbiologist or quality assurance professional to lose nights of sleep. You've heard of *location, location, location?* Well, the slogan here is *sanitize, sanitize, sanitize.*

CONCLUSION

In conclusion, it is evident that there are many things that can and do go wrong when preparing and cooking caramel for candy production. The key is that most of them can be corrected by using a little common sense. The variables are few and include sugar, corn syrup, milk, lecithin and water as the main ingredient variables and time, temperature and humidity as the key manufacturing variables. The areas mentioned here have been discussed for many years. Even though equipment has changed, ingredient stability has improved, process controls are more accurate and your employees are better trained, problems arise from time to time and many of them can be traced back to what we have discussed. These are, at the least, a good place to start eliminating variables in searching for answers.

Questions & Answers

Q: Comment on hard candy caramel regarding cooling and quality.

A: It is essential that any type of caramel be cooled as quickly as possible after reaching the desired temperature. If not, the product will continue to cook and brown. If the caramel you mention is to be used for a center in a hard candy piece, this is especially true. If it is a caramel hard-boiled sweet or a hard candy itself, this may not be as critical.

Q: I once saw an application where the final stage was to pass the product through an emulsifier. What is your opinion of this?

A: It depends on the final product. If the product is a dessert topping or an apple dip, this is a common practice. The emulsifier or homogenizer will help make the product shelf stable and will retard separation of the fats.

Q: How accurate should load cells be? What would be an acceptable +/- when weighing caramel ingredients?

A: The answer that some quality individuals would say is "zero." I would think that if you could get your larger ingredients within a pound or two, on the outside, you'd be alright. If the variance is large enough to change the desired characteristics of your product or change the nutritional statement, you have a problem.

Q: I plan to use pre-prepared standup caramel in a larger batch and to add other ingredients later. What are your suggestions on how to reheat the product so as not to burn or damage the caramel?

A: This, actually, is a very common practice. Anyone purchasing caramel from a supplier for use in other operations must reheat prior to beginning their process. The exception may be an extruded product, however. I have, on several occasions, reheated caramel for further processing. The trick is to not keep it under heat for any length of time. If you do, it will brown so much that its use will not be desirable. It will also begin to invert since time, temperature and pH are all contributors to this reaction.

Q: What causes caramel to "oil off" when cooling?

A: The fats are probably not dispersed well enough in the batch. You can either add an emulsifier like lecithin, which will help, or, if you are already doing this, try premixing the batch for approximately 10 minutes before turning on the heat when cooking.

Q: How is caramel body affected by agitation during or after cooking?

A: Most commonly, excessive agitation after cooking will cause graining in the batch. The sugar crystals will re-form, causing a more-stiff final product with a fudge-like texture.

Q: What is the ideal temperature and humidity in wrapping and storing caramels?

A: In wrapping, it depends a lot on your final product. The thing to watch for is whether the rope is sticking to the machine. Of course, I like to wrap anything in temperatures of 65° to 75°F with a humidity of 50 to 60 percent. That's just me and my specific products, however. If it is too warm and the humidity is too high, you will have more problems than you would like to deal with in wrapping.

Panning

Introduction to Panning

John S. Kitt
Kraft Foods

Pan-coated candies are produced by the application of successive layers of coating to suitably shaped centers as they tumble in a revolving pan.

HISTORY

Panned confections evolved from pills or dragées that were hand rolled in sugar by apothecaries as a means of disguising the unpleasant taste of their medicines.

According to Ron Lees, the term *dragée* is believed to have originated from Julius Dragatus, a Roman confectioner who developed a coated confection around 177 BC. In Europe, pan-coated confections are still often called dragées.

Sugar panning, as we know it, had its origins in the late 16th century when adequate supplies of refined white sugar first became available. The process started with edible seeds placed in a shallow pan suspended over a fire. A small increment of sugar syrup was added to the pan as it was swung about to keep the seeds rolling and coat them with syrup. The heat from the fire would dry the syrup, leaving a minute layer of sugar crystals around the seeds. This process would be repeated many times until the desired thickness of coating had been built up (Figure 1).

Early Pan Coating

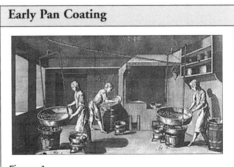

Figure 1

Ron Lees tells us that T. Buckards of the United States developed the first mechanized coating pan in 1836.

THE U.S. MARKET FOR PANNED CONFECTIONS

Panned products represent a significant portion of U.S. confectionery sales. According to government data (Figure 2), factory sales of panned chocolate confections in 2002 were $1.3 billion or 14.6 percent of the total chocolate market. Sales of nonchocolate panned products were $662 million or 13.2 percent of the category.

These data do not include coated chewing gum or bubble gum products; a significant proportion of which are also pan coated.

CENTERS OR CORES

To be suitable for pan coating, centers must have a shape that will tumble freely in a rotating pan; they must also have sufficient hardness and structural strength to stand up to the weight and attrition associated with the panning process.

Centers with sharp edges should be avoided; they tend to reject the coating.

Centers with large flat surfaces are unsuitable; they are liable to stick together to form doubles, one of the most prevalent problems in the panning process.

The centers within a batch should be fairly uniform in size and shape, otherwise uneven coating ratios can result. This is caused by the tendency of heavier units to segregate at the front of the pan.

Sometimes it is necessary to precoat centers prior to the main process. There are three main functions that precoating can perform:

- Preventing oil or moisture migration from the center.

- Filling in imperfections to provide a smooth surface for the main coating process.

- Permitting the adhesion of syrups to surfaces that tend to reject them (e.g., chocolate).

Precoating is often referred to as gumming.

CATEGORIES

Pan-coated confections are classified into three main categories: hard sugar coating, soft sugar panning and chocolate panning.

Hard Sugar Coating

Hard sugar coatings are built up by applying supersaturated solutions of sucrose or dextrose to the centers in a revolving pan.

We will be concentrating on sucrose panning in this paper. For those who wish to learn more about dextrose panning, two excellent papers were published in the *Manufacturing Confectioner*, by Bob Boutin in October 1988 and Henry Nonaka in October 1991.

U.S. Consumption of Panned Confections – 2002

U.S. government data

	Consumption	% of Category
Chocolate Total	$9,015.1	100%
Chocolate, Panned	$1,313.0	14.6%
Nonchocolate Total	$5,001.3	100%
Nonchocolate, Panned	$662.0	13.2%

Source: U.S. Department of Commerce

Figure 2

The building-up process is often referred to as *engrossing*, or the shortened form, *grossing*.

The sugar solutions are made up to specific strengths measured by refractometer and expressed as degree Brix or percent soluble solids.

A Brix refractometer actually measures the refractive index and is calibrated to read percent sucrose solids. When measuring syrups other than pure sucrose the Brix solids reading will not accurately reflect percent solids as their refractive indices vary.

Coating-syrup strengths can also be measured by hygrometer and expressed in degree Baumé (Bé). Conversion charts from Brix to Baumé can be found in textbooks such as the *Silesia Manual #4*. This book is devoted entirely to panning topics and is a useful resource for those wishing to expand their knowledge in this area.

A common term for the application process is *dosing*. The distribution of the syrup evenly throughout the centers is called *spreading*.

The sugar solution (or engrossing syrup) is dried by heating the outside of the pan or by blowing heated air into the pan. Cold drying air can also be used when processing heat-sensitive centers.

As the moisture evaporates from the syrup, the sugar crystallizes and forms a very thin layer of coating around the center. The process of dosing, spreading and drying is then repeated until the desired finished weight is achieved. Lower solids syrups are often used in a procedure referred to as *smoothing*, performed towards the end of the process.

Colors can be added to the syrup throughout the process, although common practice is to only apply color at the end of coating in a coloring stage.

Hard panning is a lengthy process, which can take from five hours to several days; the time required is dictated by the thickness of the coating to be applied.

Some examples of hard-panned items are Jordan almonds, jawbreakers, chocolate lentils, coated peanuts, coated chewy candy pieces, gum balls and chewing gum dragées (Figure 3).

By substituting suitable polyols for sugar, we can make very acceptable sugarfree hard coatings. These techniques are beyond the scope of this paper but a good source of information is a paper by Bob Boutin in the *46th PMCA Production Conference Proceedings*.

Hard-panned Items

Figure 3

Soft Sugar Panning

Soft-panned products are built up by applying a layer of noncrystallizing syrup to the centers followed by a layer of crystalline sugar. Successive layers of syrup and sugar are applied until the desired coating ratio has been achieved. The syrups usually have color and flavors added throughout the process.

Soft coatings have a translucent appearance that distinguishes them from the opaque coating of hard-panned items.

This process is much faster than hard panning, typically taking 1.5 to 2.0 hours to complete a batch. Jelly beans are by far the most common example of soft-panned candies (Figure 4).

Chocolate Panning

Chocolate is applied to centers in a coating pan by spraying, dripping or ladling. The chocolate is then hardened by the application of cold air. During cooling the cocoa butter in the chocolate crystallizes in a stable form to provide a firm, even surface.

This process is not limited solely to chocolate: compound coatings, yogurt coatings, carob coatings and other fat-based media can also be applied in this manner. Chocolate panning times are typically 45 minutes to 2 hours depending on the thickness of the coating.

There is a wide range of chocolate-coated products on the market; a few examples are malted milk balls, coated nuts, bridge mixes, coated caramels, coated raisins and bite-sized candy pieces (Figure 5).

Soft-panned Jelly Beans

Figure 4

Chocolate-coated Products

Figure 5

Combined Coatings

Products can also be made using the above techniques in combination, for example, peanuts first coated in chocolate and then given a topcoat of hard sugar.

Polishing and Glazing

Most coated candies are given a final coating of waxes, gums or shellac, which serves the dual purpose of providing a protective outer layer and enhancing appearance.

COATING PANS

A standard coating pan consists of a copper or stainless steel bowl mounted on a motor-driven shaft; the smallest pans, made for laboratory use, can process batches of a few pounds. These are usually 12″ to 18″ in diameter (Figure 6).

The most common pans are 36″ or 48″ in diameter and can process batches from around 125 to 300 lbs finished weight (Figure 7). Extra-large pans of 72″ or more in diameter are also available.

Coating pans can be almost spherical or have an elongated tulip shape. They might have a smooth interior surface or be ribbed. A key requirement of the pan shape is that it promotes good movement of the centers from the back to the front of the pan, thus ensuring an even buildup of the batch.

Pans are sometimes fitted with steam-heating coils around their outside surface or gas burners at their base. Today, it's more common to have a heated (or cooled) air source that can be blown into the pan. Often an exhaust duct is fitted to the pan to remove the damp air and dust created by the process. Pans may have a fixed or variable speed drive and sometimes the angle at which they are mounted on the shaft is adjustable.

The above variable options are selected according to the particular use for which the pan is intended.

In addition to the basic manually operated pans, there are automated panning systems that can process batches of 4,000 to 7,000 pounds. All the stages of the coating process and its key parameters are preprogrammed and controlled by a computer.

Laboratory-size Coating Pan (12″ to 18″)

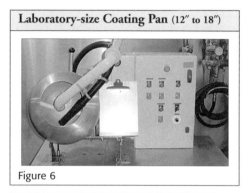

Figure 6

Production-size Coating Pan (36″ to 48″)

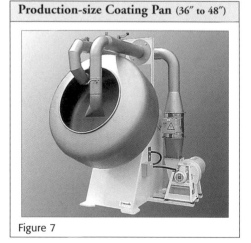

Figure 7

Most automated pans are cylindrical in shape. The cylinder's surface is usually perforated to allow the drying air to be drawn (or blown) through the product bed and out through the perforations to an exhaust vent at the side of the pan. This feature leads to the frequently used term *side-vented pans* (Figures 8 and 9).

PANNING, ART OR SCIENCE?

Pan coating, using conventional equipment, is one of the most skilled tasks in confectionery production.

The panning processes can be very sensitive to changes in ambient temperature and the relative humidity of the air. Before the days of precise climate control the expert panner could adapt the coating formulae and application techniques to compensate for these variations. This, I believe, is central to the art of panning.

Of course, the panning process can be reduced to scientific principals. Automated panning systems precisely control the key criteria at every stage of the process and maintain consistent quality from batch to batch without operator intervention. This particularly applies to hard sugar and chocolate panning. When it comes to soft panning I don't believe the automated systems have yet been perfected and cannot duplicate the accomplishments of the skilled artisan.

Side-vented Pan — Exterior

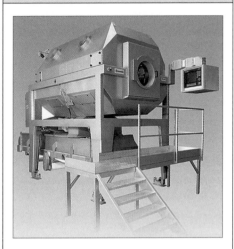

Figure 8

Side-vented Pan — Interior

Figure 9

Note: Questions and answers for this chapter appear at the end of the Panning section on page 231.

Sucrose Hard Panning

Gumming, Engrossing, Smoothing, Color Coat and Polishing

Jeff Bogusz
Ferrara Pan Candy Co.

Sugar hard panning is the process of applying a thin coat of a sucrose solution to individual tumbling centers, then evaporating the moisture so that the sugar crystallizes in a thin layer. This process is repeated until the desired thickness of hard coating is obtained. The centers can range from a grain of sugar, as is the starting point for a nonpareil or jawbreaker, to the lentil-shaped chocolate that is the center of an *M&M* milk chocolate candy. Other common center materials are chewing gum, licorice, nuts, compressed tablets or high-solids chewy candy. Any material that will not deform under its own weight and will tumble freely (no flat surfaces that may stick together) is a candidate for hard panning. For a typical panned chocolate lentil product, the coating will consist of 40 to 60 layers applied over the course of 6 to 8 hours. An extreme case would be a large jawbreaker that could consist of over 300 layers applied over the course of 2 weeks.

The goal of this paper is to provide a description of the basic equipment, processes and ingredients used in sucrose hard panning. The hard-panning process consists of five distinct steps:

Gumming The application of a protective sealant layer to the center.

Engrossing The rapid buildup of the sugar shell.

Smoothing This step ensures that the finished product will have a uniform surface.

Color Coat This step adds visual appeal to the finished product.

Polishing This step adds gloss and moisture resistance to the finished product.

The first four steps will be discussed in detail. This paper will also discuss different methods of process control used throughout the panning process.

PROCESS EQUIPMENT

Pans are manufactured in various shapes and sizes. A lab-size pan may be 16 inches in diameter and hold 4 to 8 pounds of finished product. Conventional production-size pans are commonly 36 to 60 inches in diameter and hold up to 500 pounds of

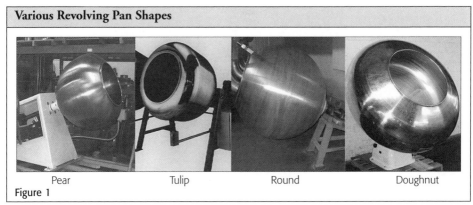

Various Revolving Pan Shapes

| Pear | Tulip | Round | Doughnut |

Figure 1

finished product. Some automated panning systems can accommodate as much as 6,600 lbs. The shape of pans will vary with the equipment manufacturer; some are round, doughnut, pear, tulip or angular (Figure 1). Generally speaking, the pear- and tulip-shaped pans will provide the most uniform depth of product and will produce the most consistent product. However, there is not one pan that is perfect for every product. The centers must tumble in a manner which will allow all of the individual pieces to be evenly coated with the sucrose syrup. For some types of large centers, the round or doughnut-shaped pans can provide better performance.

Apart from the pan, the other critical process component is the air supply. It is the air that will remove the evaporated moisture from the panning syrup and allow the sucrose to crystallize. The air flow to the pan must be of a consistent temperature and humidity. An air flow of 250 CFM per standard 38- to 42-inch pan is a good starting point. To adjust to different size pans, one can think of this as 0.8 to 1.1 CFM per finished pound of candy. For a chocolate lentil product, the ideal air conditions would be 65° to 70°F and 35%rh to 45%rh. A higher relative humidity air could be used, but the time required to complete the panning process will be longer. The amount of moisture that air can hold is increased dramatically as the temperature is increased. Thus, it is beneficial to optimize the drying rate by utilizing the highest temperature that the center material will allow without melting or deforming. Once the supply air has absorbed moisture from the product, an exhaust system should remove the moisture-laden air from the pan. It is critical to design a panning room under negative pressure so that dust is not scattered throughout the plant.

For temperature-stable products such as sugar crystals, tablets and nuts, a technique referred to as hot panning can be used. In this process, the tumbling product is heated with a gas flame, steam coils or electric heating elements to create a large driving force for evaporation. For this process air need not blow directly onto the product, but sufficient ventilation is required to remove the heat and moisture from the panning room. The hot panning process is very efficient at building up sugar layers quickly, but the layers tend to have a rough surface. As a result, the last 15 to 20 percent of the sugar shell is often applied in a more conventional process without the use of heat.

The first step in the panning process is loading of the centers. This can be performed manually or with automated conveyors. When setting up a new process, the amount of centers to be added must be determined. There needs to be a sufficient mass of candy to get uniform movement of the product in the pan. It is also important to remember that 20 to 50 percent of the finished-product weight will be added in the form of syrup. The ideal pan load is one that will end up with the finished candy at the full level of the pan.

GUMMING

The first segment of the candy shell is typically referred to as the "gumming layer." Some sort of precoat is applied to most centers with the exception of sugar-on-sugar products. There are several reasons for applying a precoating:
• It acts as a sealant layer to hold fats inside the finished products. If not sealed, fats from chocolate, nuts or flavors can migrate through a sugar shell and cause a spotted surface or peeling.
• It fills in a rough-surfaced center to create a smoother surface on the end product.
• It provides added strength to centers that are subject to deformation.
• It improves adhesion (shell less likely to peel off).
• It improves flexibility (reduced chipping of finished product).

Several types of ingredients are used to create the gumming layer. Traditionally, gum arabic or gelatin would be used. Today, the use of lower cost dextrins and starches is more common. Figure 2 describes the various ingredient systems used in gumming layers.

Gumming solutions are applied in 2 to 4 liquid doses. The doses can be manually ladled on or sprayed on with automated systems. After the gumming solution has thoroughly coated the centers, powder doses of sugar or cornstarch are added to dry the surface. The combined weight of gumming solution and powder can account for up to one-third of the total shell weight. If it is desirable to add flavor, acid or salt, it is best done in the initial gumming layer. Additional coats of gumming solution will seal in these components. Once the last gumming layer is applied, it is customary to remove the centers from the pan and allow them to thoroughly dry (2 to 12 hours). For some sensitive centers, a second gumming process is required. This could be to provide more support to a flexible jelly or to ensure a liquid filling does not leak. Gumming solutions are not typically microbiologically stable. Preparation should be limited to one shift of panning and excess solution should be discarded at the end of each day.

Gumming Syrup Formulations

Ingredient	Usage Level	Properties
Gum arabic Water	33–50% solution heated to boiling. Cooled to 80–110°F	Very good barrier properties. Makes the shell crunchier.
140 bloom gelatin Liquid sugar (67%)	1.0–1.5% gelatin dissolved in liquid sugar.	Good barrier properties. Adds flexibility to shell.
Tapioca dextrin 42DE corn syrup Water	25% dextrin + 33% 42DE corn syrup solution heated to boiling. Cooled to 80°–110°F	Very good barrier properties. Adds flexibility to shell.
Corn dextrin 42DE corn syrup Water	25% dextrin + 33% 42DE corn syrup solution heated to boiling. Cooled to 80°–110°F	Similar to tapioca dextrin. Lower cost but may impart a corn flavor.
Film-forming modified starch Water	30–40 percent solution cooked to 200°F and cooled to 80°–110°F	Excellent fat barrier. Can add a chemical off-flavor to product.
10DE Maltodextrin Water	35–40 percent solution. Cooking not required.	Low cost. Moderate barrier properties. Adds moderate flexibility to shell.

Figure 2

ENGROSSING

The goal of the engrossing step is to build up a thick layer of sugar quickly. A liquid sugar solution is applied to the surface of a center. The water is then evaporated from the liquid, allowing the sugar to form crystallized layers. This process continues until the pieces achieve the desired size.

Engrossing syrup is prepared by boiling a sugar solution. Care must be taken to ensure that all sugar crystals are dissolved in the engrossing syrup. The syrup premix must be prepared with adequate water. A mixture of one part water per two parts sugar is sufficient to ensure all crystals are melted. The solids percentage of the engrossing syrup is controlled by the cooking temperature (Figure 3). In most industrial environments, a solution of 67 percent solids will not recrystallize at ambient temperature. As a result, this is a safe syrup concentration to use without risk of crystallization prior to panning. The use of a higher solids engrossing syrup will decrease process time (less water to remove). The drawback of high-solids engrossing syrups is twofold. First, the syrup may begin to crystallize before completely spreading over the surface of the centers. These crystals can imbed themselves into the candy and cause the product to have a rough, uneven surface. Second, higher solids syrup has a higher viscosity and will not spread over the centers as quickly. Uneven coating generates a large variation in finished-piece weights. When the syrup is extremely thick it can cause individual pieces to stick together. Previous studies have stated that a syrup viscosity less than 200 cps produces acceptable syrup distribution. The ideal solids of engrossing syrup will vary with the centers being coated and the equipment used.

Liquid Sugar Viscosities							
Sugar Solids Cook Temperature	65% 219.0°F	67% 220.3°F	70% 221.2°F	72% 222.5°F	75% 224.4°F	77% 224.4°F	80% 228.9°F
Viscosity at 158°F (centipoises)	12	16	25	35	61	96	203
Viscosity at 140°F (centipoises)	18	24	39	56	105	170	394
Viscosity at 122°F (centipoises)	28	38	64	96	193	735	855
Viscosity at 104°F (centipoises)	44	63	114	179	390	735	2,250
Viscosity at 86°F (centipoises)	77	114	222	368	885	1,800	6,280

Threshold of 200 CPS for acceptable syrup distribution.

Figure 3   Source: *This is Liquid Sugar,* Hoynak and Bollenback, 1996

In addition to solids percentage, several factors play a role in the uniformity of spreading. The viscosity of the engrossing syrup is also affected by the temperature of the syrup. Warmer syrup will spread more readily over the centers. It is best to add engrossing syrup at temperatures up to 150°F, as long as the centers will not melt or deform. The storage of engrossing syrup at temperatures in excess of 150°F is not recommended due to the increased risk of inversion of the syrup prior to use and the likelihood of prematurely evaporating water from the syrup. When developing a new process it is recommended to start with the warmest syrup temperature that the centers can withstand. The solids of engrossing syrup used should be chosen such that the viscosity is less than 200 CPS (Figure 3).

To improve the spreading of engrossing syrup, it is helpful to allow it to coat the centers without air blowing on the product. This is accomplished by letting the syrup tumble over the centers before introducing drying air to the pan. Most panning systems are designed with air supply ductwork that can be easily swung in and out of the pan. After tumbling for about 60 seconds, the airflow can be restarted to begin crystallizing the sugar.

The dose size is also important. When a dose is too small, there is not enough fluid to cover the surface area of each piece. This will cause the finished product to have a wide variation of piece size. When the dose is too large, the syrup cannot dry fast enough. This causes the contact surfaces to become sticky and results in doubled or clumped product. Another sign of excessive dose size is excessive buildup on the inside surface of the pan. As the panning process progresses, the candy gets bigger. With the increasing surface area to cover, it is necessary to increase the dose size several times.

In most cases the pans will rotate at a speed of 16 to 25 RPM. Faster speeds create more pan motion which improves the consistency of spreading. High rotation speed becomes a problem when the centers are dry. If the pan is revolving too fast, the coating will begin to dust and chip. For very delicate centers or heavy centers in excess of

1 inch in diameter, it may be necessary to slow the pan rotation down to as low as 10 RPM to prevent the force of product in motion from damaging itself.

To speed the engrossing process, some manufacturers will "cheat" by adding powdered sugar during the early doses. This does allow a coating to be built up much quicker; but, the coating will be rougher and will require some care to smooth out later in the process. Also, the individual particles of powdered sugar are larger than the sucrose crystals formed during the panning process. This results in a shell that is weaker and less crunchy.

A number of additives can be used to modify the properties of the hard-panned candy shell. It is common to add 0.5 to 5 percent of corn syrup, dextrin, maltodextrin or gelatin to the engrossing syrup to provide added flexibility. This flexibility will reduce the chances that the finished product will chip during packaging. Similarly, gum arabic can be added for strength and crunchiness. All of these additives are also helpful when adding a flavor to a hard-panned shell. The larger-molecular-weight compounds reduce the amount of flavor flashed off and prevent flavor migration throughout the shell. It is not recommended to add acids at any point in the engrossing process—the risk of inversion is too great. If any sucrose is inverted into dextrose and fructose, the purity of the crystallized coating will be damaged. This will lead to pinholes developing in the shell.

Titanium dioxide (TiO_2) is added to the syrup during the engrossing process to provide a solid white background for colors to be added in subsequent steps. A typical finished panned item will contain 0.5 to 0.75 percent TiO_2 by weight. This quantity of white colorant could be added to the last 10 or 15 engrossing layers, or it could be added to all of the engrossing syrup and applied a little with each layer. The equal TiO_2 method makes it easier for the pan operator, but requires the use of additional TiO_2 to get the same effect. In other countries, calcium carbonate or rice starch has been used to provide a white base coat. In the United States, however, these ingredients are not approved for use as colorants.

SMOOTHING

To ensure a smooth surface of the finished product, several coats of a thinner, lower solids engrossing syrup are commonly added. The extra water will cause some melting of a rough surface. As the syrup dries, the low points get filled in. To increase the smoothing results, the syrup should be applied without drying air. This increases the dissolving of the high points. Care must be taken not to harm the centers. Excessive wetting will cause the coating to wear off of the points that experience the most friction. There is also a danger of creating doubles if the smoothing syrup is allowed to tumble without being dried.

COLOR COAT

It is important to have a smooth surface prior to adding colored layers because bumps and dips on the shell will result in varied color intensity. Color solutions are very similar in formulation to engrossing syrup, but with the addition of color dyes and lakes. Dyes produce brighter colors, but the water-soluble dyes tend to bleed. This bleeding could manifest as one color transferring to another colored product or as stains left when melting in your hand. Insoluble lake colors do not produce colors with the same brilliance as dyes, but they do not bleed. Most colors used in hard panning will utilize lake colors with the addition of a small amount of dye to make the color bolder.

Once the centers have reached the desired piece weight, the process is nearing completion. The last few coats of color solution are often thinned out in a similar fashion as smoothing syrups. This creates a smoother surface for polishing. In addition, it is desirable to leave a little bit of water in the final color coat. Excessive drying will create dust that will make the polishing process less effective.

FINISHING

Product must be removed from the engrossing pan to a separate polishing pan. Polishing should occur soon after the end of the engrossing process. If not, the shell will continue to dry. This allows the formation of larger crystals on the outer surface and the drier product will begin to dust when tumbled. Both of these will cause the color of the finished product to have a dull appearance.

APPLYING THE BASICS—HARD-PANNED CHOCOLATE LENTILS

There is often debate about whether panning is an art or a science. Some prefer to think of it more as a sport. There is a set of rules to follow and the more you practice the better you get. One of the best ways to improve your game is to watch others more experienced in the specific techniques. The score card for the sport of panning is the Panning Data Sheet. Figure 4 shows the data sheet for the hard-panned chocolate lentils that were made for the PMCA conference. This describes, step by step, the way a pan load of candy was produced. The nature of panning is such that the process may not be identical each time, but a great deal can be learned by analyzing the specifics of the process.

Before beginning you need to create a basic plan. In this case, 100 lbs of chocolate lentil-shaped centers were added to the pan. The average piece weight of the uncoated centers was measured. Ten centers weighed 6.7 grams. It is the weight per 10 centers that is used as a guidepost throughout the panning process. The goal from the beginning was to increase the center weight by 27 to 30 percent. This is a typical range for hard panning chocolate centers.

The gumming process used in this example consisted of four wet doses of a 33 percent solution of gum arabic. Each dose was dried with 10x powdered sugar. No drying air was used. After the first three doses a significant amount of mass had been added to the centers. To adequately cover the greater surface area, the fourth dose was increased in size.

The engrossing step began with one small dose of syrup (70% solids, 85°F). It was observed that the syrup did not sufficiently spread over the centers. On the second dose, the quantity was doubled to wet all of the centers evenly. Throughout the engrossing step, the syrup was applied without airflow into the pan. This helps the syrup spread completely. After about one minute, the air was directed into the pan to remove moisture. On doses 5 through 11, a dry dose of 10x powdered sugar was added to build the shell more quickly. In this case, the mass of dry-dosing buildup of these 7 doses was equivalent to 12 liquid-only doses. This reduced the manufacturing time by more than one hour. At dose 9, the liquid amount was increased again to compensate for the increasing surface area. On doses 13 through 23, the syrup formulation of the engrossing syrup was altered to include 5 percent of a titanium dioxide dispersion. This provided a primer coat for the color that was added later.

At dose 23, the weight count of 10 pieces had reached the benchmark of 8.6 grams. This was a sufficient quantity of engrossing and the smoothing process began. The smoothing process used a syrup cooked to 67 percent solids. The syrup was observed to be spreading well so the air flow was not removed between doses. Once the pieces were adequately smooth to the touch, the color coat process began.

The first eight color-coat doses were identical to the smoothing doses, but with the added addition of green color. At doses 9 and 10, the target finished-piece weight had been obtained. To prepare the centers for polishing, the last four color coat doses were applied at 50 percent solids. This helps to produce a smoother surface and allows a small quantity of water to be retained to reduce breakage when transferring product from the engrossing pan to the polishing pan. This moisture will also keep the product from forming dust which will make the polishing step more difficult.

PROCESS CONTROL

Several aspects of process control have already been discussed. Evaluation of syrup spreading is largely dependent upon visual cues. The average piece weight throughout the process is also an important marker of the key steps in the process. Some panning systems have been placed on scales to have a more precise control on the amount of product in and out of each pan load.

The most important aspect to control in the panning process is when to add the next dose. If doses are added too quickly, residual moisture can be locked in the shell and cause the coating to fail. If too much time is spent between doses, the shell can dry to the point of producing sugar dust or shell cracking. In addition, a slow process reduces plant efficiency. Several techniques can be used to judge when the next dose can be added.

Panning Data Sheet

	Dose #	Dose Size	Ingredient	Spreading Time Without Air (min.)	Air Drying Time (min.)	Dry Weight Per 10 Pcs.	Solids Added (g)	Percentage of Shell	Cumulative % of Shell
						6.70g			
Gumming	1	100ml	30% gum arabic	5			30g	0.182%	0.182%
			10x sugar				1,200g	7.283%	7.466%
	2	100ml	30% gum arabic	6			30g	0.182%	7.648%
			10x sugar				1,200g	7.283%	14.931%
	3	100ml	30% gum arabic	8			30g	0.182%	15.113%
			10x sugar				1,200g	7.283%	22.397%
	4	125ml	30% gum arabic	9		7.5g	30g	0.228%	22.624%
			10x sugar				1,600g	9.711%	32.336%
Engrossing	1	100ml	70° Brix liquid sugar	1	4		94g	0.569%	32.905%
	2	200ml	70° Brix liquid sugar	1	6		188g	1.139%	34.043%
	3	200ml	70° Brix liquid sugar	1	6		188g	1.139%	35.182%
	4	200ml	70° Brix liquid sugar	2	5		188g	1.139%	36.321%
	5	200ml	70° Brix liquid sugar	3	11		188g	1.139%	37.459%
Dry Dose			Powdered sugar				400g	2.428%	39.887%
	6	200ml	70° Brix liquid sugar	3	4		188g	1.139%	41.026%
			Powdered sugar				400g	2.428%	43.454%
	7	200ml	70° Brix liquid sugar	3	5		188g	1.139%	44.592%
			Powdered sugar				400g	2.428%	47.020%
	8	200ml	70° Brix liquid sugar	1	3		188g	1.139%	48.159%
			Powdered sugar				400g	2.428%	50.587%
Larger Dose	9	250ml	70° Brix liquid sugar	2	5		235g	1.423%	52.010%
			Powdered sugar				400g	2.428%	54.438%
	10	250ml	70° Brix liquid sugar	4	12	8.0g	235g	1.423%	55.861%
			Powdered sugar				400g	2.428%	58.289%
	11	250ml	70° Brix liquid sugar	4	4		235g	1.423%	59.712%
			Powdered sugar				400g	2.428%	62.140%
	12	250ml	70° Brix liquid sugar	2	17		235g	1.423%	63.563%
TiO$_2$ Added	13	250ml	70° Brix liquid sugar + TiO$_2$	2	5		235g	1.423%	64.987%
	14	250ml	70° Brix liquid sugar + TiO$_2$	2	4		235g	1.423%	66.410%
	15	250ml	70° Brix liquid sugar + TiO$_2$	1	4		235g	1.423%	67.833%
	16	250ml	70° Brix liquid sugar + TiO$_2$	1	5		235g	1.423%	69.257%
	17	250ml	70° Brix liquid sugar + TiO$_2$	2	3		235g	1.423%	70.680%
	18	250ml	70° Brix liquid sugar + TiO$_2$	2	5	8.3g	235g	1.423%	72.103%
	19	250ml	70° Brix liquid sugar + TiO$_2$	1	4		235g	1.423%	73.526%
	20	250ml	70° Brix liquid sugar + TiO$_2$	1	11		235g	1.423%	74.950%
	21	250ml	70° Brix liquid sugar + TiO$_2$	1	8		235g	1.423%	76.373%
	22	250ml	70° Brix liquid sugar + TiO$_2$	1	8		235g	1.423%	77.796%
	23	250ml	70° Brix liquid sugar + TiO$_2$	2	4	8.6g	235g	1.423%	79.220%
Smoothing	1	150ml	67° Brix liquid sugar	1	4		141g	0.854%	80.074%
	2	150ml	67° Brix liquid sugar	1	4		141g	0.854%	80.928%
	3	150ml	67° Brix liquid sugar	–	5		141g	0.854%	81.782%
	4	150ml	67° Brix liquid sugar	–	5		141g	0.854%	82.636%
	5	150ml	67° Brix liquid sugar	–	5		141g	0.854%	83.490%
	6	150ml	67° Brix liquid sugar	–	5		141g	0.854%	84.344%
	7	150ml	67° Brix liquid sugar	–	5		141g	0.854%	85.198%
	8	150ml	67° Brix liquid sugar	–	5		141g	0.854%	86.052%
	9	150ml	67° Brix liquid sugar	–	5		141g	0.854%	86.906%
	10	150ml	67° Brix liquid sugar	–	5		141g	0.854%	87.760%
	11	150ml	67° Brix liquid sugar	–	5	8.6g	141g	0.854%	88.614%
	12	150ml	67° Brix liquid sugar	–	5		141g	0.854%	89.468%
Color Coat	1	150ml	67° Brix liquid sugar + color		5		141g	0.854%	90.322%
	2	150ml	67° Brix liquid sugar + color		5		141g	0.854%	91.175%
	3	150ml	67° Brix liquid sugar + color		5		141g	0.854%	92.029%
	4	150ml	67° Brix liquid sugar + color		5		141g	0.854%	92.883%
	5	150ml	67° Brix liquid sugar + color		5		141g	0.854%	93.737%
	6	150ml	67° Brix liquid sugar + color		5		141g	0.854%	94.591%
	7	150ml	67° Brix liquid sugar + color		5		141g	0.854%	95.445%
	8	150ml	67° Brix liquid sugar + color		5		141g	0.854%	96.299%
	9	150ml	67° Brix liquid sugar + color	12	–		141g	0.854%	97.153%
	10	150ml	67° Brix liquid sugar + color	13	–	9.1g	141g	0.854%	98.007%
	11	100ml	67° Brix liquid sugar + color	12	–		94g	0.569%	98.577%
Final Smoothing	12	100ml	67° Brix liquid sugar + color	10	–		94g	0.569%	99.146%
	13	100ml	67° Brix liquid sugar + color	5	–		94g	0.569%	99.715%
	14	50ml	67° Brix liquid sugar + color	7	–		47g	0.285%	100.000%

				132 Min. Total Time	241 Min.		16,476g Start	36.3 lbs	Shell
				373 Min.				100.0 lbs	Centers
				6.2 Hours			End	136.3 lbs	Finished
								26.6%	Shell

Figure 4

The next dose can be added after all of the moisture has been evaporated from the previous coats. An experienced panner can judge this by the feel of the product. If moisture is still evaporating, the candy will be cool to the touch. Once the evaporative cooling effect has gone, so has the moisture. This control point can also be automated by measuring the differential humidity of air going in and out of the pan.

The sound of product tumbling in a pan changes as the moisture is driven off. When a wet dose is added the pan is quiet. As the shell dries the sound of product colliding becomes louder. Good panners are unconsciously reacting to the differences they hear in the candy. It is possible to place microphones inside of pans and automate this audible feedback. Unfortunately, the harsh environment and background noise make such a control system quite difficult to manage.

In addition to the audible differences between wet and dry centers, there are also visual cues. The shine on product changes as it dries. The tumbling action of centers becomes noticeably different as the product dries. These visual signs are gradually learned as a panner becomes more experienced.

AUTOMATED PANNING PROCESS

The hard-panning process has been successfully automated. Several companies manufacture completely enclosed panning systems. Generally these systems consist of a completely enclosed drum that can process 500 to 6,600 lbs of finished product per batch. If you are going to produce very large quantities of one product formulation the automated panning equipment is ideal. Benefits include the following:

- A uniform process that is reproducible batch to batch.
- A system engineered to optimum process conditions—decreased process times.
- Automated loading and unloading of product.
- Atomized spray nozzles that can uniformly spread engrossing syrup.
- Perforated drum allows increased airflow through product for faster drying of temperature-sensitive centers.
- Dust and noise are better contained within unit.

OTHER INGREDIENTS

While this paper focused exclusively on sucrose panning, it should be noted that hard panning can also be performed with pure forms of dextrose, sorbitol, maltitol, isomalt and xylitol. Hard panning with polyols has become much more popular with the increased presence of sugarfree pellet gum. For the most part, the same principles apply, but the solution concentrations and drying air temperatures change to match the crystallization properties of the coating ingredient chosen.

Note: Questions and answers for this chapter appear at the end of the Panning section on page 231.

Chocolate Panning

Bill Pullia
U.S. Flavors & Fragrances

Chocolate panning, as a process, has been employed for many years in the confectionery industry. Almost any commonly used confectionery inclusion can be chocolate coated through this process. Some of the most popular are nutmeats (peanuts, almonds and cashews), fruits (raisins, cherries) and malted milk balls. Many successful candy products on the market today are produced in this manner. Chocolate panning is also used as an intermediate step for further processing such as enrobing and sugar panning.

Chocolate panning is a fast, efficient way to add a chocolate coating to a wide variety of items. It does not require tempering; therefore, the expense of tempering equipment and cooling tunnels does not exist. Chocolate panning, when done properly, does not have the space requirements of an enrobing operation and can be more cost effective. It is a forgiving process that adds flexibility and versatility to any confectionery manufacturing operation.

The term *chocolate* is used, for the sake of simplicity, in this paper as a generic term meaning any fat-based coating material. There are many fat-based coatings used in the manufacture of confectionery today. These include milk chocolate, dark chocolate, white chocolate, yogurt coatings, chocolate-flavored compound coatings and white coatings.

BASIC PRINCIPLES

The chocolate panning process is based mainly on one major principle—heat transfer. Other factors such as humidity can also affect the process, but heat transfer is the most influential. The ability to transfer heat from the product rapidly will determine, in large part, the efficiency of the process. Cooling or drying the product between coats of chocolate is essential. The more quickly the product is cooled, the sooner the next coat of chocolate can be applied. Rapid wetting and drying of the batch will allow for faster and more efficient processing. The friction created by the tumbling action in the pan will influence the distribution of the chocolate and the smoothness of the coating.

In the chocolate panning process, the most widely used method of achieving heat transfer, is to pass conditioned air over and/or through the product intermittently. Another method in use today is adding CO_2 to the batch.

BASIC PROCESS/CONVENTIONAL PANNING

Melting

The process begins with melting the chocolate, usually in a jacketed chocolate melter. The chocolate is melted and the temperature maintained within a given range. The ideal temperature range allows for an even distribution of chocolate over the centers, yet does not require excessive cooling time. The normal temperature range is 105° to 120°F, depending on the type of chocolate used and the process.

While the chocolate is being melted, the items to be coated (centers) are added to the coating drum/pan. The pan may be fitted with baffles to aid in the tumbling action. Some centers will not readily accept a chocolate coating (e.g., due to high moisture content, a nonporous surface or high fat content) and require a precoat before chocolate panning begins. This precoat is comprised of any material that will make the centers take the chocolate more readily (gum arabic and sugar are commonly used). The centers should be at ambient temperature. If the centers are too cold, the chocolate will cool too quickly and not form a uniform coating. They will also expand and crack the chocolate coating. If the centers are too warm, the chocolate will not adhere well and will take longer to cool, thus lengthening the process and causing more chocolate to adhere to the coating drum than is desirable.

Coating

The speed of rotation of the coating drum is dependent upon the type of centers to be coated. Too fast and the centers can be damaged or the coating can chip off. Too slow and the centers will stick together, resulting in a high rate of doubles and lumps. The size of the coating drum is also important. If the coating drum is too large for the batch, the centers will not be evenly coated. This will result in inconsistent product quality and a rough surface.

Chocolate is then added to the rotating coating drum, directly onto the centers. This can be achieved either by ladling, drizzling or spraying the chocolate. The chocolate should be applied in an amount sufficient to cover the centers evenly and to cool quickly, usually 1 to 2 percent of the weight of the centers. The weight of the product and the rotation of the pan will disperse the chocolate over the centers. Once the chocolate is evenly distributed on the centers, it is then cooled so that it is dry to the touch. The amount of chocolate added each time will increase as the surface area of the centers increases. This process is repeated until the desired amount of chocolate has been added to the centers. Once the desired amount of chocolate has been added, the product is smoothed by additional time rotating in the pan. If the product is still not as smooth as desired, very conservative amounts of heated air can be used to melt the outermost coating of chocolate in order to smooth the product.

The product is then removed from the coating drum and stored, usually in trays, before moving on to the next step.

Polishing

The next step of the process is polishing. Polishing gives the finished product a shine and luster that is appealing to the eye. It also affords the product protection from moisture, sticking and scuffing. Polishing is usually achieved by applying a very thin film of gum which is then sealed with confectioner's glaze.

The polishing process is usually carried out in a separate, dedicated polishing drum. Some manufacturers polish product in the same coating drum immediately after the product has been chocolate coated. Although this method minimizes product handling, it may cause issues with scrap reclamation.

The conventional chocolate panning process, while versatile, is very operator dependent and labor intensive. It is best suited for smaller operations.

PROCESS VARIATIONS

While the basic process of chocolate panning remains virtually unchanged, many advancements have recently been made in equipment and engineering. These developments allow for more consistent quality, efficient processing, larger batches, shorter cycle times and large reductions in scrap and rework.

Belt Coating

Belt coating utilizes a plastic link belt in the shape of a pocket rather than a coating pan. Because belt coaters have a lower bed depth, they are best suited to process softer, more fragile centers. Chocolate is drizzled onto the centers through holes in a pipe positioned above the belt. This design produces a more consistent chocolate coating due to the more even distribution of weight during the coating process. The link design of the coating belt, coupled with an extraction fan on the back of the unit, draws air through the product, which allows for more efficient cooling. The belt can be reversed, which makes unloading the product less labor intensive. Excess chocolate can be easily scraped from the belt, allowing for shorter cleanup times and more efficient scrap reclamation. Aside from the belt coating unit itself, no other unique equipment is required.

Belt coating is more efficient and less operator dependent than conventional chocolate panning. There are opportunities to automate parts of the process. It is best suited for small to medium-sized operations.

Drum Coating

Drum coating utilizes a long tube fitted with solid or perforated baffles which rotate the product. Chocolate is sprayed onto the centers by a spray arm that runs through the middle of the drum. Affixed to the spray arm are multiple spray heads that force the chocolate into a fine mist with compressed air. The large capacity of these units allows for larger production runs. The perforations in the drum allow for efficient cooling. The spray system allows for excellent distribution of the chocolate and results in less chocolate adhering to the drum.

These units are usually supplied as complete, self-contained systems which include automated loading and unloading apparatus and air-handling systems. All controls are automated, allowing for the operation of several units by one operator.

Perforated-drum coating systems are very efficient, highly automated and quite expensive compared to the other systems described here, and are therefore best suited to high-volume operations.

SUMMARY

Chocolate panning is a versatile and viable process for confectionery manufacturers of every size. The products produced through this process have a history of success in the marketplace and are limited only by one's imagination.

The process itself is very straightforward and easily mastered. The necessary equipment ranges from low-tech and inexpensive setups to fully automated, high-volume systems.

Note: Questions and answers for this chapter appear at the end of the Panning section on page 231.

Soft Panning

Pamela Gesford
Colorcon

Soft panning has been around at least since 1861 when William Schrafft advertised jelly beans in a newspaper in Boston. Since then, the number of products made with a soft-panning process has dramatically increased. Even though many people think of only the jelly bean as being soft panned, there are many other new and old products made with this process. Before discussing the type of products made this way, the ingredients used, the process itself and the relationship between center and shell, we will discuss the terms used.

Soft panning is the process by which a soft coating is applied to a center. It also could be described as the process of forming a coating which includes the addition of a syrup to a center followed by the addition of dry material.

Engrossing is the process of building up the shell.

Dry charging is the introduction of dry powder by evenly sprinkling it directly onto the surface of tumbling pieces.

Finishing is the process of preparing engrossed product for polishing, including removing any of the powdered sugar on the surface.

Polishing is the process of adding the shine and possibly sealing the outside of the soft-panned product.

Products made by this process include jelly beans, some Boston Baked Beans, caramel beans, sugar-coated marshmallow eggs and even some gumballs. One of the first branded, year-round, solely soft-panned products was *Mike and Ike*, which was introduced in 1940, followed by *Hot Tamales* in 1950. These both have a gel center as do jelly beans and other products such as fruit sours. Prior to that, some brands like *Good & Plenty* (which was first made in 1896), had, by classic definition, a soft-panned undercoat, with a hard-panned shell. In addition to the traditional jelly bean there are gourmet jelly beans as well as jelly bean versions of fruity-flavored brands. Just recently, soft-panned candy fruit rocks have appeared on the market. There still seems to be a large interest in the introduction of soft and chewy items, including those that are soft panned.

INGREDIENTS

The soft-panning process has remained an art more than a science. Most candy processes start out as an art, and then, with research, the science is discovered by controlling all but one parameter at a time. One factor that seems to deter the thorough evaluation of the scientific aspects of soft panning is the complexity of the variables that influence this process. Ingredient choices have a large influence on the finished product, including the center, syrup ingredients, drying powder material and minor or optional ingredients. The majority of soft-panned products are sucrose based, so that will be the focus of this paper. However, sugarfree and dextrose-based products are also popular.

The Center

The center is commonly the largest portion of any soft-panned product. The center can be from 50 to 70 percent of the finished piece by weight. Gel centers are the most common. However, they are not all the same. The formulation and production of gel centers could make a paper in and of itself but there are a few comments that need to be made since the characteristics of any center influence the soft-panned product greatly. Centers may contain starch, gelatin, pectin or even a combination. Some of the newer modified starches or gums may also make an acceptable center for soft-panned products if the resulting gel is robust enough to hold up to the tumbling action and the weight from a fully loaded pan.

Some of the most important attributes for centers are related to uniformity. Size, shape and moisture uniformity are all important for any center. For gel centers, uniform size and shape are directly related to the quality of depositing. Size and shape uniformity allow an equal coating to be achieved on the majority of pieces in the pan since surface area is important to the amount of syrup and dry ingredients that are required. Mogul maintenance, frequent board weights and even sifting to remove depositing defects can help keep centers uniform. Starch-deposited centers with flat tops can even have sunken backs if improperly dried, creating a great surface for the engrossing syrup to glue two pieces together. For sugar-sanded centers, using a uniform size of sugar like baker's special sugar can be a good starting surface on which to base a soft-panned shell. Also, for a gel center, be aware that issues in cooking or depositing can cause centers that are softer and more easily deformed, even though they are at the proper moisture level. For instance, gelatin base that is held for an extended period at a high temperature, especially in the presence of acid, will degrade, resulting in softer, less rigid centers. Also, high methoxyl pectin can pregel if held too long after acid addition and then can easily tear during further processing. Even starch, if not properly hydrated or cooked, can create a weaker center. Any of these changes in center quality can greatly impact the ability to soft pan the centers as well as the stability of any finished product.

Other centers can present challenges of their own. Having a nut center presents a challenge due to adherence of the shell to the center as well as possible water absorption. Most choose to subcoat these centers. Subcoating ingredients will be discussed later along with optional ingredients. Uniform-sized nut centers can be selected for soft-panned products. Any other center for soft panning may have similar challenges but may also have other unique attributes that need to be controlled to produce a stable, uniform end product.

Engrossing Syrup

The composition of the engrossing syrup varies depending on the texture desired. For normal sugar-based products, the syrup is usually a noncrystallizing syrup made up of sugar, corn syrup and water. For syrup, bulk granulated sugar is regularly used. Different corn syrups can be used, for example, 42 or 62 DE. Most manufacturers seem to formulate with the type of corn syrup that they typically have on hand. Syrup preparation usually involves bringing the water and sugar to a boil to dissolve the sugar and then adding the corn syrup.

The composition of the syrup has a direct influence on the finished texture of the bean. The ratio of sucrose to corn syrup (on a solids basis) strongly affects the textural attributes of the finished product. A ratio of 1 part sucrose to 0.5 parts corn syrup (on a solids basis) produces a harder texture as opposed to a 1 to 1 ratio, which produces a soft texture. Sometimes thinned corn syrup can be used to make an even softer product. Some traditional materials suggest that solids of most syrups used should be 70 to 72 percent. More practically, however, higher solids closer to the 74 to 78 percent range are used. As with any cooked syrup, sugar inversion can play a role in possible defects. Since most syrups used in soft panning are noncrystallizing, the creation of invert sugar is less likely to slow production as in hard panning but it may cause other faults like instability of products in storage. Factors that influence the rate of sugar inversion are the ash level of the sugar, the cooking and holding time at high temperatures and the presence of acid.

Dry Powder

The next major ingredient is the dry powder that is added to the shell. Normally, two to three sizes of sugar are used for dry charging. The order that the sugar is added is from the largest to the smallest size. Particle size and particle size distribution are two of the most important factors for the dry charge material. Extra fine granular, bakers special sugar, 6X confectioners sugar and 10X confectioners sugar can be used. The larger the grain of the sugar, the more the candy pieces are reliant on the tumbling action of the pan to produce a durable smooth coating.

Optional Raw Materials

Minor and optional raw materials used in soft panning are those ingredients that are used in smaller amounts but can be critical to making the variety of products that are seen in the market today. Colors, flavors, waxes, center subcoat ingredients, confectioners glaze, acids and other flavoring or decorating ingredients are those ingredients that warrant being mentioned. Colors can be either dye or pigment based. Traditionally, FD&C dye-based colors were used in jelly beans but now many products are made with FD&C aluminum lakes as well as colors from natural sources. The use of pigments like FD&C aluminum lakes, titanium dioxide or carmine can hide some crystallization faults in soft-panned coatings. FD&C dyes and most other colors from natural sources usually produce a more transparent appearance. Colors are typically added to the engrossing syrup.

Flavors, on the other hand, can be added to a subcoat, in the engrossing syrup or even directly onto the pieces during the engrossing process. Mostly liquid flavors are used. Water-soluble powders can also be used but they may not be as cost effective. The carrier of liquid flavors may influence the panning process. Oils may interfere with tumbling and cause pieces to slide in the pan. Large amounts of propylene glycol or glycerin (common carriers for liquid flavors) may interfere with stability by holding moisture in the shell until stressed, causing sticky surfaces in packaged products. Alcohol-based flavors evaporate quickly, sometimes flashing off top notes as well.

Depending on the desired flavor, various acids can be used in soft-panned items. Buffered lactic acid solution, malic, fumaric, tartaric or citric acid can be added to the engrossing syrup, keeping in mind the effect low pH has on the rate of sugar inversion. Powdered acid can be mixed with sugar and dry charged directly onto the product. Care needs to be taken to avoid dry charging with crystalline dry acids so as not to cause pitting on the inside surface of the pan.

Subcoat ingredients are typically used with centers that are sensitive to moisture. Perfect examples are peanuts or other nutmeats that would be subject to an increase in oxidative rancidity if exposed to the moisture from engrossing syrup. Subcoat ingredients can be gum arabic, maltodextrin, tapioca dextrin, gelatin, modified starches or a combination of these.

Inclusions like colored sugar or other small particulates can be added in the last engrossing steps to provide an interesting appearance. Color dispersions or other colored films can be added as speckles or spots on the surface as well. Polishing will be discussed in another paper but the ingredients that are used in these steps also can be included in minor and optional ingredients. Waxes—typically carnauba and/or beeswax—are used on soft-panned products to impart a shine, whereas confectioners glaze can be used as a sealant over the wax polish to maintain the shine and protect the product over time. Pigmented confectioners glazes can be used as an optional ingredient to speckle finished polished products. Some of the latest versions of these products are even made with newly available pearlescent pigments. Edible ink can be printed onto various soft-panned products to denote brand name, for seasonal decoration or possibly to denote flavor or variety.

There are many variations of ingredients that allow a growing variety of soft-panned products (Figure 1).

Sugarfree and Dextrose

Before discussing the soft-panning process itself, a few comments need to be made regarding the differences in ingredients when sugarfree or dextrose panning is desired. In sugarfree it is most logical to substitute a noncrystalliz-ing syrup for the traditional engrossing syrup, followed by fine uniform crystalline sugar substitutes. Sugar substitutes may not be available in varying particle sizes so only one size of uniform distribution should be used. Remember, a high-intensity sweetener may need to be added to the engrossing syrup if the combined relative sweetness of the ingredients used is significantly lower than sugar. Despite the differences in ingredients, the examination of the cross section of a sugarfree gourmet jelly bean shows the struc-ture of the shell to be similar to any gourmet jelly bean. Most suppliers of sugarfree ingredients can give you sug-gestions for the specific use of their products in panning. Before choosing sugarfree ingredients, hydroscopicity, ease of use, performance, possible laxation effect, label acceptability and cost are all major factors to be considered.

When using dextrose to make soft-panned products, it seems the major differences are the makeup of the engrossing syrup and the use of dextrose as the dry charge sugar. A different engrossing syrup composition is needed to avoid crystallization faults in the soft coating. This major contributing factor is due to the dextrose level of the corn syrup used. Suggestions include the addition of either high-fructose (may be slightly sticky to work with) or high-maltose corn syrup to avoid this problem. Whether using sucrose, dextrose or many sugarfree substitutes, the process is the same.

Decorative Ingredients for Soft-panned Products

Pearlescent Pigmented Confectioners Glaze

Edible Ink

Vanilla Bean Seeds

Figure 1

THE PROCESS

Now that the ingredients have been reviewed the process should be discussed (Figure 2). Suggested room conditions for soft panning are temperatures between 60° to 70°F and relative humidity below 55 percent. Normally, rotary pans from 36 to 42 inches in diameter are used for most soft-panned products. These can be round or tulip shaped and they are normally stainless steel. However, for nonacid products, copper pans can be used. Pans can be ribbed or roughened with a combination of syrup and sugar prior to running to assist in tumbling.

Soft panning is probably the most challenging panning process to move into the larger automated pans. The first reason that this is such a challenge is due to the normally tender/soft nature of the typical center and the fact that some of these larger pans can have fairly deep bed depths. There are now some promising specialized automated systems available but a majority of people are still using conventional pans. In conventional pans, pan speeds from 20 to 22 RPM seem to be the most commonly used. Since the idea is to attach the dry charge material with the engrossing syrup and not to dry and crystallize the engrossing syrup, drying air is not normally used. Prepared engrossing syrup is applied to tumbling centers and allowed to distribute evenly over the pieces. The idea is to add a dose of engrossing syrup that is big enough to wet the entire surface of the center without gluing the centers together. The scoops of dry material are added and allowed to pack onto the surface. As the tumbling action continues, the syrup begins to surround the dry powder and what is typically referred to as sweat-back occurs. This means the surface appears once again to be moist. More of the dry charge material is added gradually until it does not sweat back. Sometimes it may seem that the end point has been reached but if the product is allowed to tumble a little longer the sugar can work into the surface (Figure 3).

Many factors contribute to the timing of the dry powder addition and that is the second challenge for the large, more continuous pans when making soft-panned items. The combination of one application of syrup followed by the scoops of dry charge material needed to dry the surface make up one layer. Next, another charge of engrossing syrup is added followed by scoops of dry material in a similar fashion to the first wetting. Generally, two to four layers are added but, depending on the thickness of the

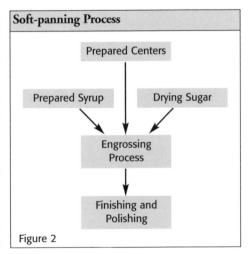

Figure 2

desired coat, there can be up to 10 layers added. Normally, the finer particle size of dry material is added in the last layer or layers. This finer material can pack in between the larger particles and form a smoother exterior, which will allow for a more easily polished surface. The last layer is usually powdered sugar. Product should be removed to trays to stand overnight to allow excess moisture to be released into the air or at least to equilibrate with the center. If an insufficient amount of powdered sugar is added to the pieces and sweat-back occurs after the pieces are trayed, the pieces will have a tendency to stick together and the coating can even peel off when separated. After standing overnight the product is ready for finishing and polishing, a topic covered by another paper.

Soft panning is a process that seems to be simple and should be easy. It is difficult, however, to do well. One might consider this a "Goldilocks" process. One porridge is too hot, another is too cold and the last is just right. In this way, dilemmas arise in soft panning unless certain attributes are just right. For example, if the dose of engrossing syrup is too high, it can lead to doubles and clumping. If the dose is too low, the distribution will be uneven across the pieces and lead to uneven coating.

If pan loading is too low the centers will not tumble correctly, which will interfere with proper coating. If it is too high the centers may crush (if soft) or pieces will become flying projectiles after the shell starts to build.

Product can stick together and form doubles if the engrossing syrup solids are too high, if the centers are improperly subcoated, if too much syrup is added at once, if the centers are too soft, if the pan speed is too slow or if the dry charge sugar is added too late.

Malformed shapes or uneven surface coating can be from too much sugar at the beginning of the process, if the application of syrup is too small to evenly distribute, if the sugar granulation is too small (or too many fines) or if the centers are nonuniform. Finished soft-panned products normally have 10 to 17 percent moisture in the shell but this does depend on the panning technique as well as any migration of moisture between center and shell.

An Experiment with Variations

Since jelly beans are still used as the main example of soft panning, an experiment to produce various jelly beans with variations in engrossing syrup composition as well as the type of sugar used for dry charging was conducted. With the

Sugar on Jelly Beans

Dry sugar on surface of in-process jelly beans

After 5 minutes of run time, sugar has worked into surface of in-process jelly beans

Figure 3

exception of the large-production-pan run done for video purposes, all samples were made in a small 15-inch lab pan for soft panning. This is not optimal since the tumbling action is instrumental to forming the coating. For comparison purposes, a typical formula was done in the small pan as well as in the production size. These formulations were made with four layers that had similar amounts of engrossing syrup and the amount of dry sugar required to dry each layer (Figure 4). This means that the resulting products may have different weight gains resulting in differing center to shell ratios. In Run 6, the one made with only sucrose in the engrossing syrup, the amount of that syrup had to be increased slightly just to wet the pieces properly. In Run 4, made with the larger seasonal jelly bean center, the amount of syrup seemed to make the pieces overly wet so there were a larger number of doubles formed. All jelly beans were placed in trays overnight and then polished. A 65° Brix finishing syrup was applied to wet the powdered sugar on the surface. When dry, this was followed by an application of wax (beeswax and carnauba) in alcohol and glazed with a shellac-based confectioners glaze.

Various evaluations were done on the six jelly bean runs. The results can be seen in Figure 5. Center and shell percentages were calculated in two ways. First, all the ingredients used were put into a formula by weight and then the percentage of center was calculated (denoted as calculated). This method does not take into account any loss of ingredients to the pan or surrounding air. The second method is based on the weighing of a number of finished beans and subtracting the original weight of the same number of centers. This method is denoted as measured in the data table. Finished jelly beans from each run were taken apart and water activities and moistures were taken on both the shell and center for each. During the production batch, samples were also taken periodically for similar evaluation (Figure 4). The trends of changes in moisture do not seem as apparent as expected; piece-to-piece variation may be to blame. Moistures were done by an outside laboratory with a loss-on-drying technique that is done slowly so as not to experience case hardening on the gel centers. The products made in the small pan had much higher moistures than the production run. The moistures found in the production run were much more typical

Production Run Sampling

Production Run/Run #	2nd Wetting	3rd Wetting	4th Wetting Before Powdered Sugar Addition	4th Wetting After Powdered Sugar Addition	Wax Only	Glazed	Glazed and Stored in Trays Overnight
Moisture and Water Activity Results							
% Moisture shell	15.9	15.5	14.6	14.2	11.7	13.7	15.4
% Moisture center	15.2	15.4	18.5	14.7	13.3	12.5	15.8
a_w (shell)	0.623	0.686	0.672	0.683	0.581	0.590	0.477
a_w (center)	0.595	0.696	0.598	0.629	0.580	0.553	0.508

Figure 4

with 10 to 17 percent finished-product moisture levels and were essentially the same between center and shell. Water activities were done with a benchtop water activity measurement device. Only the production sample, Run 1, had a higher water activity in the center than the shell.

In examining the resulting jelly beans from the above experiment, there are a few observations that need to be pointed out. Run 1, the production run, looked the best followed by Run 5, which was made with engrossing syrup comprised of thinned corn syrup (Figure 6). However, maybe this is not surprising if the total percentage of dry charge is reviewed. Run 5 has a total dry charge percentage closer to that of Run 1 and more than the other variants made in the small lab pan (Figure 5). As expected, the shell of Run 6, which had the sugar-only engrossing syrup, became opaque, crystallized and crunchy. It was almost impossible to polish,

Production Run Evaluations

	Run 1	Run 2	Run 3	Run 4	Run 5	Run 6
Pan Size	Production size	Lab size	Lab size	Lab size	Lab size	Lab size
Syrup Type	Combined corn syrup and sugar	Combined corn syrup and sugar	Combined corn syrup and sugar	Combined corn syrup and sugar	Thinned corn syrup	Sugar syrup
Gel Center Type	Small gourmet	Small gourmet	Small gourmet	Large seasonal	Small gourmet	Small gourmet
Dry Charge Sugar	Bakers special and powdered	Bakers special and powdered	Extra fine granular, bakers special and powdered	Bakers special and powdered	Bakers special and powdered	Bakers special and powdered
Center and Shell Relationship						
Center % (measured)	52.1%	66.4%	69.5%	67.6%	63.3%	63.3%
Shell % (measured)	47.9%	33.6%	30.5%	32.4%	36.7%	36.7%
Center % (calculated)	52.0%	65.4%	64.7%	65.3%	61.2%	62.1%
Shell % (calculated)	48.0%	34.6%	35.3%	34.7%	38.8%	37.9%
Syrup Formulation						
Sugar to corn syrup solids ratio	0.9:1	0.9:1	0.9:1	0.9:1	0:1	0:1
Water %	19.0%	19.0%	19.0%	19.0%	13.4%	27.0%
Sucrose %	33.0%	33.0%	33.0%	33.0%	0%	73.0%
42 DE corn syrup %	48.0%	48.0%	48.0%	48.0%	86.6%	0%
Solids—°Brix	74.9°	74.2°	73.0°	72.5°	70.7°	73.0°
Formulation						
Center %	52.0%	65.4%	64.7%	65.3%	61.2%	62.1%
Syrup %	7.4%	8.5%	8.4%	8.5%	7.9%	10.2%
Red color dispersion %	0.5%	0.6%	0.6%	0.6%	0.6%	0.7%
Berry flavor %	0.3%	0.3%	0.3%	0.3%	0.3%	0.3%
Citric acid %	0.3%	0.1%	0.1%	0.1%	0.1%	0.1%
Extra fine granular sugar	0%	0%	18.0%	0%	0%	0%
Bakers special sugar	34.1%	19.4%	5.7%	22.6%	28.3%	19.3%
Powdered sugar	5.5%	5.7%	2.1%	2.5%	1.6%	7.2%
Total sugar dry charge	39.6%	25.1%	25.8%	25.1%	29.9%	26.5%
Moisture and Water Activity Results						
% Moisture shell	15.4%	22.0%	20.6%	25.1%	26.4%	21.4%
% Moisture center	15.8%	24.6%	22.7%	24.5%	24.5%	24.9%
a_w (shell)	0.477	0.498	0.460	0.511	0.489	0.512
a_w (center)	0.508	0.482	0.441	0.494	0.454	0.494

Figure 5

Soft-panned Products — Cross Sections

Whole jelly bean from Run 1

Jelly bean 1 cross section

Whole jelly bean from Run 2

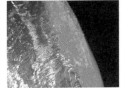
Jelly bean 2 cross section

Whole jelly bean from Run 3

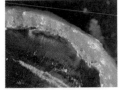
Jelly bean 3 cross section

Whole jelly bean from Run 4

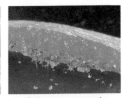
Jelly bean 4 cross section

Whole jelly bean from Run 5

Jelly bean 5 cross section

Whole jelly bean from Run 6

Jelly bean 6 cross section

Figure 6

possibly due to a rough surface or the tendency to make dust that transfers back to the polish layer from the pan surface. This is why, even when desiring a harder shell, some corn syrup still needs to be included in the engrossing syrup. The large seasonal-type jelly bean center made a decent finished product (Run 4), but the texture seemed slightly grainy. It is difficult to say which of the jelly bean variants would make a more acceptable, stable product if done in a large production pan.

CONCLUSION

In conclusion, a few other comments need to be made. The above process portion of this paper makes soft panning seem so simplistic and straightforward. As previously mentioned, knowing when to add more powder and when to add the next syrup is key to an acceptable and stable finished product. Patience may be a virtue but in the process of soft panning it has to be an essential part of the standard operating procedure. If the formulation and process are developed wisely, quality soft-panned products can be consistently produced. There are seemingly endless combinations of flavor, appearance and texture that can be combined in soft-panned products to catch the eye and please the palate of consumers.

Note: Questions and answers for this chapter appear at the end of the Panning section on page 231.

Polishing and Finishing of Panned Goods

Robert Boutin
Knechtel Laboratories

Most manufacturers finish, polish and glaze their panned products to enhance their appearance, as well as add to the product's shelf life, freshness and stability. For many consumers, the product's ultimate acceptance is based upon its finish or gloss. To a consumer, no other product attribute represents or presents wholesomeness or quality more than finish. This initial consumer reaction can trigger the purchase response and help contribute to the product's final success.

Generating these high-quality products is easier said than done, because finishing or polishing is one of the more difficult aspects to master in panning. This is mainly because the product's finish is not only related to the finishing or polishing agents used (i.e., waxes or shellacs), but also to the quality of the panning operation (engrossing) itself.

DEFINITIONS

The term *finishing* can be defined in several ways:

- The application of reduced-solids sugar syrup used to smooth the surface of sugar-panned items.
- The smoothing or rounding out of a chocolate-panned piece before the application of a sealant.
- The final application of wax or glaze to the panned goods.

For us, finishing will mean the techniques or processes used to smooth, dry or seal the surface of the pieces (i.e., the final steps in the panning or engrossing operation).

Polishing or *glazing* is defined as the application of waxes, shellac, gums or protein systems to the panned goods with the intent of generating a high gloss and improved shelf life (by reducing moisture loss, by lessening moisture absorption and lowering product agglomeration in the package).

OBJECTIVES IN PANNING

To be successful, panned goods must have a smooth surface, be hard and dry, and be

Correctly Finished Sugar-panned Mini Jawbreaker	Rough Surface Sugar-panned Mini Jawbreaker

Figure 1	Figure 2

sealed with a film former such as gum arabic, starch, gums, etc. (in the case of chocolate- or compound-coated pieces).

The complexity in reaching these common objectives comes from the fact that each type of panning method somewhat requires its own technique. To generate a high-quality product, it is imperative that we have a smooth surface to glaze or polish. If the surface is rough or irregular, the polishing agents (wax, shellac or others) will settle into the depressions or holes and not buff up to a high-quality appearance. The high spots of the candy will shine and the holes or depressions will appear dull or as white/gray spots.

Figure 1 shows a correctly finished sugar-panned mini jawbreaker and Figure 2 shows a rough surface sugar-panned mini jawbreaker. Note the whitish haze and speckled finish on the rough-surfaced piece.

So, for each type of panned good, a specific technique must be used to generate the base substrate.

SMOOTH SURFACE

Sugar Panned Products (Hard Panned or Soft Panned)

A weaker engrossing or finishing syrup is used for the last few applications (usually 65% to 67% solids down from 69% to 72% for normal engrossing). Reduce the application quantity per charge and limit the drying so as to not overdry the pieces. Every company sees modifications of this technique, but it is important that steps like this are followed to eliminate the rough surface and resulting poor shine.

How do you know when the product is smooth or smooth enough? There is a simple hot-moist-air test: take the rough jelly bean (Figure 3), place it by your mouth, take a deep breath and exhale. The moisture or humidity in your breath will coat the surface of the candy and give you a quick indication of what that piece would look like

Rough Surface Jelly Beans	Smooth Surface Jelly Beans

Figure 3	Figure 4

if polished at that stage. Repeat the same test using the smooth jelly bean (Figure 4) and see the difference. You can repeat this test using the sugar-panned mini jaw-breakers in the same way.

Chocolate Panned Goods

For chocolate panned products, the process is easier, but a little more sensitive. Here the smoothness of the chocolate- or compound-coated pieces is gained by allowing the candies to tumble in the pan after coating. The frictional heat of the tumbling allows the coating to soften and flow until smooth. Once smooth, cold air is applied to set

Smooth-tumbled Chocolate Peanuts

Figure 5

the coating and the product is then traditionally trayed off for final set. Care has to be taken here because extended tumbling can raise product temperature to a point where the coating will melt or product agglomeration will occur. If done cautiously and correctly, a smooth surface will be generated (Figure 5).

The same hot-air test will work and help you visualize surface quality.

In addition to having a smooth surface to continue and build upon, the surface of the product must be dry and hard.

DRY, HARD SURFACE

Sugar Panned Goods

Sugar-panned goods traditionally are stored overnight between engrossing and polishing or glazing. If the hard shell coating is smooth and completely dry, no further actions are required; polishing will be easy and a high-gloss (wax or shellac) shine will result. If stored for longer periods, sometimes one to two applications of reduced solids syrup will be used to eliminate any surface powder or dusting, and to expedite polishing.

Soft Panned Items

Because the centers are soft, wet and rough from all the sweatbacks, smoothing or finishing applications are needed. Just as in hard panning, reduced-solids syrup (65% solids or so, containing color and flavor) is added to the rotating product. Just enough syrup is added to wet the soft-panned piece's surface. This application smooths the surface and also dissolves any extra dry powdered sugar remaining on the candy's surface. Usually six to eight applications are necessary to form this hard, smooth coating. After the last application, the product is allowed to tumble until nearly dry before proceeding with polishing. Care must be taken here because too much of the syrup at this stage will cause product agglomeration and the forming of double pieces.

Chocolate Panned or Compound Coated Items

This dry, hard surface is generated by sealing the nutmeats, dried fruit, malted milk balls, etc. This technique or step is frequently called *gumming*. Various gum solutions are used, and certain formulations are designed specifically by each company, containing ingredients such as gum arabic (or acacia), gelatin, starches, corn syrups and/or maltodextrin.

The sealing solution generally is applied to the product in a rotating pan by spray or ladle and allowed to tumble coat until evenly distributed. The application quantity should be sufficient to totally wet the product, while being careful not to overwet or dissolve previous coatings. Actual application quantity will depend upon pan load and the surface area of pieces being coated, as well as sealant concentration (overwet pieces can generate a rough, white, hazy surface). Depending upon the formulation used, after distribution the pan is usually stopped and conditioned air applied (60°–65°F and 50%rh max). Frequently, a second application is done in the same way, except after drying the pan is allowed to rotate and the sealant is buffed out to a gloss (Figure 6).

In addition to forming a hard, dry surface ready for polishing, this sealing or gumming also provides an oil barrier, reduces oxygen migration, delays rancidity in nutmeat products and improves adhesion if subsequent sugar panning is needed or desired. The amount of time needed

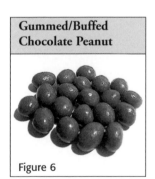

Gummed/Buffed Chocolate Peanut

Figure 6

for it to thoroughly dry depends upon the sealant used, and the product is frequently trayed off overnight before proceeding to the polishing or glazing process.

POLISHING AND GLAZING

Sugar-panned items

Normally carnauba wax, beeswax, candelia wax and blends of each are used to polish the surface. Usage levels vary from 0.05 to 0.1 percent (depends on the total surface area of the pieces more so than product weight). These waxes are applied in a dry crystalline form or in alcoholic solutions/suspensions. Both will work great, but the alcoholic solution is a little easier to work with. These alcoholic wax solutions lessen the wax's tendency to settle in the candies' low spots. They can also tie up moisture (helping to polish a slightly wet product), as well as even out the color on an overly dry piece.

For added stability and shine, shellac, corn zein or other film-forming lacquers can be used, in follow-up coats, and applied over the wax-polished pieces. Regardless of which finishing resin system is selected, application methodology is similar. The resin solutions are applied to the rotating confections in such a manner and at such a usage level to promote the formulation of a thin, uniform coating or film. As with all coatings, the coverage should be complete while avoiding overwetting. Application quantities will depend upon the product batch weight, as well as its overall surface area.

As the solvents used in the resin solution evaporate, the resins become sticky. Jogging the revolving pan with repeated on/off cycles (one-half turn each time) will prevent the confections from sticking together. This technique will also minimize the possibility of coating being pulled off surrounding pieces when separated and the resulting pull or kiss marks.

For finishing, best results are achieved when the procedure is completed in an environmentally controlled clean room. Ideal conditions are temperature 55° to 70°F, low relative humidity 40 to 60 percent, airflow 200 to 400 CFM. These conditions are broad because the actual parameters will depend specifically on the type of shellac used, the panning products, the products' bed temperature and actual piece temperature. Ideally, warm dry air accelerates solvent evaporation and film polymerization, so the warmer and drier the better.

Chocolate- or Compound-coated Items

The process of polishing or glazing chocolate- or compound-coated items is a simple one-step optimization.

One to two applications of confectioners glaze or other film formers are applied to the sealed and gummed pieces. The technique used is the same as discussed for the waxed sugar goods. This glaze provides the moisture barrier needed, helps delay the melting of the chocolate when the candies are accidentally exposed to higher than normal temperatures and supplies the high-luster, glossy appearance associated with high quality—considered highly important to the consumer.

In some countries or religious groups, the use of shellac is restricted, so aqueous coatings must be used. The aqueous coating formulations are quite similar to those used on the sealing or gumming step, except usually of lower solids to reduce their stickiness. Application of this solution is added at levels of 0.3 to 0.75 percent and, while tumbling, air is added to dry this polishing agent. Once thoroughly dry, a second application is usually applied. These two applications usually form a continuous film, and during drying and tumbling the buffing action of the product movement produces its gloss. Sadly, these products' hygroscopicity lowers their usefulness and consumer acceptance, due to dulling or becoming sticky in humid environments.

EQUIPMENT

Types of equipment used in finishing or glazing are typical revolving pans, belt coaters or automated computer-controlled drums. All should be equipped with variable-speed motors and controlled volumes of warm or cold dehumidified air. Depending upon degree of automation, the ingredients are added via ladles or spray systems. All will yield excellent results. The use of newer automated computerized systems allows more efficient manufacturing and consistent product. These units are generally expensive to purchase and to install, so many operations are still regular revolving-pan driven.

INGREDIENTS

Gumming and Sealing Solutions

Generally, the old tried and proven sealant has been gum arabic or gum acacia solution, i.e., 25 to 40 percent solids in water with the solids being adjusted by product weight and shape. Smaller pieces seem to require lower-solids syrup to reduce their sticking together or agglomeration, while the higher-solids syrups form stronger films so less applications are required.

While gum arabic is considered the norm, its price and availability have opened opportunities for other formulations. Alternate sealants are available, some of which eliminate the need for an overnight tray-off and dry, which is needed when the gum arabic solutions are used.

These formulations using gums, starches, maltodextrins, etc., also work well, but frequently these formulations are less forgiving to changing environmental conditions and manufacturing problems can arise. Some require a winter and summer formulation or changes for high-humidity conditions.

Waxes

Generally, dry, crystalline carnauba wax is used. While it is inexpensive and generates an excellent gloss, newer wax blends or alcoholic solutions/suspensions continue to grow in popularity.

Wax- and Shellac-polished Jelly Beans

Figure 7

Frequently, beeswax is added to the carnauba to allow faster, easier polishing (the beeswax is a better softener and allows the blend to buff easier compared to other waxes). Addition of oil, along with waxes (for example, gummi bears) improves product shine, reduces stickiness and improves stability properties.

But wax does not offer generally sufficient product protection and stability to the candies (other than gummies and jellies). Subsequently, many pan-coated products are shellac glazed (Figure 7).

Shellacs

Just like the gums and waxes, shellac has undergone changes and improvements over the years. Originally, most companies used standard 2.5 lb, 3 lb or 4 lb cuts of shellac in an alcoholic solvent. Many companies still use this, but some of the newer shellacs are easier to use and worth consideration.

For example, several suppliers offer highly modified continuous shellac, which is somewhat idiot-proof. It is continuous run shellac, meaning you apply the solution and just let the product slowly tumble dry. Gloss is nearly as good as regular 3 lb shellac and you forego the jogging and the associated shellacking skills required. Another feature of these shellacs is that they dry very quickly, allowing for increased production efficiency and immediate packaging after drying. This eliminates the customary overnight dry of regular shellac which allows all of the solvents to evaporate. This overnight drying is important if regular shellacs are used. If packaged too quickly, a solvent taste can be absorbed by the candies.

There are concerns about the solvent fumes and volatile organic compounds (vocs) associated with shellacs. As mentioned previously, a high percentage of a shellac formula is alcohols and other flammable liquids. Care must be taken during storage and handling as well as air exhaust to eliminate fire, explosion, pollution issues and hazards. To counter these general characteristics, newer shellac products are designed to be less flammable (safer to handle) and to generate lower VOC emissions (thereby helping to address the air pollution issue). Overall performance of these low-VOC shellacs is pretty good; dry times are slightly longer, but still acceptable to general productions.

Regardless of how excellent the panning job has been, it frequently takes 4 to 6 months for products to reach consumers. For prolonged gloss, stability, product freshness and high quality, packaging films with good moisture- and oxygen-barriers are suggested.

SPECIALTY FINISHES

Burnt (or French) Peanuts

Burnt (or French) peanuts are hot-panned—meaning gas burners or steam coils are used to elevate the temperature of the pan. In this product, roasted peanuts are placed into the revolving pan and, after heating, coated with repeated applications of a sugar/corn syrup solution, color and flavor (2:1 sugar/corn syrup at around 70% solids). The syrup is allowed to coat the rotating nuts and, with the added heat, the water is evaporated quickly. But because of the corn syrup, the coating is reasonably tacky and as it dries its tackiness or stickiness generates the rough, pimpled surface.

Syrup solids, corn syrup levels and temperature of the pan all affect the magnitude and quality of pimples or bumps generated. Once the desired surface texture has been obtained, several final coats of simple sugar-water syrup are added to color, smooth and finish the pieces. The candies are then removed from the pan, trayed overnight and generally shellac-glazed the next day (Figure 8).

Silvering or Pearling

Silver pearls are normally used as cake decorations (Figure 9). There is an actual silver plating on top of a small jimmy or nonpareil sphere. These candies and this process are for decorative purposes only. The manufacture of these items is usually done in glass or sugar-lined pans. The process involves the earlier manufacture of very smooth dry cores, which are coated with a gelatin or acetic acid adhesive solution. Powdered aluminum or silver leaf is then added to the pan.

Tumbling here not only spreads the metallic powders, but also beats and softens the metal into a continuous coating on the core. Because of the fumes and dust generated, these pans are sealed. Panning times of one to two hours are typical and after the pearls are highly glazed they are tray stored for at least two days to evaporate all acetic acid. Shellac is sometimes added to improve gloss stability. If money is not a restriction, a similar process can be done with gold dust.

Burnt/French Peanuts	Silver Pearls
	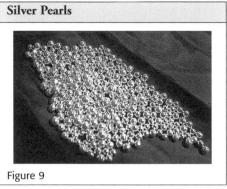
Figure 8	Figure 9

Marbling

Running one color into another produces this special effect. The results are seen on products frequently sold as pebbles or Easter eggs. Several methods can be used to manufacture these effects. One incorporates highly colored syrup, which is applied to the revolving pieces and immediately dried up with an application of dry powdered sugar, allowing the colored syrup to coat only portions of the centers. This is repeated for additional colors. Finally, a weak sugar solution is applied and allowed to dissolve and smear the colors.

An alternate method, most frequently used now, involves the use of solvent-based colors, which are applied to the rotating centers. After several colors are added, an application of pure solvent (alcohol) is added and as it spreads and coats the pieces, its solubilizes/dissolves some of the previous colors, generating a mixing or blending of colors.

Pigeon Eggs

This process is usually done on pan-coated, sugar-shelled malted milk balls and involves the use of solvent-based edible colors applied to a finished colored core. As the cores are rotating, a stiff bristled brush is gently raked in the pan opening, allowing the color to sprinkle randomly on the candy. The amount of spots depends upon the pan rotation speed, the amount of color applied and the raking technique used. Once dried, the spotted finish is generally waxed and shellacked (Figure 10).

Pearlescent Finishes

These are rather new coatings that can be applied to the panned goods. Unlike the pure metallics (pearling of silver or aluminum), the product is edible. This technique involves the use of a topical colored (blue, green, red, purple, gold or silver) application of approved colorants on a prefinished shellacked, colored base. The resulting effect is metallic without the use of any metals (see Figure 11).

Pigeon Eggs	Pearlescent Almonds

Figure 10	Figure 11

Satin

A semi-gloss or dull finish can be obtained from the various shellac suppliers. Application techniques are the same as for regular shellac.

Cocoa and Acid

These dry powders can be topically applied to the panned pieces. This is accomplished by adhesion of the powders to the piece's surface. Solutions similar to sealing or gumming syrups (i.e., 25% to 40% gum arabic or maltodextrins in water) are applied to the tumbling candies and pieces are allowed to wet. After the syrup has been fully dispersed, one or two applications of powder (be it cocoa powder, cocoa powder and sugar, citric acid or others) are added to the revolving pan. The powders are added slowly or via sifters to help ensure a uniform piece dosage. The pan is allowed to revolve slowly until all of the powders are affixed onto the candies before stopping and storing in trays overnight for hardening.

Do not allow product to overdry in pans while revolving; the extra tumbling will wear off the powdered topical coating, returning the pieces to their original pan coating.

CONCLUSION

This paper highlighted some of the actions normally taken or seen in the finishing, sealing and polishing of the various panned items. It is impossible to cover any of the individual items in sufficient detail to make you experts.

Panning is a science, but deeply rooted in art, so the techniques discussed should supply you with some insight. You should expect some trials and failures while developing the exact techniques for your equipment and operation.

Full Panning Panel
Questions & Answers

A panel discussion on panning with John Kitt, Jeff Bogusz, Bill Pullia, Pamela Gesford and Robert Boutin.

Q: How is it that a flat surface tends to lead to doubles?

A: I think the highest contribution to doubles in chocolate panning is certainly flat surfaces. Flat surfaces will find each other, they like to get married and not only will they find each other they will find any flat surface on the pan, be it a baffle, a rib, the pan itself, etc. So definitely watch the shape. Also, there is a fine balance between the rotation speed and the size of the pan. The baffles are also very important. The ribs' keeping the product tumbling is key, especially with chocolate being as viscous as it is. Making sure that they don't stick together and looking at the viscosity of the coating are important.

Most of the time the shape of the center is key. Many times one of the limitations people have is talking about depositing centers for soft panning, where automatically there is a potential for a flat side and you can't shape that upper side. There are some ways of over-filling and making sure that you don't overdry so you don't get a sunken back because that is even worse than a flat surface. Sometimes, in soft panning, it will collect the syrup and make it even more of a glue and stick the piece. With soft panning one of the things I see is when you apply the syrup, if you let the syrup on there too long and it's completely covered, it will actually start to glue together. There are a whole bunch of different things but shape is definitely the biggest key.

The amount of syrup and the viscosity of the syrup you put on there are also important. If you ever get to a position where you've almost wet the coating off of the inside of the drum so that it doesn't have the abrasive texture anymore by adding so much syrup, you can actually cause the pieces to stop moving. If the pieces stop moving they have the chance to bond themselves if they're not continuously tumbling, so anything you can do to keep the pieces moving at all times helps avoid doubles as well.

Many times you have too many people applying too large of a quantity too fast. If you add too large of a quantity you can almost guarantee that you're going to get doubles or triplets.

Q: Can you comment on what might cause dark- and light-colored centers in the same pan after coloring? (The centers are the same size.)

A: The product can dry unevenly in the trays. You get a white appearance on the part that dries because you have more sugar crystallization there than you do on the opposite side. If you're having different colors in the same pan I would look back to the smoothing step and make sure that you had a smooth product before the color was applied.

On occasion, where the product is totally smooth but still doing that, we got it down to insufficient air distribution in the pans. With the conventional pan and it coming through the pipe with no fishtail on the end, it was blowing on one area of the pan. Consequently, these parts dried faster during the finishing stage in the front than in the back and they were consistently darker. This probably happens with dyes but not with lakes.

You see a lot more problems with dyes where you get a mottling. The moisture in the dye will flow around so you get much more of a mottling or marbling effect with dyes but I actually have seen it with lake colors if the pieces aren't dried and you don't have enough buildup.

The other thing is the tendency to go with as little as you need. Sometimes you actually need more lake than what people use and so there's not enough color in that coating itself. Sugar crystals start to show through because it is less distributed than you think it is.

Some manufacturers color the engrossing sugar used throughout the coating process; others only add color in the final stages. Uneven appearance can result if insufficient color is used in the latter process.

Q: Does chocolate actually temper in the panning process?

A: It is my opinion that chocolate does temper in the process. While it is untempered when applied, the cooling in the pan, as well as its rotation, generates an environment that allows tempering to take place. If I recall correctly, in some parts of the world where waxes and shellacs are not allowed, I remember working on a project where after chocolate panning is finished the candies are lowered to run in the pan with moderate cooling. After a short period the candies' gloss began and the end result was very highly polished pieces, and all that was done was that the chocolate actually tempered itself during rotation.

I have spoken with several people on this subject and some say that they have been able to prove that chocolate does temper during the panning process under the right conditions.

Q: Could the panel address the VOC issues in glazing?

A: There is a big concern about the solvents from the shellacs and the VOCs (volatile organic compounds) and that has been somewhat addressed. People have been putting scrubbers on their units and things of this nature and exhaust. But the newer high-tech shellacs have been reformulated to be lower in VOCS and it's a major concern as these things are flammable and explosive. How you handle it all has to be seriously considered. These newer low-VOC shellacs have been working very well. They are a little slower in performance compared to the originals but safer and easier to handle.

Q: How small can hard-panned seeds be made? I have seen one millimeter in diameter. Can they be any smaller?

A: Initially you start with a sugar crystal and build up and that's a starting point of a jawbreaker; it can be a very small surface to start with. A sugar crystal is about 60 microns and it depends on what size powdered sugar you use.

If you start with a starch piece and it is panned and sifted you can make a pretty small piece.

Some of the seeds they started the jawbreakers with were very small and sugar crystals are difficult. I think they usually add starch to help keep them separated during the initial stages.

Q: Discuss bloom formation on chocolate pieces. Do panned chocolates still bloom? If not, why not?

A: In my experience, bloom problems associated with chocolate-panned products are generally sugar bloom. That can easily be addressed by working with the compound or the chocolate manufacturer to balance out the formula for your specific application. Generally, what I have seen happen is that fat bloom is something that is not readily apparent after the product is polished. But when you start to bloom sugar crystals, you're going to get the same thing as in some of the other panning processes that is going to be much more apparent even under a nice shellac. These are things that can be addressed through temperature control and also can be addressed through viscosity issues and types of fats and actually achieve the finest finished coating.

Chocolate panned candies can bloom, even though protected with a sealant and shellac—not a pretty sight. While the shellac coating will offer some temperature protection, if exposed to high enough temperatures and for sufficient time periods, the base chocolate will soften and the tempered chocolate will lose its seed and become untempered and bloom, normally forming a mottled-looking surface appearance. The shellac outer coating will generally keep the pieces from melting all together unless heat is extensive.

Q: Could you re-emphasize what is the normal composition of the noncrystallizing syrup for soft panning?

A: Depending on what texture you want to get, you can use thinned corn syrup that can easily be used as an engrossing syrup, as well as basically the combination of sucrose and the corn syrup. When I said corn syrup solids what I meant was the solid content of the (liquid) corn syrup—straight 42 DE corn syrup not the dry corn syrup solids that are currently available.

Q: *What is the difference between adding coating syrup to the bottom of the panned product versus the top of the panned product? Is one way more effective then the other?*

A: It depends on the pan to a certain extent. If you have good movement in the pan and your syrup solids are low enough you are going to cover all the pieces evenly with whatever syrup you put on. If you are going to a higher solid syrup you might need to distribute more across the bedded product to get the coverage. It is one of these things that an operator becomes in tune to when looking at the product after it has been coated.

Application location can be important, but that is a difficult question to seriously address. A lot depends upon what type of product is being coated and the shape and style of pans being used. Then it may or may not be of significant importance. A revolving pan does have limited mixing capabilities and application location can help increase product quality and lessen doubles and uneven buildup. There was a good simple article recently written in *Confectionery Production*, March 2004, pages 16–18, "Work Circulation in Coating Pans." I think it answers your questions better than I did.

Q: *With automated drum coating for hard panning, is polishing done in the same drum?*

A: It can be done in the same drum or you can have another automated pan to transfer it into afterwards.

I think the high-tech pans are designed for engrossing sugar crystallization and while that's being done I usually try to transfer it out and have an operator, who is kind of just watching the pans anyway, do the polishing in some conventional pans. It's easier, works well and is less expensive. You also don't dirty the pan, and shellac is hard to get out of pans.

Let me add to the answer in the above paragraph. While I remain strong in using other pans for polishing as well as sometimes even precoats, the real answer to this question is costs and efficiencies. Each method will generate excellent product, and depending upon your labor rates, availability of personnel, extra pans and automated pan needs, each scenario has its pros and cons.

Q: *Is it possible to make low-carb coatings?*

A: Under the current labeling laws there are many options for low-carb coatings, with the range from chocolate-flavored to white coating to fruit-flavored coatings to, believe it or not, cheese-based coatings.

For soft panning what you are trying to do is find something that functionally is acting like the typical full-carb ingredient, then replace it with things that have a low-carbohydrate content. With different ingredients that are being produced, from the standpoint of the sugarfree type of ingredients, I think you just have to work with your suppliers to see which ones would fit the bill of having a noncrystallizing syrup followed by a fairly uniform—as uniform as possible—powder to dry charge on the product. Of course, any gel or candy center would need to be reformulated as well.

This answer is more difficult to state. Sugarless coatings (i.e., maltitol, isomalt, etc.) by some companies have been called low- or no-carbohydrate coatings and that is somewhat correct as they are sugar alcohols, or polyols. The FDA now has defined them as nonsugar carbohydrates, I believe. Without a good definition, this is a difficult question to answer. Let me propose that one could generate low- or no-carbohydrate coatings by applying an adhesive coating (maybe made with vegetable gums) and dry powder dose the pieces with calcium carbonate or another noncarbohydrate ingredient. The resulting coating would be dry and hard and in my thought be noncarbohydrate based.

Chocolate Moulding

Introduction to Chocolate Moulding

Michael Ferraro
Godiva Chocolate (retired)

Unlike sugar confectionery, which traces its beginnings back to the Egyptians candying fruit, sesame seeds and nuts in honey some 3,500 years ago, chocolate moulding has a very lean history. Cortez brought cocoa, along with vanilla, back to Europe during the 16th century. Chocolate (or cocoa) was consumed only as a drink until the mid-1800s. It was a very rich, cloying drink with the 54 percent of cocoa butter typical in the ground nib. Additionally, any attempts to make a product for eating yielded a dry, crumbly confection after mixing with sugar due to the low fat content.

To improve on the drinking quality of cocoa, Van Houten developed a hydraulic-pressing method to remove some of the fat from the cocoa, making a much more palatable drink.

This led to a cocoa butter surplus, which was experimentally added to a mixture of chocolate liquor and sugar, resulting in a product with better mouthfeel and moulding properties.

This product, when tempered, exhibited contraction and gloss, making the process of moulding possible. Fry and Sons of Bristol, England, moulded a solid bar named *Chocolate Delicieux à Manger* in 1847 and sold it commercially. Cadbury followed with a commercial product in 1849.

CHARACTERISTICS

Moulded articles share some characteristics:

- Detail on the products can be exquisite.
- A large range of textures on the same article, from matte to high gloss, can be achieved.
- There is an exact size duplication of product, important for weight control and ease of packaging.
- Liquid centers are a possibility.
- Hollow products may be made.

TYPES OF MOULDING

The five types of moulding that will be covered here are solid moulding, classic shell, cooled punch, one-shot and hollow moulding.

Solid Moulding

For solid moulding, such as solid chocolate bars, the tempered chocolate is deposited into a mould; the mould is vibrated to settle the chocolate and release any air bubbles; the product is then cooled and the piece demoulded (Figures 1 and 2).

Classic Shell

For the classic shell process the tempered chocolate is deposited in a mould, filling the cavity. The mould is vibrated to remove trapped air, then the mould is inverted and shaken, leaving a coating of chocolate or a "shell" within the mould. The "stalactites" of chocolate are removed, the shell is allowed to harden and a filling is deposited. Chocolate is deposited on the filling or in some cases the mould is flooded. The excess chocolate is scraped off or "backed off" and the mould is cooled, allowing the candy to fully contract. After that, the chocolate is demoulded (Figure 3).

A variation of this process is book moulding, in which two moulds are sandwiched back to back and locked together immediately after backing off. This would form a 3-dimensional piece such as a walnut (Figure 4).

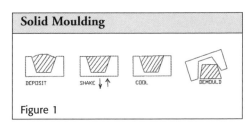

Solid Moulding

Figure 1

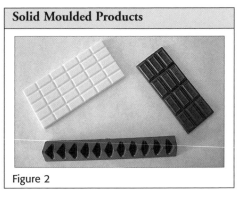

Solid Moulded Products

Figure 2

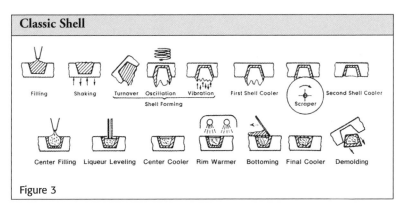

Classic Shell

Figure 3

Cooled Punch

In November of 1922 a patent was issued to William Boyd and William Yates for moulding chocolates using a cooled punch to harden the chocolate. Some of the release agents tested were water, alcohol and turpentine. Needless to say, not many commercial applications were spawned from this initial concept.

Although each major equipment manufacturer has handled the forming and releasing of shells in various ways, the implementation of a cooled punch process has recently been quite successful, providing the confectioner with a unique way to mould his shells.

Essentially the process of the cooled punch works like this: the precise amount of chocolate is deposited in the mould and a cooled male plug is pushed into the mould, displacing a shell with the desired thickness. The shell is filled via a depositor and the product is backed off. Then the mould is cooled and the chocolates are demoulded (Figure 5). A variation of this is to book mould two empty shells to create a hollow moulded figure.

One-shot

Although continuous coextrusion had been in place in the baking industry for many years on products such as the Fig Newton, the center within a chocolate shell or one-shot was not developed until the mid-1930s by Cadbury for use on the *Caramello* bar.

In the process of one-shot, the chocolate and filling are deposited through concentric nozzles with precise timing to ensure that the center is fully contained within the bubble of chocolate. The mould is vibrated very slightly so as to not disturb the fragile bubble and then the product is cooled and demoulded.

Figure 6, a schematic of the one-shot process, shows from left to right the concentric nozzles, the timed depositing of a center within a "bubble" of chocolate and the final product in the mould cavity.

Shell Moulded Products

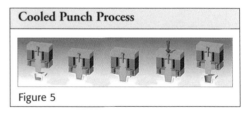

Figure 4

Cooled Punch Process

Figure 5

Schematic of One-shot Deposit

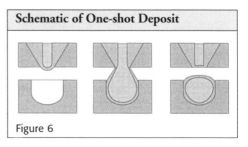

Figure 6

Figure 7 is a further schematic of a one-shot depositor, showing chocolate on the left side and filling on the right with a mould traveling underneath the depositor left to right.

Some one-shot articles show the precise control that can be achieved using the one-shot process (Figure 8).

Hollow Moulding

In hollow moulding, chocolate is deposited into one side of a mould. The mould is closed and rotated through all axes to distribute the chocolate. After hardening, the mould is opened and the figure is removed (Figure 9).

A schematic drawing of this process is difficult to portray but a photograph of a 4-head spinner showing the moulds rotating about in a planetary gear fashion will help you understand how the chocolate is spread on all surfaces of a mould (Figure 10).

Some examples of hollow moulded products are shown in Figure 11.

CONCLUSION

New processes have been developed, and new materials are used for moulds, going from metal to polycarbonate. The principles of chocolate contracting and taking the detail of a mould remain the same, yielding perfectly formed, perfectly finished pieces.

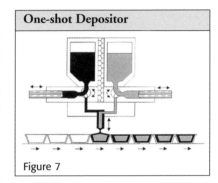

One-shot Depositor

Figure 7

One-shot Articles

Figure 8

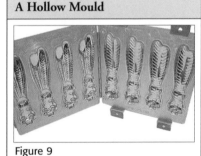

A Hollow Mould

Figure 9

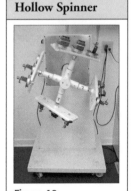

Hollow Spinner

Figure 10

Hollow Moulded Products

Figure 11

Questions & Answers

Q: What is the highest temperature at which the center can be deposited?

A: This is dependent on many factors: shell thickness or type of chocolate, for example. A conservative stance would be to not exceed 90°F. Some companies, however, supercool the shell and deposit a hot (120°F) caramel into the shell followed by aggressive cooling to prevent melt- through.

Q: What are the typical proportions of center to shell in one-shot versus classic shell moulding?

A: Careful control with one-shot can yield an 80/20 center shell ratio but mould design is critical. Closer to spherical, i.e., truffle, is better. Shell moulding generally yields a ca. 65/35 center to shell ratio. One-shot has come a long way.

Q: Which company was the first to make a hollow moulded piece?

A: It does not seem very clear who marketed the first hollow figures. Some attribute it to the Germans who sculpted hollow chocolate eggs in moulds with the very coarse paste of the mid-1800s to mimic the papier-mâché eggs given to children at Easter. Certainly after the First World War hollow moulding came about with many other industrialized processes, initially in Belgium.

Designing and Developing Chocolate Moulds

Paul M. Harbecke, PhD
Agathon GmbH & Co. KG

Chocolate moulds have always been the means by which chocolate can be formed into all kinds of beautiful shapes that are pleasing to the eyes and the taste buds, and that are nourishing as well as a luxurious but inexpensive good food. This paper will cover the development of moulded chocolate items from the idea to the final product, and the designing of the plastic mould and its production, including the types of moulds, the handling of moulds and the materials they are made of.

DESIGNING THE IMPRESSION

This is probably one of the most decisive factors to ensure a trouble-free moulding process. Marketing has an idea that they want to produce a certain moulded item. First, and above all, the new creation should bring out the image the chocolate manufacturer wants to give his product. The appeal to the customer is the first requirement. At first sight, this is a question of marketing and not to be discussed here. In reality, however, the wishes of marketing are frequently diametrically opposed to the facilities of engineering and the abilities of production. To this extent it must be our concern to clarify these points of designing, which will avoid problems in producing the item.

Given the marketing information, expert artists with many years of experience in this field will be able to produce a 3-D picture of the item on the computer screen, which can then be sent electronically to the customer for his comments. It can be modified easily. The item can be looked at from all sides with the help of a viewer or can be sent as a 2-D picture or as a print, whatever is suitable.

The data can be converted into a milling machine program for either producing a model or the master tool directly.

Also, the volume of the new item, as well as the weight of the shell and the center of a filled item, will be calculated. That way, of course, a computer simulation for a cold-stamping process is also possible. Normally, however, models are produced of certain materials, and then vacuum-formed or thermoformed moulds will be made from which product samples can be demoulded to check the appearance and to verify the weight or volume.

The picture of the new item and the vacuum-formed sample should reflect the following important points.

Demouldability

Good demouldability, avoiding breakage during moulding, at demoulding, and during packing and transportation, easy consumption of the product and, in the case of hollow or filled items, even shell formation and perfect bottoming are of highest importance. These qualities of chocolate products can be achieved in the following manner.

The tapers or draft angles should be large enough to allow the product to be released from the mould. Thus 8° to 10° should be considered a minimum. Sharp angles should be avoided by all means and at any time. If not, air bubbles will remain in the cavities, which not only give the item a bad appearance but also hinder good demoulding.

Engravings

Engravings or decorations on the product not only give the item a certain appearance or publicize the name of the product or the producer, but they also further an easy demoulding process, as they enlarge the surface of the item and thus help its cooling and contraction (Figure 1). This way, cooling spots or pull marks can also be avoided. The engravings should be about .18 mm deep and well rounded. The tools should have a taper of about 15° to 20°, in order to avoid the chocolate sticking in the engraved area or leaving pinholes.

Detailed Engraving Example

Figure 1

In the case of a flat, thin item, engraving lines have a direct helping function for demoulding, if incorporated in the sidewalls of the cavities. The reason is that during shrinkage a small vacuum might establish itself, which will hold the product in the mould. The engraving lines will help air to get into the cavities and release the vacuum. I have seen such small items also held in the mould by static; particularly during demoulding the moulds will charge up with static. Also, the chocolate does charge up. In that case a discharge or an ionizing device will be helpful in releasing the chocolate from the mould.

A certain surface texture or a degree of matte texture applied to the surface of the cavities will be helpful in demoulding, due to an increase of the surface area. A certain doming, i.e., a convex instead of a flat surface area, helps demoulding, due to better contraction of the chocolate.

Sometimes it is advisable to leave the whole area of a cavity at a certain degree of matte texture, if the fine lines of a picture are important for the character. The perfection depends on the toolmaking process. A speciality is laser engraving. Looking at the bar from one side you will see an image and looking from the other side you will see a different image. This is a patented process.

Avoiding Breakage

Avoiding breakage during the different stages of production can be achieved in the following ways.

Since the best contraction of a chocolate piece can be achieved with an even circumference, ideally a sphere, deviations from that shape tend to impede an even contraction of the chocolate. In extreme cases this will result in breakage, particularly when tempering of the chocolate or the cooling process is not perfect. The breakage will already occur in the mould. This again points to the necessity of having radii as big as possible.

Breakage during demoulding will occur when the product clings to the mould due to sharp corners in the cavities, or parts of the chocolate may stick if the surfaces are too flat or not engraved.

Some irregular shapes of an item will also cause breakage during demoulding. Take, for example, a filled bar with humps or cubes. If the base or raft of such a bar is too thin compared to the height of the cubes, the bar will break when dropping out of the mould, if not already during contraction. For a typical 100 g bar, the base or raft should be at least 5 mm thick compared to the total height of the bar of approximately 12 mm (Figure 2). If a thinner base is desired, there should be reinforcing ribs of chocolate (Figure 3), preferably around the outside of the bar between the cubes. Between the base and the

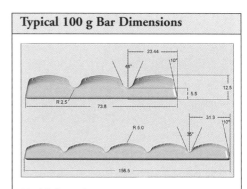

Typical 100 g Bar Dimensions

Model dimensions—X: 156.6mm; Y: 73.8 mm; Z: 12.5 mm; volume: 81.30 ccm; weight: 100.00 g; density: 1.23 g/ccm

Figure 2

cubes of such a bar, big radii are necessary in order to achieve an even contraction of the chocolate bar. A higher strength of the bar can also be achieved by scalloping on the outside.

Easy Consumption

Easy consumption of a chocolate item is partly determined by its shape. In the case of a bar, it should easily be broken into palatable pieces or the piece itself should be bite size without causing

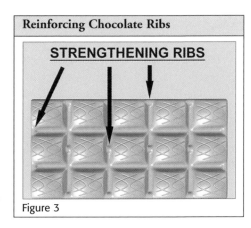

Reinforcing Chocolate Ribs

STRENGTHENING RIBS

Figure 3

breakage of the whole bar. So-called breaking grooves or guidelines engraved on the bar raft will help to this end.

Easy wrapping of the product is also a function of the design of an item. Sharp corners, for example, should be avoided to keep the wrapper from ripping. A corner radius of 1.5 to 2 mm is considered safe.

A wrapping angle of a height of 2 mm and 4 degrees will help in the wrapping process, as the bars will more easily push each other on the feeder to the wrapping machine, instead of shingling.

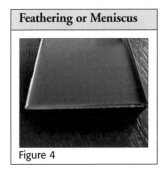

Feathering or Meniscus

Figure 4

Feathering is a thin rim of chocolate or meniscus around the bottom of a chocolate product (Figure 4). It is caused by the shaking of a solid product or, in the case of a filled product, by severe scraping.

Even though a certain freeboard is necessary when producing a solid product in order to avoid spillage during vibration on the shaker table, this should not be more than .5 mm in the case of a small piece of up to, say, 50 g, or in the case of a bigger item above 50 g it should not be more than 1 mm.

When producing a filled item, scraping should be done in two directions and the wall of chocolate to be moved in front of the scraper should not be too large in order to avoid erosion.

When a meniscus occurs, which usually breaks off during demoulding or wrapping, an ionizing device should be used, so little crumbs will fall off instead of scuffing the product.

DESIGNING OF THE MOULD

Type of Moulds

The general design of a complete mould depends, of course, on the particular chocolate machine: there are loose-mould plants and chain-mould plants, depending on the method of transport or fastening of the moulds in the plant. Also, there are plants where the mould is moved by a plastic screw.

Strength

The strength of a mould is the most important matter besides correct dimensions and adaptability to the particular machine.

Ribs

Ribs give a mould most of its strength besides the general design. They are put into the back of the mould either length- and crosswise or as a continuation of sidewalls of the cavities (Figure 5). In some cases diagonal ribs are used in order to achieve top rigidity.

Ribs on Back of Mould for Strength

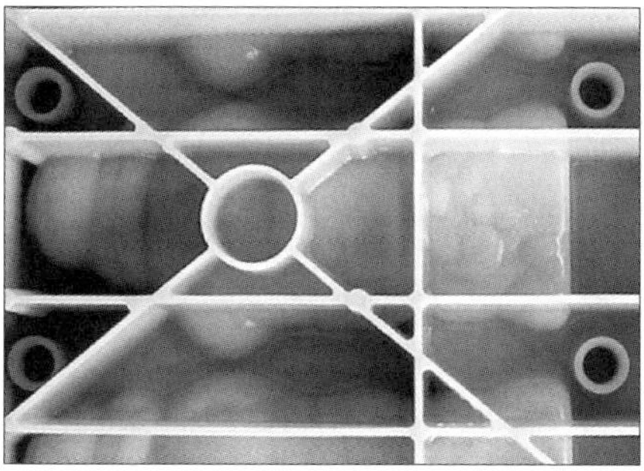

Figure 5

Experiments and experience have proven that a more rigid mould with more ribs and thus more material will last longer. There is another advantage to a rigid mould: the shaking of a mould is more even and therefore better because the vibration is not absorbed in the same way as it would be in a flexible mould. As to vibration, the important factor is that the vibrators have a high frequency and low amplitude, and the contact between the vibrators and the mould should be as close as possible.

The ribs have a further function: they are runners for the good distribution of the plastic material during the moulding process in the injection moulding machine. Furthermore, they serve as connecting points between the outside frame to keep or pull the moulds in a straight position; in other words, to keep them flat.

Wall Thickness and Radii

In order to produce a good mould, other factors have to be considered: thick sections or rather uneven sections have to be avoided as they will result in sinks or voids during the shrinkage of the material.

Uneven sections may also impede the even flow of the polycarbonate material and thus result in the buildup of stress in the mould.

The wall thickness of a mould or its section should be at an even 3 mm for polycarbonate moulds, except in areas of the frame and faceplate.

Radii on the back of the mould are of utmost importance. Any notch or not-rounded area will very soon result in breakage of a plastic mould. For chocolate moulds which undergo special and rough treatment, radii of 0.5 to 1 mm are considered to be safe in order to avoid early breakage.

Other Criteria

The gating or distribution system for the polycarbonate is also of very high importance: at a wall section of 3 mm, the flow length of a typical polycarbonate will only be about 280 mm or 11 inches. Any flow length above 280 mm could result in stress formation.

Therefore, the bigger the mould is, the more gates are needed. When you see moulds with few gates or just one gate, no doubt they are much cheaper to produce, but the consequences can be unwanted. Sometimes flow-additives are used. Also, any additive will weaken the polycarbonate mould. The flow length of the material can, of course, be increased by raising the temperature of the material, but this will result in early aging or degrading of the material itself.

There have to be vents in the back of the tool in order to let the air escape, which is compressed during the injection process. Air should also escape between the front and the back tool. Insufficient venting can result in flow lines which are visible in the mould and, therefore, also in the product.

Ejectors are used in the back tool in order to release the mould or push it out easily. The mould comes out straight and will not be distorted.

The temperature of the material should be between 280° and 300°C during the injection process. If the temperature is higher the problem will be degrading of the material itself.

A very important factor in injection moulding is the temperature of the tool in order to achieve a flat mould. Due to the fact that the material is not evenly distributed between the front and back of a mould, the temperature of the back and the front tool will have to be different in order to make up for these incongruities. In no case is it good for the mould if it is put into a jig after coming out of the press in order to keep it flat. This is highly dangerous because the stress will just be captured and at some point, particularly at extreme temperatures, the stress will be released and the mould will bow.

After a mould is taken out of the injection moulding press, it should cool off and then be put into a tempering furnace and left in there between 2 and 3 hours at a temperature of about 90°C in order to get rid of any little stress that might be in the mould despite a good moulding process. In any case, it must be understood that the mould must be flat before and after the tempering or annealing process.

MATERIALS

Materials used for the production of chocolate moulds are polycarbonates or derivatives of polycarbonates or blends respectively. Tests and trial runs have been done with various modified polycarbonates. A material can be chosen that is more resistant to certain processes, such as extreme exposure to cold or hammering. Another mould could have an additive of silicone, which gives it a higher notch impact strength and an extreme flexibility. This material has been tested for many months, and so far no negative reports have been received. It is, however, fairly high priced.

Colors are often used to distinguish one mould set from another. It should be noted that any addition of pigments may degrade the material and should therefore be used as little as possible.

OTHER DEVELOPMENTS

New technologies of cold pressing or cold stamping as well as the one-shot technology increasingly emphasize that the requirements are becoming more rigid as to the tolerances of the dimensions of chocolate moulds. Tolerances of as little as .05 mm are requested and can be achieved.

There are book moulds of various types, for chain plants with carriers in which the two halves will be booked by the mechanics of the mould together with the moulding plant, and there are various types of book moulds with the front or top mould being flipped over onto the bottom or back mould. Even though the moulds might be in a carrier or a frame when booked together, it seems that the use of magnets has proven to produce a better double item, be it hollow or filled (Figure 6). As to the one-shot book mould type, the moulds are together when being filled, and the top part is taken off the bottom mould for demoulding. Here again magnets are applied. It has to be considered that magnets must be well sealed into the mould by inserting them— from the bottom to keep the top

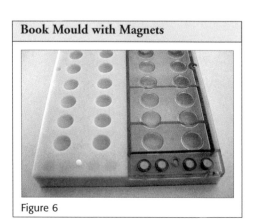

Book Mould with Magnets

Figure 6

clean—into a moulded tube, which then is closed with a cap by ultrasound welding.

There have been developments with electronic chips being sealed into moulds for various purposes (Figure 7), such as counting the hours the moulds have run, counting the times the moulds have been washed, signalling to the depositor the amount of chocolate to be deposited in each cavity, if, for example, the next mould has a different

Mould with Computer Chip

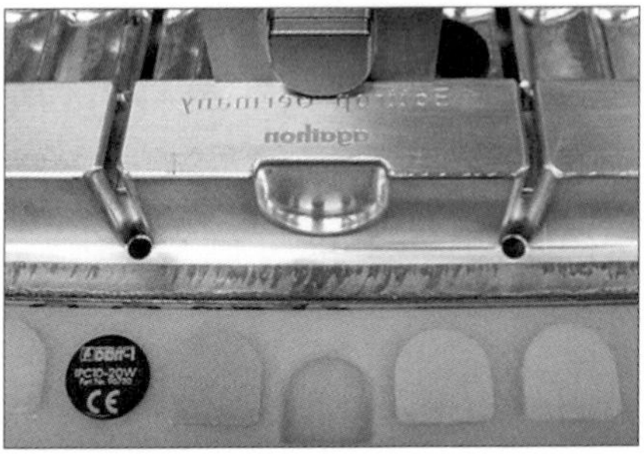

Figure 7

item and different layout so the correct amount of chocolate will be deposited.

Nowadays, lugs and the bushings where the chain pins go into the moulds are made of nylon and are interchangeable, if this is possible. The benefits are clear: first of all, nylon is a much better material to take impacts from a chain pin and, secondly, if the bushing breaks, it is easily exchanged by a new one.

HANDLING OF MOULDS

Moulds should preferably be stored in carts where each mould has its own compartment. Otherwise when they are piled up one on top of the other, the ribs on the underside of the mould might cause little notches on the cavities of the mould underneath, causing damage.

When washing moulds, several things should be considered. First of all, only wash when it is absolutely necessary. Since chocolate will leave a very thin film of fat in the cavities, there is a definite advantage in demoulding. A washed mould has to build up this film again. Furthermore, the water temperature should not be higher than 60°C or 140°F. The choice of detergents, if they are used, is very important.

The supplier of the washing machine will give you all necessary information about the type of detergents, rinsing agents and, most importantly, their dosage.

SUMMARY

There are many considerations in the designing of a new moulded chocolate item and the development of a plastic chocolate mould.

Obviously, computer programs are used these days to design and produce the tooling for chocolate moulds. An item developed on the computer can be sent by email, and the mould maker can, with the help of necessary equipment, produce a master tool right from those data, without ever having to look at a picture.

But there will be no top chocolate moulds without the many important side considerations during the development of the mould or without the artistic and manual input of the sculpturers and engravers, nor without the many manual jobs of the toolmakers and those who do the fine-tuning and set up the injection moulding machines, so all parameters will be right for a good and lasting chocolate mould.

Questions & Answers

Q: Who are local polycarbonate mould makers with foreign offices?

A: I don't know of any local U.S. polycarbonate mould makers with foreign offices.

Q: What is the life of a polycarbonate mould? When does it need to be replaced?

A: The life of a polycarbonate mould varies very much. There are moulds in daily use up to 12 years, and there are many that are much younger and should not be used anymore. For example, when the mould cavity surfaces are scuffed by ingredients in the chocolate or wafer items, then they become dull and should be replaced.

Q: What specific applications is the KU 1238 material used for?

A: Makrolon KU1-1248 is a polycarbonate developed by the Bayer company especially for chocolate moulds. The material is FDA approved. According to the Bayer company it is tougher or rather less prone to breakage than the regular polycarbonate. It is used particularly when the moulds have to take a lot of beating or undergo extreme temperature changes.

Q: What type of material is best for low-temp conditions with excessive stress on the mould (knocking)?

A: It seems that the KU1-1248 material by Bayer and especially EXL polycarbonate lend themselves to low-temp conditions with excessive stress by vibrating or knocking the moulds. EXL gives the moulds extreme flexibility due to added silicone.

Q: How far away are we from having moulds that can be detected by metal detectors?

A: Many tests have been done to detect moulds by adding metal dust or flakes to the polycarbonate, for example. The problem is that any inclusion will dramatically reduce the strength of the polycarbonate. Plastic material with metal inclusions does exist for caps that are used to cover up tubes where magnets are placed underneath a mould.

Q: Any comments on the shape of castellations when inclusions are added?

A: When chocolate with inclusions is moulded in shapes with castellations, problems might come up when the castellations are too deep, i.e., when the inclusions rest between the castellations, breakage may occur.

Q: If a mould is under filled to obtain a lower-weight piece, will this affect demouldability?

A: When a mould is under filled to obtain a lower-weight piece, demouldability is affected in the sense that a meniscus will develop which may impede demouldability because the meniscus, particularly when it's very thin and small, will adhere to the sides of the cavities.

Q: Are embossed or debossed images preferable for best demoulding?

A: In principal, it makes no difference whether the images are debossed or embossed. There are always mountains and valleys. On the other hand, when there is a certain image or a logo, the mould maker could advise which of the two possibilities is better.

Q: When EXL material is used for moulds, is eventual distortion a problem?

A: When using EXL material, we have not so far found any distortion, unless the material is over stretched.

Q: What is the "comparative" life of various mould substances?

A: It is virtually impossible to give a time limit on the comparative life of various mould substances.

Q: When designing a chocolate bar, what is the ratio between bar thickness and the breakup score?

A: The ratio is approximately 5 mm base to 12 mm total height for a 100 g bar with approximate dimensions of a 150x70 mm footprint.

Q: What is the proper detergent needed to clean polycarbonate moulds? How impor-

tant is pH in the cleaning solution?

A: The proper detergent for mould washing will be determined by the producer of the washing machine. Also, the producers of the polycarbonate material publish guidelines for washing moulds. These guidelines can be sent by request.

Q: Do any additives to the polycarbonate enhance the demoulding process?

A: We do not know of any additives to the polycarbonate which will enhance the demoulding process. The demoulding process is determined by the quality of the cavities, the quality of the mould itself, the quality of the chocolate and the moulding process.

Q: How can we avoid cooling spots?

A: As to the mould, cooling spots can be avoided by proper engravings and domed surfaces; in other words, an increase of the surface of the cavities to ensure an even cooling process. Of course, there are other factors like temperature, humidity and crystallization of the chocolate that are important.

Q: What software is used in mould design? Is it commercially available?

A: The software for the designing of the item is Free form and for the mould itself, Cimatron. Both software programs are readily available commercially.

Selecting the Right Chocolate Product for Moulding

Marlene Stauffer
Blommer Chocolate Co.

The principle objective of a candymaker is to provide a product that will please the consumer and hopefully bring him back for a repeat purchase. The principle purpose of a chocolate manufacturer is to provide chocolate that meets the needs of the candymaker. This paper about the selection of chocolate for moulding has three parts: definitions, chocolate properties and selection.

DEFINITIONS

In the confectionery industry, when someone speaks of a chocolate coating, it is in reference to a pure chocolate that contains properties making it flowable for a specific application. A confectionery coating is sometimes referred to as a compound coating—this would contain vegetable oil rather than cocoa butter but would still maintain flowable properties. I will be specifically focusing on chocolate (versus compound). Chocolate consists of "an intimate mixture of solid particles suspended in fat." This mixture will develop the unique character that determines exactly how it will function in specific applications.

To help us understand this mixture, let's take a brief look at the manufacturing process for chocolate. Cocoa beans are grown within an area approximately 20° north and south of the equator. These cocoa beans are roasted, shelled and ground into chocolate liquor. Some of this chocolate liquor is pressed to remove its component parts—cocoa butter and cocoa powder. Chocolate itself is manufactured by mixing sugar, chocolate liquor, an additional portion of cocoa butter and milk ingredients (if it is a milk chocolate). This mixture is then refined (particle size reduced) for a specific smoothness to the tongue. The flake is conveyed to a conche where flavor development, shearing action and further coating of the solid particles with fat occurs. Once the conching process is complete, the product will be standardized to a specific viscosity. This entire process, along with controls and formulation, will determine the unique character of the chocolate and how it will function in a given application— such as moulding, enrobing and dipping. Let's look a little closer and see what role this unique mixture plays in the outcome of chocolate products for the moulding process.

CHOCOLATE PROPERTIES

The properties of a chocolate that would influence chocolate behavior for a moulding application are product flow (viscosity), particle size (fineness) and temperability (type of fat). Equipment and troubleshooting are also important.

Viscosity

Viscosity is a measurement used to describe the flow properties of a product, specifically its resistance to flow. Some ways of measuring viscosity are the MacMichael, Brookfield and Haake methods. All of these methods are used in industry today, with Brookfield being the most common.

MacMichael viscosity measurement began in 1915 using degree MacMichael as the measurement of this single-point system. The product is tested at a specific temperature, using a specific cylinder diameter and depth-measuring torque. It gives a number indicating how thick or thin a product is, but does not tell the complete picture about the flow characteristics of the product. This is not as commonly used today, but the original numbers generated from this method are still referred to when selecting a specific coating and are easy for us to relate to. For example, a 65 viscosity chocolaate is very thin and refers to chocolate suitable for hollow moulding, a 145 viscosity chocolate might be used for enrobing or moulding with inclusions, and a 200 viscosity chocolate would be considered thick and can be used for solid moulding.

In 1988, the USA Brookfield viscometer or rheometer determined a two-point result showing a more absolute measurement of the chocolate performance or flow properties. Brookfield, at a specific temperature, can take readings at increasing rates of shear, followed by similar readings at decreasing speeds. Using Casson's calculations, typically on a computer program, plastic viscosity and yield value can be determined.

Rheology is defined as the study of the deformation and flow of matter with stress. Viscosity is the name given to this internal friction of fluids. Essentially, there are two types of liquids, Newtonian and non-Newtonian. Newtonian fluids are independent of shearing—you can stir as much or with as much force as you want and they will not change. Examples would be water, alcohol, liquid fat or glycerol.

Chocolate is non-Newtonian and its viscosity varies according to the rate at which it is stirred (sheared). It is affected by the presence of solids in suspension because chocolate is a suspension of particles in a fat phase; these particles need a force to start them to flow. This is known as yield value. More specifically, the yield point should be defined as the shear stress at which not only deformation occurs but stationary flow begins. Examples of products with yield value would be ketchup, meringue or mayonnaise. Left on their own, they have their own "standup," meaning a high yield value.

Yield value (YV) is reported in dynes/square centimeter. Plastic viscosity (PV) is then the force needed to maintain this flow once it is moving, which is known as poise. Brookfield can measure these Casson values. Let's look at how to measure viscosity using a Brookfield viscometer.

Example: Brookfield Model DV-III Programmable Rheometer, small sample adapter, 27 spindle.

- Brookfield reading at 40°C, 20 rpms.

- 20 rpms X 3.4 (some say 3.7) = MacMichael reading (NCA).

- Readings at speeds of 5, 10, 20, 50 and 100 rpms forward and back can be plugged into a computer equation calculating YV and PV.

- Exact values must be determined based on supplier, equipment and historical data.

A lower yield value is desired for moulding so product will flow evenly into a mould, especially with inclusions, so proper shakeout can occur and removal of air pockets is successful. A higher yield value is desired in enrobing to prevent decorations from collapsing and to avoid feet formation in the bottom of pieces.

Emulsifiers also influence flow properties of chocolate (Figure 1). The standard of identity for chocolate allows up to 1 percent emulsifiers. Soy lecithin is the most typical emulsifier utilized in chocolate manufacturing. Lecithin has both lipophilic (fat-loving) and hydrophilic (water-loving) properties. This surface active agent greatly affects chocolate fluidity. The addition of 0.3–0.4 percent lecithin has the same viscosity-reducing effects as over ten

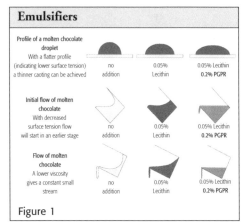

Emulsifiers

Profile of a molten chocolate droplet
With a flatter profile (indicating lower surface tension) a thinner caoting can be achieved
no addition | 0.05% Lecithin | 0.05% Lecithin 0.2% PGPR

Initial flow of molten chocolate
With decreased surface tension flow will start in an earlier stage
no addition | 0.05% Lecithin | 0.05% Lecithin 0.2% PGPR

Flow of molten chocolate
A lower viscosity gives a constant small stream
no addition | 0.05% Lecithin | 0.05% Lecithin 0.2% PGPR

Figure 1

times this amount of cocoa butter. At greater than 0.5 percent levels of lecithin, the chocolate viscosity actually starts to increase.

Polyglycerol polyricinoleate (PGPR), a unique surfactant, is another approved emulsifier for the chocolate manufacturer that greatly reduces and can even eliminate yield value of chocolate. PGPR will also reverse the effects of minor increases in the moisture content of chocolate caused by a high humidity or coating high-moisture products. The exact amount required depends on the yield value you would like to achieve. Typically, a combination of lecithin and PGPR can be used to manipulate chocolate to meet your needs.

Viscosity is controlled by the ingredients utilized in the formula, the amount of surface area created during the manufacturing process, the amount of fat in the system, and the type and amount of emulsifiers. Ranges of viscosity for moulding can be from very thin to very heavy. Cold press technology is quite independent of viscosity and can achieve the perfect pieces using its unique systems.

Particle Size

A particle is any object having definite physical boundaries in all directions without respect to size. Traditionally, fineness is determined by handheld micrometers measuring only the largest particle in the sample. This measurement can be in inches or microns. A blend of approximately one part oil with three parts chocolate mixed together and tested on a rotational micrometer will give the largest particle in the mixture.

It is a great tool to use online in the production process or for a quick check as products are received into your manufacturing plants.

The micrometer does not tell you the distribution of the particles—only the largest particle.

Laser-light-scattering measuring equipment has been developed and is widely used to look at all the particles of a mass. This unit can identify the size and amount of all particles within the determining range of the instrument. One way of measuring is to take a very small amount of sample, disperse it into a solvent and inject that mixture into a measuring unit. Particles will diffract the laser beam at different angles depending on their size. The laser beam is focused on a field of particles and then the angle of diffraction is observed. Smaller particles diffract light at wider angles and different intensities than larger particles. This type of fast QC check can tell the distribution of the particles—information that is needed to evaluate fat requirements, yield value and mouthfeel.

Moulding products may require a range of particle size dependent on the finished product. A more fine product will increase the surface area, increasing viscosity and causing flow issues into the mould. If viscosity is critical, a more fine product will require more cocoa butter to maintain required viscosity, creating a higher cost product. If a product is being manufactured with inclusions that create noise in the chewout, a fine particle size might not be necessary. Consideration of all of these options will help select the ideal coating.

Type of Fats

Again, we are focusing on cocoa butter products here because cocoa butter is the ultimate fat with desirable melt in the mouth, enabling proper flavor release. Cocoa butter with its unique melting characteristics (as shown in Curve 1 of Figure 2) requires tempering. Tempering is the process of inducing partial crystallization of cocoa butter to ensure a finished product with acceptable gloss and shelf stability when cooled properly. Proper temper and storage result in an increased absence of bloom.

If we look at specific recipes for semisweet chocolate and milk chocolate, the major difference is that semisweet chocolate typically contains very little or no amount of milkfat. Milk chocolate must contain a minimum of 3.39 percent milkfat and high-quality milk chocolate will contain more.

Cooling Curves of Cocoa Butter and Butterfat

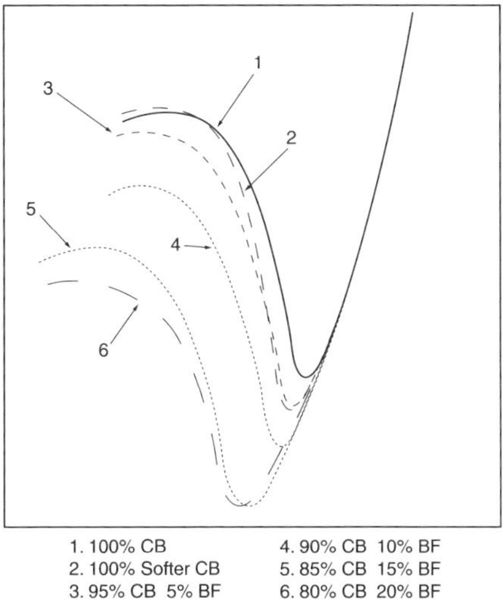

1. 100% CB	4. 90% CB 10% BF
2. 100% Softer CB	5. 85% CB 15% BF
3. 95% CB 5% BF	6. 80% CB 20% BF

Figure 2

The ratio of milkfat to cocoa butter can result in different functional properties of chocolate. Milkfat tends to soften chocolate, making it more plastic and less heat resistant than semisweet chocolate. Since milkfat is 75 percent liquid at room temperature and does not share the same crystal form as cocoa butter, it is incompatible and creates a softening effect. As the level of milkfat to cocoa butter increases in the Jensen cooling curve, the crystal-initiating temperature decreases and as a result the time required for a complete crystallization becomes longer. Practically speaking, the more milkfat, the longer a product takes to seed and set up properly. It is known that a small amount of milkfat in semisweet chocolate aids in bloom stability. In moulding, contraction is critical for successful demoulding of products. Improper ratios of milkfat to cocoa butter may result in soft products leaving fat behind in the mould, causing the next round of products to have mottled fat on the piece.

Rules of thumb:
- More than 5 percent milkfat will require modification to tempering and cooling parameters.
- A 1:3 milkfat to cocoa butter ratio is ideal.
- 2–3 percent milkfat in semisweet chocolate will provide protection against bloom.

PRODUCT DESIGN/SELECTION FOR MOULDING

When selecting a chocolate for the moulding process, certain questions must be asked:

• What type of finished product do I want?

• Do I need a milk, semisweet or white chocolate?

• What flow properties do I need to request?

• What fineness do I need for my product?

Let's explore a product specification sheet so we know what to look for and what to request. Specifications can be geared to maintain flavor, appearance and cost, and also to focus on specific characteristics the manufacturer must achieve during the production process.

A typical supplier of chocolate will provide a specification sheet for chocolate including but not limited to the following:

• Product ingredient listing in descending order.

• Physical parameters (viscosity, fineness, fat).

• Microbiological parameters (product safety).

Product Ingredient Listing

An ingredient listing will include in descending order a list of what is in the product.

Example #1: sugar, cocoa butter, chocolate liquor, milk, soy lecithin (an emulsifier), vanillin (an artificial flavor).

One interpretation of this ingredient listing is that this milk chocolate contains a low amount of milk, therefore it would have a low milkfat to cocoa butter ratio and typical tempering parameters would produce quality products.

Example #2: sugar, milk, chocolate liquor, cocoa butter, soy lecithin (an emulsifier), vanilla.

Due to milk being the second ingredient in the listing, it is a high milkfat-containing chocolate, therefore the milkfat to cocoa butter ratio might be higher and may require slightly lower tempering parameters and a longer cooling time. This product may yield a softer finished product.

Example #3: sugar, chocolate liquor, cocoa butter, milkfat, soy lecithin (an emulsifier), vanillin (an artificial flavor).

This is a typical semisweet chocolate containing milkfat to aid in bloom prevention.

Physical Parameters

Some physical parameters that could be listed on a specification sheet might be viscosity, fineness and percent total fat.

Viscosity A viscosity of 190–200 MacMichael, 55–60 Brookfield at 20 rpms, 40°C, would indicate a heavy or thick product, while a viscosity of 65–75 MacMichael, 19–22 Brookfield at 20 rpms, 40°C, would indicate a very thin product.

If you were to specify in plastic viscosity (PV) and yield value (YV), this would be where to analyze what works best in the specific moulding application.

Fineness (Particle Size) Fineness specification would typically be reported in inches or microns. A particle size of .0006–.0008 inches or 15–20 microns would be very fine and silky smooth to the tongue. It would be desirable for flavor release and complement a smooth, creamy center.

A particle size of .0018–.0020 inches or 45–50 microns would be a more coarse product and perceived as sandy to the tongue and could be incorporated into products containing crisp rice or nuts. It has been stated that a fineness greater than 20 microns is not perceived by the tongue.

Percent Fat A reading of 24–26 percent fat would indicate a very low fat content for a chocolate and a resultant high flow characteristic and most likely a lower-cost product.

A reading of 34–36 percent fat would indicate a higher fat content for a chocolate and a very flowable, thin product with a higher cost.

Microbiological Specifications

Microbiological standards are basic to the confectionery industry and would be performed using AOAC/BAM methodology by an accredited laboratory. With good manufacturing practices, there should be no issue meeting microbiological requirements.

- APC: <25,000/g
- Coliforms: <0.3/g MPN
- *E. coli:* 0.3/g MPN
- Yeast and mold: <100/g
- *Salmonella:* neg/750 g

PUTTING IT ALL TOGETHER

Let's look at several scenarios to help us decide what coating we need to select for a specific moulding application.

Solid Moulding

Solid moulding typically can tolerate a heavier viscosity. Selecting a fineness for solid moulding is very dependent on meeting flavor release requirements and whether or not you are adding any inclusions. The intricacy of the moulds will also influence your selection.

An example of a solid moulded specification sheet might be as shown in Figure 3—it would be used for a solid moulded chocolate due to the high viscosity, low fat and also low fineness.

One-shot Depositing/Shell Moulding

One-shot requires the center viscosity to be very close to the coating viscosity. The particle size must match the center of the piece. For example, if you are pairing a truffle center with a coating, the specification will require a very fine coating. If nuts or crunchy centers are desired, a more coarse coating will work fine.

Solid Moulded Specification Sheet		
Milk Chocolate A		
Description: A blend of sugar, cocoa butter, milk, chocolate liquor and soy lecithin (added as an emulsifier). The product is refined, conched and standardized for flavor, color and viscosity.		
Physical Characteristics		
1. Fineness		.0008–.0010 inches 20–25 microns
2. Standard Viscosity		190 +/- 10 NCA 53–59 Brkfld, 20 RPMS, 40°C
3. Moisture		Less than 1%
4. Color and Flavor		To match standard
5. Total Fat		27.5% +/- 1%

Figure 3

Figure 4 shows the coating heavy and the center thin. You can see how it changes the forming inside the piece, risking the integrity. Figure 5 shows the coating thin and the center heavy, risking the chance of the center leaking out through the coating.

An ideal coating and center viscosity shows exact fill and the integrity of the piece is perfect (Figure 6).

An example of a one-shot/shell moulding specification sheet might be as shown in Figure 7; this could be used for moulding with inclusions or one-shot depositing due to its compatibility with center viscosities and ease of flow into the mould with inclusions.

Viscosity Effects—Coating Heavy, Center Thin

Shell viscous, filling low viscous

Shell mass   Filling mass

Figure 4

Hollow Moulding

Hollow moulding requires a thin, flowable viscosity for complete coverage of the mould during filling, agitation and rotation. Particle size is typically based on the desired mouthfeel or price point.

An example specification sheet for hollow moulding might be as shown in Figure 8.

This coating would most likely be used for a hollow moulded product to aid in total coverage of the mould, filling all the intricate designs in the mould. Note the high fat content.

The coating shown in Figure 9 would be used for either a lower-price product or a product containing inclusions such as crisp rice or nut pieces.

Example ranges for moulded products are in Figure 10 for a reference.

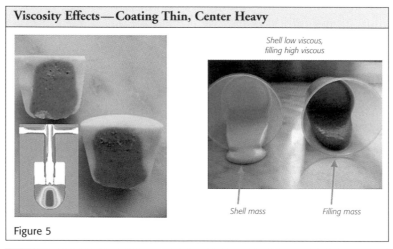

Figure 5

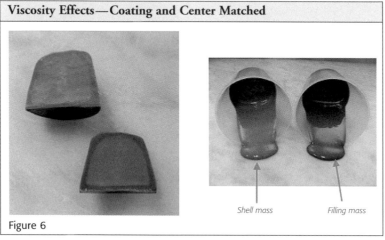

Figure 6

One-shot/Shell Moulding Spec. Sheet

Milk Chocolate B

Description: A milk chocolate manufactured from a blend of sugar, cocoa butter, milk, chocolate liquor, soy lecithin (added as an emulsifier) and vanillin (an artificial flavoring). The product is refined, conched to create a mild chocolate flavor and standardized for color and viscosity.

Physical Characteristics

1. Fineness	.0006–.0007 inches 15–18 microns
2. Standard Viscosity	145 +/- 5 NCA 41–44 Brkfld, 20 RPMS, 40°C
3. Moisture	1% max.
4. Color and Flavor	To match standard
5. Fat	32% +/- 1%

Figure 7

CONCLUSION

In summary, it is critical to define the goal of the final product. Are you targeting a specific particle size, flavor melt characteristic or price point? There is quite a diverse selection of milk, semi-sweet and white chocolate available. Evaluation of the chocolate properties and what works best in your system will enable the selection of the coating to match and achieve your goal.

Ultimately, the perfect coating is the one that meets the flavor profile at the intended price point and that runs well on your plant machinery.

Hollow Moulding Specification Sheet

Milk Chocolate C

Description: A blend of sugar, cocoa butter, whole milk, chocolate liquor, soy lecithin (added as an emulsifier) and vanillin (an artificial flavoring).

Physical Characteristics

1. Fineness	.0009–.0011 inches 23–28 microns
2. Standard Viscosity	65 +/- 5 NCA 18–21 Brkfld, 20 RPMS, 40°C
3. Moisture	Less than 1%
4. Color and Flavor	To match standard
5. Fat	36%–38%

Figure 8

Hollow Moulding with Inclusions

Milk Chocolate D

Description: A blend of sugar, cocoa butter, whole milk, chocolate liquor and soy lecithin (added as an emulsifier). The blend is refined, conched and standardized for flavor, color and viscosity.

Physical Characteristics

1. Fineness	.0018–.0020 inches 46 –50 microns
2. Standard Viscosity	145 +/- 5 NCA 41–44 Brookfield, 20 RPMS, 40°C
3. Moisture	Less than 1%
4. Color and Flavor	To match standard
5. Fat	29%–31%

Figure 9

Example Ranges

Type	Viscosity (NCA)	Fineness (microns)	Fat (%)
Solid	140–200	15–50	28–32
Hollow	60–70	15–50	32–36
One-shot	140–150	15–30	30–32

Figure 10

Questions & Answers

Q: How much variation can there be in viscosity of chocolate for a given center viscosity for one shot?

A: The goal is to have the viscosities at time of depositing as close together as possible to obtain even distribution of the center and the coating on the piece. Adjustment of the center temperature without jeopardizing the temper of the chocolate may be required. A quick check would be to evaluate flow of tempered chocolate and center from a small cup to help establish parameters.

Q: Comment on compound versus chocolate on mould release.

A: As long as parameters are maintained and you have good contraction, mould release should be very similar for compound versus chocolate.

Q: How easy is it to control the yield value and plastic viscosity for a specification?

A: Pv and YV are affected by raw materials used, processing parameters and equipment. Once all elements are established, control can be maintained. If you are changing suppliers, parameters may require evaluation. Historical data of what works best on specific equipment will help establish ranges. PGPR can also be used to reduce yield value.

Q: What are some of the factors that contribute to viscosity creep upon storage?

A: Viscosity creep upon storage can be caused by the environment. Humidity will cause viscosity to increase. Pumping action will create shear and may cause a change in viscosity. The addition of rework can also contribute to viscosity change.

Q: What is the conversion from MacMichaels to centipoise? Does PGPR encapsulate free water as well as lecithin does?

A: Brookfield reading at 20 rpms, 40°C multiplied by 250 will give centipoise value. PGPR is water loving and will encapsulate free water, increasing flowability.

Chocolate Moulding– Soup to Nuts

Graham Nice
J. Holland Corporation

As long as chocolate has been around, people have been finding ways to mould it into different shapes to find novel ways to sell it.

MOULDING PROCESS

The process of chocolate moulding consists of the following steps: mould conditioning (heating), depositing, vibrating (shaking or tapping), cooling and, finally, demoulding.

For more complex products the first four steps may be repeated several times, e.g., for layering, shell moulding and for making inclusion products.

One type of moulding that does not follow these steps is roller forming. Here the mould consists of a pair of chilled rollers that the chocolate is forced between and then "shock" cooled to the plastic state, in a sheet or web. After some minutes of conventional cooling the product pieces are separated from the web in a rotating drum (Figure 1).

This method of forming is usually used to make semi-finished pieces or centers that are subsequently processed by panning (lentils) or polished and foil wrapped (egg- and ball-shaped novelties.)

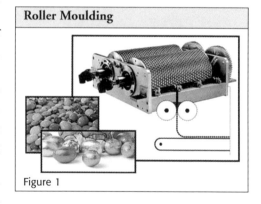

Roller Moulding

Figure 1

TYPES OF MOULDING LINES

Solid moulding is the simplest technology, has been around the longest and is generally used for blocks and bars.

Shell moulding has the most variants, and can be accomplished in one step by the one-shot method or in multiple steps of making a shell and subsequently filling it.

Hollow moulding is generally achieved by spinning a mould that has been partially filled with chocolate and closed.

MODULAR UNITS

Before considering the details of various moulding plants, let's look at the basic modules that appear in all chocolate moulding systems, namely mould conditioning, depositing and vibrating.

Mould Conditioning or Heating

Moulds are generally returning from a cold environment (cooler) after demoulding, so they have a cold surface and core temperature. If tempered chocolate were deposited onto this cold surface it would be shocked, which would mean that it would not flow over the mould surface evenly and could potentially cause stresses in the fat structure which would affect shrinkage and demoulding. A well-conditioned mould not only demoulds properly, but will also result in the correct shine.

The temperature to warm the mould up to will depend upon the critical nature of the moulding. For example, for large blocks or bars the mould temperature could be lower as there is more thermal mass, but for small pieces or delicate shells, the mould temperature would need to be fairly close to the temperature of the deposited chocolate.

Two main types of mould heating are hot air and radiant (IR) (Figure 2).

Hot air consists of a large box where warm air is blown across the mould surface—in some ways similar to a cooler but with the opposite desired effect. Advantages include precise control of mould temperature and even temperature. Disadvantages are that this takes longer (more moulds in circuit) and uses more energy.

Radiant (IR) heating consists of a radiant heat source, usually an electric lamp, mounted above the mould, shining down on the mould surface. Some of the advantages include energy efficiency (as it only acts on the mould surface), simplicity and less time (and therefore fewer moulds). Disadvantages are that the temperature is never 100 percent even and it is difficult to get heat into the bottom of a deep mould cavity.

Note that overheating moulds is to be avoided, as this will break the temper of the chocolate and cause spots or fat bloom on the product surface.

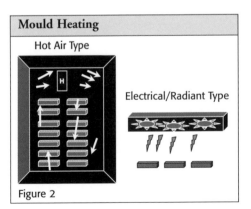

Mould Heating

Hot Air Type

Electrical/Radiant Type

Figure 2

Most automatic mould plants will be equipped with a sensor to measure the temperature of the mould surface after the heating. This reading can be used to tell the depositor if it should fill the mould or not, or to sound the alarm if there is a serious temperature-related problem (hot or cold), in this way avoiding moulds full of chocolate that cannot be removed by the demoulder.

Depositing

Being a low-melting-point, fat-based material, usually with a fairly high yield value, chocolate does not want to flow, so it has to be pumped into the mould cavities. These glorified pumps are generally referred to as depositors.

Having said this, there are occasions where a simple valve is used from a pressurized chocolate circulation pipe to fill a large block mould. This method is also sometimes used where weight accuracy is not critical, i.e., flood filling or backing off of a shell-moulded piece.

The two most common types of depositors are piston and rotary.

Most systems use a valve to open and close the route to the depositing nozzles, but differ in the design of the pump itself. The Knobel-type depositing pump uses a profiled piston, which rotates in place of a valve to either draw from the hopper or pump down to the nozzles.

Piston depositors are the most common and widely used depositing method (Figure 3). Here the pistons are horizontally mounted and draw chocolate from the hopper above. There may be a stirrer or sweeper mounted in the hopper to keep the mass flowing and to help keep the pump chamber flooded. Hoppers have to be water

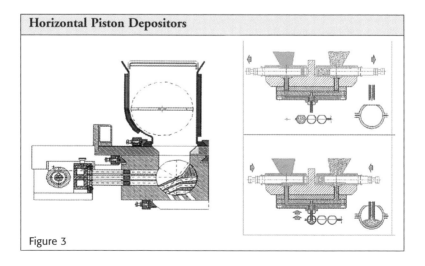

Horizontal Piston Depositors

Figure 3

jacketed with temperature control to maintain the desired chocolate state. Depositors themselves should be located in a warm (~80°F) chocolate environment out of the way of drafts from air-conditioning vents.

Pistons, as they draw out from the hopper, are exposed to the air, so in the case of center depositing they may require some lubrication (fat for fat-based centers, H_2O for water-based).

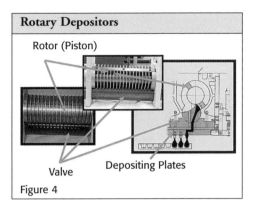

Rotary Depositors

Rotor (Piston)

Valve

Depositing Plates

Figure 4

Pistons can be made in a wide range of diameters, so they can be used when great weight accuracy is required, and can be used for very fine or small deposits like decorating.

Rotary pumps consist of a shaft with slots milled into it that pumps the mass when it rotates. Rotary depositor pumps are fully enclosed in the hopper and perform the same function by turning in conjunction with the valve. As these are flooded and not exposed to the air there is no need for lubrication for center depositing (Figure 4).

Most modern depositor pumps are now commonly driven by servomotors, for accuracy and repeatability. This enables control over the suck-back action, which is a feature that ensures a good cut-off and reduces dripping.

A third servo may be used to move the head with, or relative to, the moulds during the depositing cycle. A fourth servomotor is sometimes also used to motion the depositor in the vertical axis, though this motion is more commonly made by use of a simple mould-lifting device.

For depositing of center materials, piston and rotary depositors, of the same design, are most commonly used; there are, however, circumstances in which special depositor executions are applied. One example would be when depositing very fluid liquids, like liqueurs, where a suction leveling device may also be employed.

In certain instances where center masses are too viscous to be deposited, an extruder with a knife or wire cutter will form a slug of material to be dropped into a chocolate shell.

The metal plates (usually a stack of plates) mounted under the depositor valves are called *depositing plates*. Their function is to channel the mass towards the nozzles or holes that are arranged in the right location for the corresponding mould layout. The use of plates allows a single set of pumps to be used for multiple mould layouts by simply changing the channeling employed. On most machines, these plates are easily removed from the side to aid in changeover.

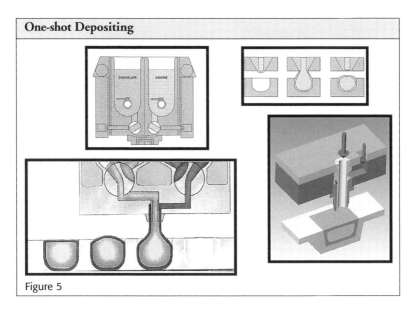

Figure 5

ONE-SHOT DEPOSITING

One-shot depositing was developed by Cadbury in the 1930s but only became common on commercially available machines in the 1980s.

The process involves simultaneously depositing the center inside of a shell of chocolate, encapsulating it in the "drop" of chocolate. Two separate hoppers, each with its own set of pumps and valves, are shown in Figure 5. The chocolate and center are brought together in a concentric nozzle in the depositing plate at the last moment, prior to depositing into the mould.

The advantages are that a filled piece is made in a single step and the capital cost is low as there only needs to be a single depositing station on the line. However, there are limitations in the types of products that can be produced with the one-shot method. The centers generally need to be similar in temperature and viscosity to the chocolate being used, and this method does not work well where inclusions are to be deposited.

INCLUSION DEPOSITING

Small-diameter nozzles are most commonly used for depositing liquids, whether chocolate or center material. This approach, however, does not work when there are inclusions mixed in with the chocolate. In this case the openings must be large enough to let two inclusions travel through side by side. So, for example, if the rice crispy piece is 4 mm long then the outlet needs to be at least 8 to 10 mm across. With such a large opening dripping would occur, so a shut-off knife or valve is sometimes fitted to the underside of the plate to physically close the hole in the plate after depositing is completed.

The pump diameters or rotor slot width must also be sized for the desired inclusion, with a similar approach to sizing to handle the inclusion size.

For very large or single inclusions (e.g., cherries), a separate dropper or counting system may be used to place the inclusion into the mould before the depositor, or into a formed chocolate shell.

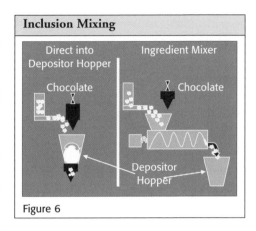

Inclusion Mixing

Direct into Depositor Hopper — Ingredient Mixer

Chocolate — Chocolate

Depositor Hopper

Figure 6

Most inclusions are mixed into the chocolate before it gets to the depositor. This could be done in a batch process in a kettle or in a continuous dynamic mixer (Figure 6). Inclusions are sometimes introduced directly into the depositor hopper with the chocolate in the correct proportion, where the depositor agitator is used to complete the mixing.

Again, there is a limit to the amount of inclusion that can be mixed into chocolate; the mass must be fluid enough to be pumped by the depositor, and able to be vibrated flat in the mould. With too much inclusion the mass will have a dough-like consistency and will not be able to flow.

Generally, low-density inclusions like crisp rice will be in the 5 to 15 percent range (by weight) whereas denser ingredients like nuts and fruit could be in the 10 to 30 percent range.

Temperature is again a factor as cold ingredients will cool the chocolate and cause it to stiffen prematurely, and if too hot could affect the temper. Also, ingredients that are less dense than chocolate will tend to float and heavy ones will sink, so this needs to be taken into consideration when vibrating or tapping the mould. Lastly, the piece design needs to be considered, e.g., a thin bar with large inclusions will have weak points, making it more delicate for demoulding and subsequent wrapping.

Vibrating

Chocolate is a viscous, thixotropic material with a potentially high yield value, so there is a need to hit the mould, first of all, in order to make the chocolate flow evenly over the surface, but also to flatten the back of the piece in the mould. Most importantly, it is to remove any air bubbles that are trapped under the chocolate.

The most common vibrator designs are vertical vibrators, (shakers or tapping tables); here the mould is hit from the bottom over a preset period of time as the result of motion from an eccentric motor or air cylinder. This period of time could be as little as a few seconds for a small piece to a minute or more for a large bar or block with inclusions.

Normally both the frequency and amplitude of this tapping motion should be adjustable to obtain the desired effect for the particular product.

Horizontal vibration is used in some instances to spread a small amount of chocolate over a large distance to make a thin piece.

Lastly, orbital shaking is a special application used to ensure even coverage of a chocolate shell during the traditional fill-and-dump method, while the mould is upside down during the dump cycle.

However, there is first a more basic machinery distinction with loose moulds and captive moulds.

Loose moulds are moulds pushed through the circuit by a chain pusher or screw, and conveyed vertically in the cooler. Captive moulds are moulds fixed to a chain circuit and conveyed in a back-and-forth manner through the line.

Loose moulds are generally simpler (and less expensive) as they do not have any features moulded onto the end of the mould, as do captive moulds. Loose mould plants are also generally intermittent in motion, and can have various layouts including "racetrack" or square, L- or U-shaped. Captive mould lines are straight line, and are more often used with continuous mould motion, and for dedicated high-volume production.

Loose moulds are more flexible systems and are applied more often for specialty moulding such as book or hollow (spinning.)

SHELL MOULDING

The basic filling technologies for shell moulding are one-shot (which was covered under depositing), wet shell, air jet forming, traditional shell moulding and cold pressing.

Wet Shell

Wet shell is the simplest of the shell methods. This is where a defined amount of chocolate is deposited into a mould and immediately following, without any cooling, an article is placed onto the wet chocolate. This article could be nuts, a cookie or a wafer. The product could then be cooled as it is with the article showing, or it could be subsequently "backed off" to encapsulate the article inside the chocolate.

Air Jet Forming

Air jet forming is used where the mould is a paper cup, e.g., peanut butter cups.

A small amount of chocolate is deposited into the cups and an air blast pushes the chocolate up the sidewalls. Peanut butter, marshmallow or something similar can then be extruded into the cup while the chocolate is still wet (Figure 7).

A blast of air can also be used on chocolate moulding lines for creating a marbling effect on the chocolate piece. This is done by depositing a small quantity of a white chocolate into a mould and hitting it immediately with an air blast to produce a marbled effect on a dark chocolate piece (i.e., seashells).

Traditional Shell Moulding

The technology for modern shell-moulding lines is basically the automation of the hand-moulding method, which has been around for generations (Figure 8).

The following steps usually take place:

- Fill mould with chocolate (to the top), making sure it is a properly conditioned mould (temperature, 2° to 4°F below chocolate temperature) as this has a great effect on the amount of chocolate that is retained by the mould.
- Shake or tap the mould.
- Invert the mould to dump out excess chocolate. Usually around two-thirds of the chocolate is recycled (dumped, detempered, then retempered).
- Shake and tap while inverted (orbital shaker).
- Clean off excess chocolate.
- Cool while inverted 1 to 2 minutes until chocolate reaches a plastic state where it no longer flows.
- Clean mould surface again.
- Right the mould and cool again. This cooling is essential if a high-temperature center is to be used.

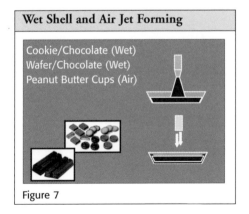

Wet Shell and Air Jet Forming

Cookie/Chocolate (Wet)
Wafer/Chocolate (Wet)
Peanut Butter Cups (Air)

Figure 7

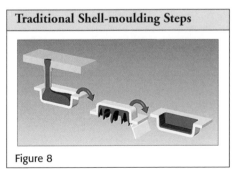

Traditional Shell-moulding Steps

Figure 8

- Fill with center/inclusion (e.g., cherries, whole nuts, etc.).
- Cool again (center cooling).
- Add backing chocolate, which becomes the base of the piece.
- Scrape off excess chocolate.
- Final cooling.
- Demoulding.

Some of these steps (like inverted cooling) may be omitted depending on the piece to be produced. But there are multiple steps involved and this of course makes it a complex forming method. The reward for all of this pain is that it is the most versatile of all moulding lines and produces the widest array of products.

Cold-pressing Technologies

This is a relatively new, alternative shell-forming method, which has been commercially available since the early 1990s. Instead of the fill-and-dump method, the exact amount of chocolate for the shell is deposited into the mould; a cold (frozen) metal plug is then inserted into this chocolate for a couple of seconds, pushing it up the side of the mould, therefore forming the chocolate shell very quickly without the mess of dumping and tempering a lot more chocolate than is needed to actually make the shell (Figure 9).

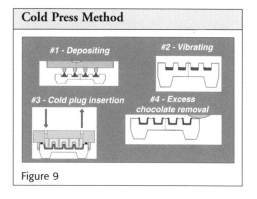

Cold Press Method

#1 - Depositing

#2 - Vibrating

#3 - Cold plug insertion

#4 - Excess chocolate removal

Figure 9

The main advantages of the cold-pressing method follow:

- Greater control/precision of shell thickness all over the piece (particularly true for complex shapes, and for book and hollow moulding).

- Energy savings, as only a fraction of the amount of chocolate needs to be tempered, typically only a third of the amount required for traditional shell moulding.

- Saves space over the traditional method. Less equipment is required as there are fewer processing steps and it is easier to build straight-line plants.

Next are the disadvantages:

- Higher capital cost as each mould shape/mould layout needs its own metal tool.

- More dedicated/less product-flexible than the fill-and-dump method.

- Cold temperature of tool (below dew point) usually requires it to be located inside a dehumidified/desiccated air chamber.

Book Moulding

In this moulding method two half moulds are brought together in the moulding process to make a filled piece that has 3-D contours (i.e., without the flat base that is present in typical shell and solid moulding.). Moulds are filled and processed in two halves and are usually brought together prior to final cooling after the chocolate rims have been reheated, so that the final piece is bonded together (Figure 10).

In loose mould plants, book moulds are usually coupled in the vertical plane, and location pins are used to secure the moulds together while they travel through the final cooler. On cap-

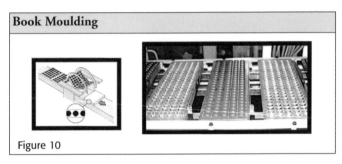

Book Moulding

Figure 10

tive mould plants, generally a metal frame holds both moulds and a spring-loaded mechanism brings the two halves together.

Hollow Moulding

Many of the shell technologies have been applied to hollow moulding. However, the greatest volume of products, particularly the large seasonal hollow novelties, are produced in a batch method on a spinning machine.

Moulds consist of two halves, and are held together with clips or magnets. Chocolate is metered in and the closed mould is placed on a drum which has turning arms attached, the drum rotates and the arms spin, therefore turning the mould through 360° in two axes.

The moulds may be predecorated with colored coating prior to the main chocolate charge, e.g., to produce the eyes, basket and other features on hollow Easter bunnies.

After spinning, when the chocolate has cooled enough to where it no longer flows, the mould is placed inside a cooling cabinet or on a belt through a conventional cooling tunnel for final cooling and setting.

Questions & Answers

Q: What do you recommend to prevent aerating the chocolate so that there are no bubbles in the moulded solid bar?

A: Ensure tempering system, pumps and pipework are not leaking air into the chocolate. Also, run tempered chocolate down an angled pipe or over a plate to prevent "plopping" into the depositor hopper.

Make sure that depositor hopper stirrers do not break the surface of the chocolate and fold air into the mass.

Ensure that depositor pump seals/clearances are functioning correctly with no air leakage into the pump chambers when the pumps aspirate.

Have good vibration/tapping.

Have the correct mould temperature so that chocolate stays fluid enough to let air escape during vibration.

Do not overtemper the chocolate as this results in viscous chocolate which can hold more air.

Q: What is the ideal mould temperature range? For depositing?

A: For fine depositing, like shell or one shot, moulds should ideally be 2°F to 4°F below chocolate temperature. For heavy block or bar deposits this is less critical, the +5°F to -10°F range relative to the chocolate temperature is probably OK under most circumstances, though the tighter the control within a ±5°F range is preferable.

Q: Are there any drawbacks to using one-shot depositing rather than traditional shell moulding or frozen cone forming?

A: Chocolate shell thickness is not as perfectly consistent over the whole piece.

Complex or awkward mould shapes with many details cannot have as much filling with the one-shot method.

Centers for one shot are limited to small or no inclusions plus they must be made for a narrow viscosity and temperature range close to that of the chocolate being used.

Another drawback of one-shot moulding is for products with fat-based fillings. These can tend to have shorter shelf lives (bloom sooner) due to the amount of liquid oil migration that happens during the initial moments after depositing and before the outer chocolate shell solidifies

Q: How is the rim reheated for book moulding?

A: Electrical lamp (IR) heating from the top is used to soften or melt the rim slightly before mould booking or doubling.

Q: Is air entrapment more of a problem in frozen cone versus traditional moulding?

A: Possibly with complex mould shapes that have detailed relief on the mould and frozen cone tool surface. But I do not have direct experience of this, so talk to users of the frozen cone technology to get an opinion.

Q: Why use a continuous mixer rather than a batch mixer for fruit inclusions?

A: The continuous method works all day once it is set up right to run. Batch is good, too, but a manual batch system relies on an operator to get it right. Large batches of chocolate will have a different temper from the start to finish of running the batch through the depositor, so that could affect the depositing of the batch.

Q: In book moulding, how do you remove excess chocolate?

A: Normally you have a licking roller or scraper to remove excess chocolate from the rims before combining the mould, but you can not remove all the chocolate as you need a slight excess in order to make sure that there is enough to fill in all the spaces when the two mould halves come together. Any excess that remains after combining and pressing will come out of the side of the mould book and some will remain as a fine web between the pieces on the mould top surface.

Q: In radiant heating is mid IR or near IR preferred?

A: No experience, but if pressed for an answer I would have to say that the choice may somewhat depend on the heat absorbency of the chocolate being used (i.e., white chocolate would reflect more IR heat than dark chocolate).

Chocolate Cooling and Demoulding

Dave Cruickshank
Cadbury Trebor Bassett

Tempering and cooling are best regarded as two parts of the same process, i.e., the solidification of chocolate. There are interactions between the two processes, and they both need to be right to get an efficient process and a high-quality product.

The functions of cooling are to remove specific and latent heat, contract the chocolate such that it releases cleanly from the mould, and produce a stable and attractive product.

PRODUCT FACTORS

The product recipe has a major effect on the cooling requirement and cooler performance. For cocoa-butter-based systems the aim is to crystallize the fat into the stable Form 5 polymorph. This gives a stable, attractive product, and also gives rise to the contraction required to allow clean demoulding.

However, the requirement to crystallize fat into small crystals of Form 5 limits the rate of cooling that can be applied. If this is exceeded by either low cooling temperatures or short cooling times, then less stable lower polymorphs such as Form 4 will result that do not give the stability or contraction needed.

Other recipe factors will affect the maximum allowable cooling rate, such as the proportion of butterfat present, and the presence and type of vegetable fat (where legally allowable). These ingredients both have the potential to reduce the crystallization rate of Form 5, and thus longer cooling times will be required.

The other factor that must be considered is the rate of heat conduction through chocolate. This is low, and thus requires cooling times on large chocolate bars to be longer to allow heat from the center to be conducted to the surfaces where it can be removed.

The level of temper present in the chocolate will also have an effect on contraction, and both very low or high levels will reduce contraction, and may lead to incomplete demoulding.

For noncocoa-butter-based systems, the polymorphism is less complex and faster cooling rates are possible because at chocolate cooling temperatures only one poly-morphic form is possible. Here the only constraint is to avoid cooling into a glassy amorphous state. The constraints of heat conduction, though, are the same as for cocoa-butter-based systems.

COOLER CONDITIONS

Heat Load

It is possible to calculate the heat load from the crystallizing fat in a typical moulding plant cooler. Assume that the chocolate contains 30 percent fat, and that the temperer crystallizes 1 percent of that. The final stabilized solid fat content of the chocolate is measurable by NMR, but in the United Kingdom, 55 percent solid fat at 20°C (68°F) is typical. The cooler then first has to remove the latent heat from a net 54 percent of the fat as it crystallizes. In a moulding plant running at 6t per hour this requires 46kw to be removed.

In addition, there are other factors that will add to this theoretical heat load:

• Specific heat from other ingredients, e.g., milk, sugar, etc.

• Centers or inclusions, if any.

• Moulds, chains, mould frames.

• Air leakage.

• Conduction through the fabric of the cooler.

Cooler Conditions

Temperature Cooler conditions should be set on the basis of the temperature that the product needs to achieve. Apart from temperature settings, which are normally con-trolled and measured close to the heat exchange coils of the chiller plant, there are other factors such as track speed and air flow that need to be taken into account.

It is normal to consider coolers as having three distinct temperature zones:

• Zone 1 is mainly for specific heat removal and has temperature settings of 12° to 15°C (54°–59°F). Product is in this zone typically for 5 minutes.

• Zone 2 is where the majority of the latent heat is removed. It can be seen in Figure 1 that latent heat is much larger than specific heat, and tends to be

Specific and Latent Heat	
Specific Heat of Fat	1.5 kg/kg K
Latent Heat of Crystallization	25 kj/kg
Contraction Measured Between	0.3% & 0.8%

Figure 1

released quite suddenly as crystallization sets in. This zone will have lower temperatures than zone 1, and potentially a much longer time. Large units or bars will require 30 to 40 minutes of cooling in zone 2. Typical temperatures are 7° to 10°C (45°–50°F).

- Zone 3 is where product is warmed prior to exiting the cooler. The main purpose is to heat product to a temperature above the dew point of the packing room. Temperatures and times are typically the same as in zone 1.

Dark chocolate or milk chocolates with low butterfat contents will not require such low temperatures and 2° to 3°C can be added to the temperatures quoted above for this type of recipe.

Air speed The main requirement is to have turbulent flow across the product and moulds, and this is generally agreed to occur once the air speed has reached 5 m/sec (990 ft/min). There is little advantage in exceeding this rate unless the air is heated significantly on its return to the cooler coils.

Residence time This is controlled by varying the track speed, normally measured in moulds per minute. Large solid units require more cooling time than small thin ones.

Humidity control It is vital to avoid any condensation forming on product while in the cooling tunnel. Condensation will lead to sugar bloom, a surface defect caused by sugar first dissolving in the condensation, and then recrystallizing. It can, in extreme circumstances, cause molds or yeasts to start to grow on the chocolate surface.

For these reasons, air in the cooling tunnels is dehumidified. Air simply cooled to, e.g., 13°C (55°F) will be saturated with water vapor (100% rh) at that temperature. To dehumidify the air, it is "overcooled" to, for instance, 1.5°C (35°F) and then reheated to 13°C (55°F). This air then has a relative humidity of 45 percent. Dehumidification requires additional energy use, and thus it is important that the process is optimized.

Intense coolers It is sometimes necessary to deposit a hot center, e.g., a caramel, at 55°C (140°F) into a chocolate shell, and the purpose of intense coolers is to prevent the center from melting or detempering the chocolate. Typically the shell is cooled to 10°C (50°F) prior to depositing the center, and cooling continues immediately after depositing to ensure that the chocolate is undamaged

COOLER DESIGN

Single-level Cooler

The single-level cooler (Figure 2), seen after most enrobers, has an elegant simplicity of design that makes it easy to understand how it operates.

The chillers introduce conditioned air at the center of the cooler that passes towards each end of the tunnel (Figure 3). Air passing back towards the enrober runs counter-current to the units, which in itself introduces the basis of the required temperature profile. Essentially, the air that the units first experience has been warmed partly by units further into the tunnel, with adjustments from strategically placed heaters. Air passing forward in the same direction as the unit flow is also heated close to the exit to warm the units prior to leaving the tunnel.

The basic layout of the tunnel makes it easy to arrive at the correct temperature profile. While it is relatively common to accommodate a single-level cooler with a residence time of 15 to 20 minutes (which is adequate for most enrober products), larger moulded products require much longer times, for which a single-level design would be impracticably long. This has led to multilevel designs which are used in most moulding and shell plants.

Single-level Cooler with Enrober and Infeed

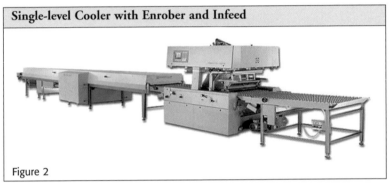

Figure 2

Airflow Diagram of Single Level Cooler, with Central Chiller Unit

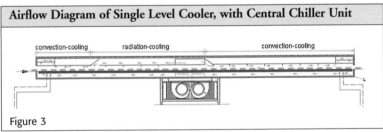

Figure 3

Multiple Zone Cooler

A four-zone cooler is designed where moulds enter from one side and, in groups of three or four, are raised to the top of the tower, and then lowered to the bottom on the other side (Figure 4). There are four separately controllable chillers, two on the up side and two on the down side. These blow air from side to side across and between the moulds. Coolers that have chillers and coils on one side and racks that carry the moulds on the other side can be used singly or in series and the same basic design can also be used as a mould heater. In a shell plant there would be three cooling stages: after the shell-forming stage, after the center deposit and after the units have been backed off.

Paternoster 4-Zone Cooler	Multizone Cooler in Background with Depositor Station in Foreground

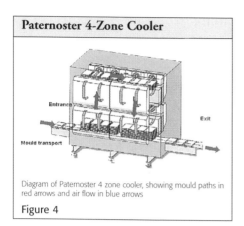

Diagram of Paternoster 4 zone cooler, showing mould paths in red arrows and air flow in blue arrows

Figure 4

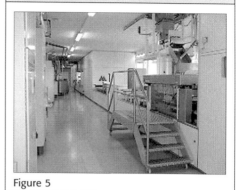

Figure 5

Multilayer Shell/Moulding Plant

This is the most complex layout with coolers stacked above the depositors and shell-forming sections (Figure 5). It is also the most space efficient of the options. The compact nature of the design means that the control of airflow is done by a variety of guides, baffles, etc., that over time are at risk of being moved or damaged during cleaning or maintenance, sometimes to the detriment of their performance.

In all designs, the aim is to produce the ideal temperature profile for the product.

INNOVATIONS IN COOLING

Radiant Cooling

This is not a recent development, and features in some commercially available coolers, particularly single-level designs. It comprises matte black cooled panels that act as an additional cooling source to supplement the cold air flow and cold tables, where fitted. They provide a small proportion of the total cooling capacity of the tunnel.

Mars Inc. U.S. Patent 6,419,970

This patent covers the use of extreme cooling conditions at low or ultralow temper levels. It claims improvements in gloss and detail retention from cooling using air temperatures below 0°C (32°F) in a rapid cooling process. It also necessarily provides for rewarming in a humidity-controlled environment to maintain good appearance.

Jet Turbulence Coolers

Here the use of air moving at 20 m/sec (3,960 ft/min) is claimed to offer advantages over conventional processes at lower air speeds. Jet coolers are most effective at the point in the process where crystallization occurs. The emission of latent heat is sudden, and as can be seen from Figure 1, latent heat is much larger than specific heat.

DEMOULDING

If the tempering and cooling processes have been optimized, then demoulding is a minor part of the process with good quality product cleanly leaving moulds that are returned to the start of the process.

A small amount of force is normally needed to part the product from the mould, and this either takes the form of a hammer or a mechanism that twists the moulds. Units tend to be held in place by electrostatic charges, which is more of a problem with light or small units than moulded bars.

Units are demoulded onto either plaques or a belt, depending on subsequent packing arrangements.

CONCLUSION

The processes of tempering and cooling are related and are best considered as a single two-stage process. The parameters must be matched both to the plant and the recipe in order to give high-quality work and efficient operation.

Questions & Answers

Q: What is the ideal humidity in a moulding plant and/or packaging area?

A. It should always be below the dew point of the coldest surface to avoid condensation. In reality this means around 50 percent RH in both cooler and packing room.

Q: What effect does humidity play on demoulding?

A. High humidity can lead to condensation on the moulds. Once this happens, there is no alternative to removing and cleaning the moulds through a mould-washing plant. Very low humidity leads to high levels of static electricity in the demoulding area, which can cause units, especially light ones, to stick in the moulds. This only applies to polycarbonate moulds, not metal ones.

Q: What specific visual problems can be caused by improper cooling of chocolate?

A. There are several:
1. Fragments of chocolate pulled from the unit remain adhered to the mould.
2. White/grey areas of chocolate similar to fat bloom in appearance.
3. Lack of gloss, especially on the unmoulded surface.
4. Water marks caused by condensation on moulds.
5. Concentric circular marks (pull marks), usually near the center of the moulded surface.

Q: What can be used to demould chocolate articles that use low-melting-point fats in the chocolate, which inhibit contraction?

A. Soft fats normally crystallize more slowly, so longer cooling time is the best route. Careful reduction of the center zone temperature can help, but too cold will cause bloom to develop after packing.

Q: Is there a standard cooling time per given mass of chocolate (considering air temperature and surface area)?

A. Theoretically, yes. Practically, no. There are so many variables, e.g., bar dimensions, recipe (especially butterfat content) and mould design, together with the plant variables, that each product and plant has to be treated individually.

Q: Is underfilling the mould cavity in order to decrease the piece's weight using the same mould a problem in demoulding?

A. No, but you do tend to create more chocolate fragments in the demoulding area from the broken pieces of the meniscus.

Q: What are the desired cooling stages for CB and compound chocolate?

A. I'm not sure I understand the question. Cooling requires three temperature zones, with the coolest and longest zone being the center zone. The only significant difference between cocoa butter and compound-based products is that compound fats are simpler polymorphously, so it is possible to use shorter cooling times and/or lower zone 2 temperatures.

Q: Are there risks of shock cooling in the various cold punch techniques?

A. It seems that if you go cold enough, then shock cooling is not a problem. So Jensen rolls, cold punch processes and even ice cream coatings work well, and give no problems. The conditions between these processes and conventional cooler temperatures seem to be where shock cooling causes problems. This is discussed in Mars U.S. Patent 6,419,970, which covers extreme cooling conditions.

Q: What are the symptoms of shock cooling?

A. There are several:
1. Pull marks and lack of gloss.
2. Lack of contraction.
3. Soft product leading to dirty belts.
4. White patches or, in extreme cases, bloom which develops after packing.

Q: What are the optimum ambient conditions for a moulding process? °C? % RH?

A. The product only needs humidity control in the packing room and coolers to around 50 percent RH. A room temperature of around 18°C is acceptable. Cooler temperatures are covered in the paper.

Q: Do postproduction conditions in the package affect the chocolate? There is some indication that chocolate continues to solidify after packing. How long does a chocolate bar continue to crystallize after demoulding?

A. An increase in solid fat content after the cooler can be followed by nuclear magnetic resonance (NMR) and at 20°C continues for around 120 days. The proportion of fat crystallizing is small, so the usual warehousing conditions (8°C and ambient RH) are adequate to deal with this.

Q: How do different levels of protein (from the milk source) affect contraction?

A. I have no knowledge of proteins having this role, and can think of no mechanism which would link the protein content with contraction.

Q: Can you comment on what is the best way to remove heat trapped in the center of a finished filled chocolate?

A. Heat has to be conducted through the bulk of the chocolate to a surface before it can be removed. The rate depends on the thermal conductivity of the chocolate and filling, which are physical constants for any given recipe. This means that they are outside of our control or influence. The plant variables of time, temperature and airspeed are the only ones that can be employed.

Q: What do you recommend for cooling bars with layers of different chocolate, for example, white and dark chocolate?

A. Use conditions that are appropriate for the most sensitive of the chocolates in the product. This usually means the one with the highest butterfat content.

Q: On the cold punch process, as the chocolate cools and contracts, how is the chocolate released from the punch?

A. On Jensen rolls an antifreeze fluid is normally used. For cold punch there is no need for this as the units do not adhere to the cold forming components.

Q: Can turbulent air flow across moulds in the cooling tunnel disturb the surface of the chocolate and increase possibility of fat bloom?

A. It must be possible, but I have never come across this. I would expect that the air handling in plants using very high-velocity air would be designed to avoid any such effect. Once chocolate has started to crystallize, the yield value would be very high, and would need a very concentrated air jet directed onto it to make visible marks.

Aerated Confections

Aerated Confections Introduction

John Cooke

It seems that there is not a good printed definition for *aeration* in the dictionaries to describe accurately how this term applies to confections. The *Standard* says that the word means to *supply or charge with a gas* or to *expose to the circulation of air for purification* and to *expose to oxygen as in the purification of blood*. None of these definitions really sends your thoughts to candy or the topics that are presented in this Back to Basics series. In fact, they bring to mind the aeration of lawns or bottled water or the Red Cross bloodmobile.

The methods used to aerate candy would be considered much more brutal than anything described above. We push and pull, beat rigorously, shear and inject until the mass of candy submits and changes into something quite different than it was previously.

Our Back to Basics authors will examine the aeration of several well-known confectionery products. The topics cover hard candy, nougat and taffy, as well as marshmallow.

In the case of hard candy, the purpose of aeration is to change the color from clear to a nice white or pastel opaque appearance and to change the texture of the mass from a glass which is not at all chewable to a lighter, chewable product. The difference can be explained by comparing the texture of a butterscotch disc and a light and airy candy cane.

Nougat and taffy are actually very similar confections and there have been debates throughout the years as to whether some saltwater taffy is actually nougat and vice versa. The debate stems from whether or not taffy is taffy if it is whipped instead of pulled to aerate.

Marshmallow is marshmallow; however, there are different types of this product, too. There is eating marshmallow, like the ones we roast over a campfire; grained marshmallow, which usually comes in the shape of a bunny, chick or peanut; and there is enrobing marshmallow, which must be able to stand up and hold its shape throughout an enrobing process.

The demonstrations include microscopy and offer examples of the various foam or air pocket structures in these different types of aerated items.

Some of the reasons to aerate confections are to change the texture, increase the volume of the mass, change the appearance or to modify the mass for the purpose of providing a suitable product for further processing, such as enrobing.

Many different food manufacturers use aeration, and examples of other food products include the following:

Ice cream

Homemade confections such as divinity

Aerated chocolate bars

Snack cakes such as *Twinkies*

Lookout Moon Pies

Whoopie Pies

Bubble gum

Circus peanuts

Creme and meringue pies

Crisped rice/marshmallow treats

Whipped cream products

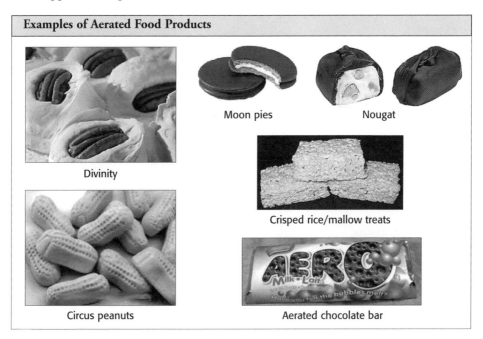

Examples of Aerated Food Products

Divinity

Moon pies

Nougat

Crisped rice/mallow treats

Circus peanuts

Aerated chocolate bar

Note: Questions and answers for this chapter appear at the end of the Aerated Confections section on page 318.

Nougat and Marshmallow Processing

Ralph Lee
Masterfoods USA

Nougat and marshmallow, while not necessarily identified as such, have been around for a long time. Both are aerated sugar syrups with or without the addition of flavorings and/or inclusions. Their roots can be found in the recipes for traditional products such as montélimar and torrone. Large-scale commercial production of nougat products began about 85 years ago, during the 1920s. At that time everything was batch processed. Eggs were separated by hand (Figure 1). Egg whites were whipped in large mixing bowls. Cooked syrup was manually poured into the egg whites and whipped further to make a frappé. Frappé was combined with other ingredients, flavoring and rework in a large blender. After blending, the candy was dumped onto a table and spread by hand. The slab was marked off to the correct dimensions, then armies of workers moved in with large knives to cut the pieces to size.

1920s Processing—Cracking and Separating Eggs

Figure 1

PROCESSING STEPS

The recipes and general process steps for producing nougat and marshmallow really have not changed much since the 1920s. The whipping agent is prepared and beaten; the cooked syrup is added to the whipping agent; the mixture is aerated; flavors and other ingredients are blended into the mixture; the mixture is cooled; and the product is formed. Each of these process steps will be addressed, with an emphasis on aeration.

Batch versus Continuous

While nougat and marshmallow recipes and process steps have not changed much, process equipment has evolved. The first process decision that needs to be made is whether to use a batch, continuous or hybrid batch/continuous process. This decision will depend upon the required volume of product.

Batch processing, while previously used to produce large volumes of products, is now reserved for small-volume and/or high-price specialty products due to ergonomic concerns. In particular, carpal tunnel syndrome is a strong argument against manual cutting. Small volumes are typically in the thousands of pieces per day.

Continuous processing is appropriate for large volumes, typically above 300 to 1,000 kg/hr. Hybrids of batch and continuous processing can and should be used for the in-between volumes.

Whipping Agent Preparation

Common whipping agents are egg, soy, milk proteins, gelatin or combinations. Preparation of the selected whipping agent is necessary to ensure functionality of its protein. Proper mixing and hydration are key. The whipping agent is beaten only after this has been completed. Proper mixing is accomplished by using high-shear mixers (Figure 2).

Once mixed, sufficient time must be allowed for proper hydration. For albumen and gelatin, a minimum hydration time of 30 minutes is recommended. After hydration, the whipping agent is ready to be used in the aeration process.

Note that a protein and water mixture is a very good medium for bacterial growth. As such, it is obviously important to keep the equipment clean, keep the whipping agent cool and use the whipping agent as quickly as possible.

Syrup Cooking

Syrups are mixtures of sugars: sucrose, invert and corn syrups. They are formulated in ratios driven by the desired final texture. In general, the more sucrose, the more grained or short the final product will be. With more noncrystallizing sugars (corn syrup, for example) the product will be longer or chewier. The purpose of cooking the nougat or marshmallow syrup is to deliver the syrup at the correct moisture content into the process. Nougat syrups generally have lower moisture percentage than marshmallow syrups. Syrup solids will typically be measured with a refractometer.

The actual cooking process is quite straightfor-

High-shear Mixing Head

Figure 2

ward. Batch kettles and continuous plate heat exchangers are equally effective for syrup cooking and both are easy to clean.

Generally, there is a hold time after the syrup is cooked and before it is added to the whipping agent. Reducing sugars will develop during this hold time. This can be desirable or undesirable since reducing sugar levels impacts product texture at the forming step.

Note that, if at all possible, cookers should be closely coupled with subsequent process steps to eliminate manual handling of potentially dangerous hot syrups.

Aeration

The function of all aeration systems is to create small, evenly dispersed bubbles of air to give the finished product desired density and light texture. There are several different methods that may be used to accomplish this. Key elements are shear and beating (residence) time. Batch aeration systems have residence times measured in minutes, while continuous aeration systems have residence times measured in seconds.

Batch Aeration Traditional batch aeration systems use open mixers, such as the vertical planetary mixer and the larger horizontal mixer (Figure 3). These mixers typically rely on close operator attention to achieve correct aeration. While this may result in products with a wider range of final densities, these mixers have the advantage of being very flexible for smaller operations as all process steps can be carried out on the same equipment.

Batch pressure beaters allow greater control of the aeration level (Figure 4). The whipping agent is first whipped in the beater under pressure. The cooked syrup is added, then the mixture is whipped further. This creates many small bubbles that expand when the pressure is released.

Horizontal Batch Mixer — Interior

Figure 3

Batch Beater with Two Cookers

Figure 4

Process control variables include beating (residence) time for both whipping steps, beater pressure and beater speed (rpm). Consistent product quality should be expected as all variables can be automatically controlled.

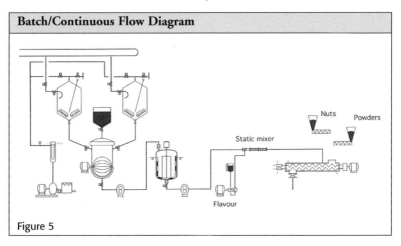

Batch/Continuous Flow Diagram

Figure 5

Batch/Continuous Aeration The batch pressure beater system can feed a continuous process if a pressure buffer tank is installed after the batch pressure beater (Figure 5). This would be advantageous for a company looking to start with a small batch system and expand to a larger capacity batch/continuous system as demand increases.

Continuous Aeration Continuous aeration is similar in layout to the batch/continuous system except that a continuous pressure beater is used (Figure 6). Typical designs for a continuous pressure beater consist of a cylindrical shell enclosing a rotor: the aeration head (Figure 7). Both the shell and the rotor are studded with many metal pins.

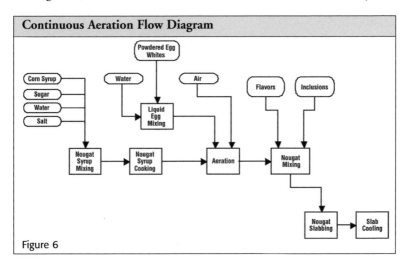

Continuous Aeration Flow Diagram

Figure 6

Continuous aeration systems may have single or dual mixing heads. In the single-head system, whip agent and cooked syrup are injected at different points along the length of the head. The whip agent is added first to allow it to be whipped before it is combined with the syrup. For the two-head system the whip agent is whipped in the first head, then the cooked syrup is added and the combined mixture is whipped in the second head. Both arrangements are successful in producing good product.

As with the batch pressure beater, the control variables are whipping time (residence time), beater pressure and beater speed. The shorter residence times require higher shear rates. Higher shear rates result in heat buildup in the mixing head. Heat buildup requires that the mixing head be provided with a cooling jacket to remove the heat. Depending on the size of the mixing head and production rate, the rotor may also need cooling. Pressure inside the mixing head is controlled by a backpressure device such as a valve or a pump.

Continuous aeration systems require metering of the aeration gas. In the past, rotameters provided adequate but hard-to-control metering. Compact mass flow meters are recommended, as they are easily incorporated into automated systems. Continuous aeration is appropriate for large-volume production.

A few comments are in order regarding equipment design. Nougats tend to have higher viscosity than marshmallow. Their higher viscosity requires higher pressure for proper aeration in both batch and continuous systems. Seal design is important. Mechanical seals are required for the higher pressures associated with nougat processing. O-ring seals are adequate for the lower pressures associated with marshmallow processing. In either case, seal maintenance is critical to maintaining correct aeration levels.

Mixer headpin design in continuous systems has evolved over the years. There are basically two methods of manufacture, machined and inserted. In the machined case, the pins and rotor (or stator) are machined from a solid block of metal. In the inserted design, the pins are made separately and are welded or screwed into the rotor and stator. While there are arguments for and against each type, both work quite well. Note that a piece of tramp metal or even a chunk of crystallized sugar could possibly bend a pin. A bent pin in a machine operating at 500 RPM can quickly lead to complete

Continuous Aeration Head

Figure 7

catastrophic failure. Be sure to clean your pressure beaters thoroughly after running to prevent hardening of leftover ingredients.

Flavor and Ingredient Blending

Plain nougat and marshmallow, while texturally very nice, taste pretty bland. More often than not, flavors and other ingredients are added to the base whipped material. The range of materials that can be added is nearly limitless, with due care. This is also a good place to add rework.

It is preferable to add flavors and other ingredients to the whipped material while it is still hot to help prevent breakdown of the light structure. For batch processes these materials can be added in virtually any type of low-shear mixer. For continuous processes, liquids and colors can be added using an in-line static mixer. Inclusions (solids) can be added using a powered continuous blender.

Cooling Cooling can occur either before or after forming, depending upon the product. The key is to minimize shear. The foam structure is more readily broken down the cooler it gets. Low-shear methods, such as cooling wheels and cooling belts, are preferred.

Keep in mind that these materials are very low density and good insulators. As such, they cool very slowly.

Forming Common forming methods used for nougat and marshmallow include batch slab and cut, extrusion, continuous slabbing and starch casting.

Batch Slab and Cut Batch Slab and cut is the simplest forming method for nougat and marshmallow. The product is poured onto a chilled table, allowed to cool, then cut manually with knives. Properly cooled product slabs may also be individually fed into mechanical slitters and cutters.

Extrusion Extrusion is more suitable for marshmallow due to its lower viscosity. In addition to the traditional marshmallow shape, many interesting cross-section shapes can be made.

Continuous Slabbing Continuous slabbing is best for large volume production of square and rectangular nougat bars. The slab is formed by chilled forming rolls and deposited onto a cooling belt. The properly cooled full slab is fed into slitters and cutters.

Starch Casting Starch casting, where the product is deposited into starch, is an old but effective method of forming. It offers the opportunity to flexibly create more diverse individual shapes. The high capital costs of mogul-type systems and the large storage space required for final drying generally limit this process to large-scale process plants, although there are smaller scale starch-casting systems available.

IN-PROCESS TROUBLESHOOTING MEASURES

Density

The key output variable for an aeration system is density. A change in density at any given process step will quickly indicate something is wrong at that step. Keep in mind that the density will change during the process as components are added and the temperature changes. It is important to know the desired density at every process step.

There are many methods used to measure density. Volumetric methods work well when the material is still fluid. Water-displacement methods work well for finished pieces.

Graining (Shortening)

It is also important to know the desired product texture and viscosity at each process step.

A change in texture can indicate a misformulation, incorrect cooking temperature, incorrect hold times and under- or over-aeration.

CONCLUSION

Nougat and marshmallow are the basis for a tremendous number of products. Nougat and marshmallow products can be and are made on a very small to very large scale. A little bit of product creativity and some process know-how are all that it takes.

Note: Questions and answers for this chapter appear at the end of the Aerated Confections section on page 318.

Basics of Nougat and Marshmallow Formulas

Greg C. Johnson
Russell Stover Candies, Inc.

Nougat and marshmallow confections share similar ingredients and processes. The basic formulas for nougats and marshmallows are shown in Figure 1.

Both are made using similar ingredients. Both candies consist of three major components. The first component is a medium in which to carry the whipping agent. The second component consists of the whipping agent, usually rehydrated in water to assist incorporation into the final candy. These two parts are added together, then mixed with the final part. The final component is a cooked syrup base into which the combined first two parts are added during the whipping stage of manufacturing. In the hands of a talented confectioner these same raw materials are transformed into a multitude of tasty treats. Both nougat and marshmallow can stand alone or be combined with other candy centers to make a wide variety of confections. Since both nougat and marshmallow use the same basic materials, what is the difference? The differences lie in the proportions of the ingredients and the preparation of those ingredients. With a common base consisting of a cooked syrup, the first difference comes from the ratio of sugar to corn syrup in the base syrup. The second difference is the choice of whipping agent and the method of aeration. In general, marshmallow tends to be more highly aerated than nougat. These two differences result in obvious differences between the two confections.

MARSHMALLOW

Marshmallow (Figure 2) can be formulated in a variety of methods. Cut marshmallow is a marshmallow that is aerated, extruded and cut in a single

Basic Formulas	
Nougat	**Marshmallow**
Part 1	Part 1
1½ lb Sugar	12 lb Fine sugar
11 lb Corn syrup	3½ pt Water
Part 2	Part 2
1 lb Fine sugar	13 oz Bloom quick-
6 oz Dried egg albumen	setting gelatin
12 oz Water	5¼ pt Water
Part 3	Part 3
5½ lb Sugar	12 lb Corn syrup
2 lb Corn syrup	1½ lb Invert sugar
½ oz Imitation vanilla flavor	2 oz Vanilla flavor

Choice Confections—Manufacturing Methods and Formulas, Walter Richmond, MC Publishing Company, 1954.

Figure 1

operation. The finished product is rolled in powdered sugar to seal any exposed surfaces. Another type of marshmallow can be cast into a starch mould. This allows the confectioner to mould the candy into a multitude of shapes. After curing in starch, the marshmallow can be removed from the starch mould, cleaned of excess starch and coated with a variety of coatings. Some marshmallow formulations are made so the resulting product is nearly dry. The center can then be panned and the moisture from the panning operation softens the center. Marshmallow can be formulated in a manner that results in a grained marshmallow; a common example is a circus peanut. This is usually accomplished by adding powdered sugar to the candy just prior to or during aeration.

Marshmallow also works well with other candy centers such as caramel (Figure 3).

NOUGAT

Nougat (Figure 4) is another staple of the confectionery industry. Nougat is a mixture of a hard candy syrup and a whipped candy. There are two types of nougat, short nougats and chewy nougats. As with marshmallow, it is the percentages and handling of the raw materials that distinguish the two types. In general, chewy nougats contain a higher percentage of corn syrup compared to short nougat. Short nougats have a slightly higher percentage of sugar. Nougat formulations range from soft, light, delicately textured products like divinity (Figure 5) to a candy with a dense, short-grained consistency, like a peanut log. Nougat can stand alone as a candy coated in a variety of coatings. It can be combined with other center formulations. This is typically done in candy bars, many of which are familiar to us all. Nougat formulations are very compatible with combinations of fruits, nuts, spices, chocolate and a variety of flavorings.

Marshmallow

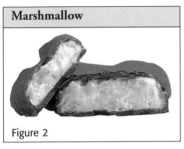

Figure 2

Marshmallow and Caramel

Figure 3

Nougat

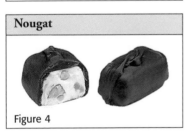

Figure 4

Divinity

Figure 5

WHIPPING AGENTS

It is the choice of whipping agent that determines the final texture of the finished candy. This choice depends on what the candymaker wants in the finished product. Each whipping agent has advantages and disadvantages. It is up to the candymaker to determine the attributes that may best result in the desired candy. A brief look at the characteristics may help in picking the correct whipping agent. Several characteristics must be considered when picking a whipping agent. Shelf stability, volume (specific gravity), density, pH, cost and flavor all figure into the choice of a whipping agent. A cross section of the types of whipping agents available to the confectioner includes egg albumen, soy protein, milk protein and gelatins (Figure 6).

SWEETENERS

By weight, sweeteners represent the largest percentage of ingredients in nougats and marshmallows. Their function is to add sweetness, bulk and texture (Figure 7). The two major sweeteners are sugar and corn syrup.

Whipping Agents

Egg Albumen
- The use of egg albumen results in a large increase in the volume of the candy batch.
- The foam made by whipping egg albumen is delicate and light in texture.
- Egg albumen is sensitive to pH and has a limited range of pH values. Lower pH values reduce the whipping ability of the protein.
- The delicate texture of the foam does not hold up well over time, so the resulting confections made using egg albumen are best suited for products with a shorter shelf life. Heat can denature the protein, reducing the effectiveness of the whipping agent.
- Egg albumen is expensive compared to other whipping agents. This must be figured into the cost analysis of the confection formulated with egg albumen.
- Egg albumen generally is perceived by consumers as a high-quality ingredient. It is considered a natural product.
- Egg albumen is a protein and is one of the most common food allergens. There must be proper labeling of this ingredient for compliance with existing labeling regulations and to assure that sensitive individuals are not adversely affected.

Soy Protein
- Soy protein is one of the most heat-stable whipping agents, working well over a wide range of temperature applications.
- This stability makes soy protein more versatile than other whipping agents. It yields a wide variety of finished products from a very fluffy to a rather dense whip.
- Soy protein works well over a wide pH range.
- It is more difficult to mask the flavor of soy protein than other whipping agents.
- Soy protein is an allergen and must be listed on all labeling to warn sensitive consumers.

Milk Protein
- Milk protein is a stable whipping agent.
- Milk protein does not whip to as light a foam as other whipping agents. The use of milk protein produces a texture that results in a denser finished product.
- The use of milk protein results in a distinct flavor. This may or may not be desirable.
- Milk protein is expensive when compared to other whipping agents.
- Milk protein is an allergenic substance and must be labeled to alert the sensitive customer to its presence.

Gelatins
- There are several sources of gelatin including hide stock and bone stock.
- Gelatin is the most stable of the whipping agents.
- The foam that results from aerating gelatin is versatile and ranges from delicate to a very rubbery texture.
- Gelatin works well over a wide range of pH values.
- Gelatin is a good value for the versatility it provides.
- The use of some gelatin products may have religious prohibitions so the confectioner must address these issues during formulation.

Figure 6

Sugar

Sugar (sucrose) is the gold standard for sweeteners.

Corn Syrup

Corn syrup is a generic term that, in the past, has meant glucose syrup. Today, corn syrup can be formulated to meet very specialized needs, resulting in a wide range of textural properties and levels of sweetness.

Polyols

Polyols are a group of compounds that are hybrid molecules. One end of the molecule looks like a carbohydrate and the other end of the molecule looks like an alcohol. In recent years various polyols have found more acceptance as sweeteners in confectionery products.

OTHER INGREDIENTS

Other ingredients play important roles in the manufacture of nougat and

Sweeteners
Sugar • It is reasonably priced. • It has very versatile properties. • Sucrose has a known level of sweetness. **Corn Syrup** • Corn syrup is used as a bulking agent and for final texture of the confection. • Corn syrup is inexpensive compared to the cost of other raw materials that serve the same purpose. • Corn syrup is versatile in that it can be formulated for the specific needs of the confectioner. • Corn syrups come in a variety of dextrose-equivalent (DE) values for different applications. **Polyols** • Historically, sorbitol has been used as a humectant. • Polyols open a wide variety of new applications ranging from sugarfree products to reduced-calorie formulations. Polyols can be used to manufacture products for the diabetic market. • Polyols are very expensive. • They also require a new understanding of raw materials. • Polyols have a laxative effect and may be limited in how much may be used in your products. • Polyols have a cooling effect. This characteristic tends to limit the use of certain polyols. • The legal status of some polyols varies from country to country.

Figure 7

marshmallow formulas. While minor ingredients constitute only a small percentage of the finished formula, their impact is large on the final outcome of the candy.

Fat of any type in any aerated formulation must be handled with care. Aeration is the process of encapsulating air molecules in a matrix made from a whipping agent and a syrup base. Much like bubbles in dishwashing soap that break when they come in contact with the greasy residue on dishes, fats attack the emulsion made with the whipping agent. Fats are an important part of nougat formulations so they must be incorporated gently into the formulation. This gentle mixing allows the confectioner to maintain the aeration of the product without breaking it down by the incorporation of fat.

Cocoa powder and other ingredients high in fat have to be monitored carefully at the time of incorporation. If the confectioner is making batches, the reuse of cooking pots and utensils may affect subsequent batches due to remaining fats and oils on the vessels, resulting in poor quality of the next batch.

Nut meats and **oil-based flavorings** can cause failure if care is not taken at the time these ingredients are incorporated into the candy. The confectioner must take care to assure that the addition of a flavoring at the end of the manufacturing process does not break down the candy.

Emulsifiers help to keep the fat in suspension. Lecithin is a common emulsifier used in the confectionery industry.

Water must be from a potable source for which the confectioner is aware of the hardness, pH and level of dissolved mineral. These components of water affect the whipping agent, texture and flavor of the finished candy. Problems arising from the water used in making candy are easily overlooked when troubleshooting problems with a formulation.

Air is the final component that can cause the confectioner a multitude of problems if it is not clean and dry. Air may be injected into a confection by a variety of methods using various equipment. If this air is contaminated with oil from pumps it can ruin an emulsion. Moisture added by compressed air may result in a product that is sticky and difficult to handle. The environmental air of the plant must also be conditioned and dried to a temperature and relative humidity that will assist in handling the confection prior to coating in chocolate or wrapping.

CONCLUSIONS

It is ultimately up to the candymaker to take similar ingredients and manipulate them so they result in a desirable end product. By starting with a basic understanding of the function of the raw materials and how they react to make nougat and marshmallow, the confectioner can manipulate the ingredients by the amount of each ingredient present, the processing conditions and the whipping agent used to make the candy. The variations are nearly limitless and technology continues to give the candymaker new materials to work with in the making of marshmallow and nougat. Improvements in existing raw materials also allow for better end product. Yet a basic understanding of the differences between nougat and marshmallow formulations is only half of the story. Just as technology has improved and modified the raw materials used to make nougat and marshmallow, it has also changed the equipment used to manufacture these candies.

Start with a basic understanding of the function of the raw materials and manipulate those materials to achieve desired results. Improved raw materials allow for new and improved products.

Whether it is an improved formulation or the latest piece of equipment, we should never forget the simple joy of savoring a tasty piece of candy.

Note: Questions and answers for this chapter appear at the end of the Aerated Confections section on page 318.

Hard Candy Aeration

Jim McGovern
Jelly Belly Candy Company

Pulling hard candy is one of the oldest methods of changing the basic characteristics of the hard candy texture. Pulling incorporates air by hand or mechanical means with the intention of a uniform distribution of air to change the "bite" or crunch when eating, as well as to change the appearance.

The process of pulling is literally a stretching of the hard candy mass, causing air to become entrapped in the candy. The incorporation of air during the pulling action forms elongated "tubes" of air and thus additional surfaces from which light can be reflected. This changes the outward appearance of the candy to that of a lighter or a whiter color. A clear cooked hard candy can literally produce a white candy piece (such as a starlight mint) without use of artificial colors when pulled, or aerated. A red-colored candy will appear pink following the pulling application. A candy without color added will appear whiter, almost silvery. The items will also have the intended advantage of the bite or crunch caused by the pulling.

If you remember that we are adding additional surfaces from which light can be reflected, so, too, will the candy surfaces be increased to give a better flavor experience. The basic hard glass structure of hard candy will be interrupted as well, and changed to a lighter, easier-to-eat piece. Always remember that a pulled hard candy piece will not necessarily be soft enough for chewing.

Before a batch of hard candy can be pulled, the cooked candy mass must first be tempered, or cooled uniformly, to allow for the candy to be handled in the pulling operation or on a mechanical device. A hard candy batch cooked to 290°F to 300°F would be tempered to approximately 220°F to 230°F before being introduced to the pulling action. The viscosity increase caused by cooling enables the batch pulling method.

If there is an intention to produce a pulled, colored hard candy, color and flavor may be incorporated into the batch before tempering and pulling. This yields the desired texture in a pastel-colored hard candy piece.

Flavor may also be added to the batch as it is being pulled for a uniform mix of flavor throughout the batch, eliminating a step, provided pulling time allows for good distribution of flavor.

TRADITIONAL PULLING

Hand Pulling

Hand pulling on a hook is a traditional small-batch pulling method. A portion of a cooked, flavored, colored hard candy is tempered and then literally hung on a hook attached to a wall or a post and pulled by muscle and gravity, with the pulling process repeated until the desired consistency is achieved. This method is quite interesting to watch, but requires a bit of skill, a bit of muscle and the time it takes to process the entire batch while still warm and formable.

Drawbacks include fatigue, fluctuations in batch-to-batch consistency, ergonomics and being labor intensive.

You might still witness this method being performed in a small candy shop where small batches and working space are also factors.

Vertical Machine Pulling

Vertical batch pulling was a great improvement over hand pulling where larger quantities of candy were required to supply the candymaking operation. The larger machines are capable of handling 150 lb batches per cycle; smaller versions would be used for up to 50 lbs. These machines are workhorses powered by heavy electric motors and drives; some are equipped with water-cooled arms (hooks) or plastic sleeves to keep the candy from sticking to the arms. In this method, a tempered batch of candy is loaded on the puller arms, the operator jogs the machine and the pulling gradually starts. Once the candy is begun on its pulling cycle, the operator is free to add flavor to the pulling batch or begin preparation of the next batch in tempering. When the pulling cycle is completed, the operator or timer stops the machine, strips the pulled candy from the puller arms and transports the pulled batch to the next operation on the candy line.

The control of the degree of aeration is through the timing of the batch while in optimal pulling action. This may be done by an electronic timer, automatic cycling by PLC or similar device. A shorter pulling cycle will produce a less-pulled piece with a slightly harder texture and less-pastel appearance. This is described by some candymakers as *lightly pulled*. Occasionally, it is difficult to hang the batch quickly and get the pulling action moving steadily without additional attention by the operator. This might influence the batch-to-batch consistency if a timer is activated before the desired action is achieved.

Advantages of the vertical batch-pulling process include a relatively low initial cost, the fact that it is a simple machine requiring only basic maintenance and easy changeover of flavors and/or colors between batches. Skilled workers can produce more than 1,000 lbs per hour depending upon the degree of aeration and other product-specific requirements.

Disadvantages begin with the exposure to injury of the operator due to the interaction of the operator's arms in close proximity with the powerful machine while in process (extensive, regularly inspected and maintained safety guards are necessary to protect the worker). The precision of specific gravity control is difficult because it is determined by human action with time and attention to a dynamic process. Loading and unloading of candy is heavy work and considerable effort is required to strip candy from the arms quickly and completely. Plastic sleeves and water-cooled arms require vigilance to avoid product contamination by those substances.

A final step, following the pulling of the batch previous to or immediately following assembly of the batch, may be the application of clear, cooked candy to the batch in a very thin layer. This is to seal the outside of the pulled candy from the atmosphere, much the same as wood might be sealed with varnish. Incorporating air in the batch increases the surface area of the candy, providing a greater number of surfaces for air and moisture to affect the candy quality. Hard candy will dull and grain with exposure to humidity; applying shine will retard the effects of the atmosphere on the candy.

Aeration by Chemical Action

Aeration can also be induced by chemical action, as is done by the addition of sodium bicarbonate (or baking soda) to the cooked batch of candy. This is a classic method used to produce peanut brittle. One can demonstrate this at home or in the laboratory by melting butterscotch hard candy in a microwave oven and stirring in peanuts when liquid. The final step is performed when baking soda is mixed into the peanut and hard candy mixture immediately before pouring onto a cool surface, such as a cold table or cool, greased cookie sheet.

The major drawback of this aeration method is control of air bubble size and distribution, size of batches and handling.

NEWER PULLING DEVICES

Horizontal Machine Pulling

Horizontal batch pullers are a great improvement over the vertical machines in safety. However, they require more space and are more expensive. The operation consists of a flat, chilled metal- or plastic-covered surface, or table, onto which the cooked, tempered batch is loaded (Figure 1). A guard is lowered, closing off the operational area from outside access. Then a central arm is lowered, or raised, into the center of

Horizontal Pulling Machine	Air Injection

Figure 1	Figure 2

the batch automatically, immediately prior to the start of the pulling operation by two opposed rotating pulling arms moving at the outer dimension of the pulling table. The batch is then pulled for a predetermined time period, after which the pulling arms retract back in the direction from which they were inserted. The batch is then removed from the machine and moved on to the next step in the operation. (Often this machine is a part of an automated system mated with mixers, feeders and take-away conveyors which eliminate the manual loading/unloading operation.)

This machine is far more safe and automated than the vertical batch pullers, yielding similar results in specific gravity. The advantages are evident by the safety guarding, ease of loading and unloading, greater productivity and yield, and lessened need for operator attention.

Disadvantages are relative expense, space required for the machine and attending services for load/unload, and a greater complexity of the machinery itself.

There is some dispute as to the quality or degree of pulling when compared to the vertical puller because the horizontally pulled batch rests on the horizontal plate, giving rise to a different pulling action.

Automated Air Injection

Today's larger automated cooking lines are 24-hour, 6- or 7-day per week operations using automated blending, cooking and aeration in consecutive steps on equipment capable of many thousands of pounds per hour (Figure 2). This equipment can run with very few operators and produce a quality product similar or superior to many of the other methods at far greater capacity.

The process begins with an automatic sugar and corn syrup blending and cooking system yielding a continuous mass of hard candy that is fed into one or more mixing cylinders. These mixers are used to incorporate colors and flavors, and to inject oil-free compressed air via carefully controlled nozzles. These nozzles can be controlled to yield reproducible aerated candy throughout the entire production period by varying temperatures and viscosity of the candy mixing with controlled rates and volumes of air using mixing speeds and number of air injection nozzles.

Advantages begin with the controlled volume of candy produced with consistent density and flavor due to machine controls. Safety is greatly improved due to lack of need for human intervention directly with the hot candy, tempering on line as it is conveyed by machine and improved ergonomics. Piece-weight variations, due to more accurately controlled density, are minimized.

Disadvantages include the complexity of the machinery itself and the many key process parameters to be monitored continuously. Because the machinery can produce larger quantities of candy continuously, longer production runs are more efficient and changeovers are less frequent. Cleanout times are more expensive and therefore must be minimized. The operators must be more technologically advanced and carefully trained and supervised. This equipment can easily support large sales requirements and is less versatile than the other aeration methods discussed. Cost of equipment of this magnitude is significant, as well as the space to house a line that cooks and mixes colors and flavors, and aerates, tempers and feeds a forming line.

REFERENCES

Schleuter, Juergen A. Aeration of Hard Candies. *Manufacturing Confectioner,* June 1982.

Mann, Julian. Air Injection: The Automation of Hard Candy Aeration. *Manufacturing Confectioner,* 1995.

Note: Questions and answers for this chapter appear at the end of the Aerated Confections section on page 318.

Taffy Processing

Gianni Ruffinatti
Ruffinatti

In continental Europe, taffy is defined as fat-containing, low-boiled candy having a residual moisture content ranging between 4.5 and 9 percent. Types of product that fall within this category are varied and include plain, unpulled milk caramels, fudges, traditional English toffees and all types of pulled or aerated chewy candies with or without milk and butter.

The production process for all of these items starts, however, in the same manner, so we can safely include them in our discussion.

BASIC PRODUCTION METHODS

Batch Cooking and Cooling

Historically, batch cooking was the original production method (Figure 1). All quantities are recipe driven. First, preweighed quantities of water and/or milk and sugar were combined in a gas-heated copper pan. When the mix was brought to complete solution and boiling point, a preweighed quantity of glucose was added. The new mixture was again brought to the boiling point before fats, emulsifiers and any recipe-specific ingredients were added. At atmospheric pressure, continuous mixing was performed as the desired cook temperature was reached.

When steam cooking replaced gas-fired batch cooking, standard production was carried out in double-jacketed kettles with

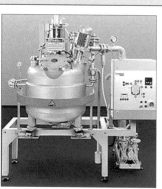

Batch Cookers — Old and New

Figure 1

integrated mechanical mixers. The recipe-driven cooking ingredients, methods and procedures remained essentially the same as under the original gas-fired system. Traditional confectioners shut off the kettle's steam supply approximately 1°C below the final cook temperature to cope with latent heat retained in the copper cook vessel. With the mixer still running, heat-sensitive ingredients such as gelatin mixtures and varieties of flavors and colors could be added. After that, the cooking vessel would be emptied.

Originally, hot and liquid product output from the cooking vessel was discharged into wheeled carriers and then spread onto cooling slabs (Figure 2) to facilitate heat dissipation. At this stage, if required by recipe, additional ingredients, such as dry acid crystals or icing sugar and rework product were sprinkled onto the product surface. Then the long sheets of cooled candy were cut into smaller pieces, allowing them to be folded over one another, facilitating homogeneous distributed temperature reduction.

When sufficient heat dissipation had occurred to achieve proper product temper, the pulling process could commence, or, in the case of plain, unpulled toffee products, the rope-forming process.

Cooling Table

Figure 2

Before examining the following pulling, aerating and forming processes, I want to backtrack and briefly explain the continuous cooking and cooling methods that in recent years have often replaced the traditional systems.

Continuous Cooking and Cooling

The continuous cooking and cooling process for the production of low-boiled candies offers a higher level of automation, which usually translates into greater output.

Weighing & Mixing Vessel

Figure 3

All the basic ingredients such as water, sugar, glucose and fats are automatically received and weighed, one after another, into a weighing vessel (Figure 3), usually fitted on load cells. In the vessel, a high-speed propeller mixer combines the individual ingredients together into a slurry. When the mixing process is complete and the batch weighed, it is then released into a hot-water-jacketed buffer tank, frequently located below the weighing vessel, utilizing gravity feed. Ingredient weighing and mixing are the only parts of the continuous operation still done batch-wise because of the need for precision and control.

The premixed slurry is continuously pumped into the continuous cook system, where, passing through the cooking elements, it reaches the desired cook temperature. The slurry is then released into an open chamber where the water content is allowed to flash off.

Different machinery manufacturers offer different types of cookers utilizing different types of cooking elements or heat exchangers (Figure 4).

When the premix slurry is a basic sugar, water, glucose and fat mixture, without milk proteins, the choice of cooker type is wider because almost all types of heat exchangers used for cooking hard candy can be used to cook these slurries efficiently and quickly. Coil-in-chest, plate-in-frame and the shell-and-tube heat exchangers are examples of these types of cookers.

Unfortunately, these types of cookers are not suitable for the production of milk chewy candies. Scraped-surface cookers are required for this sort of application.

However, it is possible to combine the high efficiency and simplicity of the plate-in-frame heat exchanger with the facility of the scraped-surface-cooker principle.

Such a combination allows the production of all types of milk caramels by keeping separate the cooking of the basic slurry from the cooking and caramelization of the milk. In this system, the basic slurry, without milk, is passed through the plate heat exchanger and then the milk is

Various Toffee and Caramel Cookers

Figure 4

added to the boiled syrup by a synchronized metering pump, just as it flashes off its moisture upon entering the caramelizing chamber.

The steam-jacketed caramelizing chamber is fitted with a variable speed wall-scraper mixer that assures perfect mixing of the milk with the cooked syrup and prevents any sticking and/or burning of the caramel on the steam-jacketed wall. The inflow of the product into the caramelizing chamber, as well as the outlet of the ready caramel, is continuous, allowing variability in the degree of caramelization (i.e., the color and flavor of the finished candy) by adjusting product residence time and by controlling the level of the product in the caramelizer. A vacuum pump can be used to enhance the natural water evaporation when a lighter color of the product is required, therefore a very short residence time in the caramelizer is allowed.

As mentioned earlier, chewy candy needs to contain some ingredients that make it chewy (a little bit gummy) but keep it soft for the first bite. This is often achieved with the addition of animal gelatin. A combination of gelatin and gum arabic or other types of colloidals can be used. All of these items have temperature sensitivity and degrade with prolonged exposure to high temperature. In a continuous production process, the addition of these ingredients must be done after the cooking operation and immediately before the cooling stage. It is critical that once these new ingredients are added, they are well mixed and the entire product rapidly cooled down, minimizing the exposure time to high temperature.

In automatic and continuous production plants a dynamic or a static in-line type of mixer (Figure 5) is often fitted on the jacketed pipe that brings the cooked product from the continuous cooker to the cooling drum or to the stainless steel cooling band. The dissolved gelatin is continuously metered in by a dosing pump and, of course, the other liquid or heat-sensitive ingredients such as flavors, colors or foaming agents can also be individually dosed and thoroughly mixed to the ready product in the same way. Coming out of the continuous mixer, the product is fed onto a cooling drum or a stainless steel cooling band.

The introduction of the cooling drum concept more than 45 years ago in continental Europe created an opportunity to redesign many taffy production departments, making them much more compact thanks to the great saving of floor space obtained by replacing the old rows of cooling tables with one or more cooling drums (Figure 6).

A further development and improvement that

In-line Mixer

Figure 5

came from the use of the cooling drum's concept is the automatic dosing for acid powders, icing sugars and liquid flavors, which are introduced directly onto the cooled film of taffy coming off the drum as it is layered onto a weighing belt. Together with the ability to continuously weigh the cooled product as it is layered on the receiving belt under the drum, the possibility to automatically cut the outcoming taffy film when the required weight of cooled product has been reached and automatically move forward the collected batch to the next stage of the process makes the original cooling drum into a fully automatic production system that does not require any human intervention.

Pulling and/or Aerating

While many types of milk, chocolate or licorice plain toffee do not contain gelatin or foaming agents and are not pulled or aerated, most chewy candies are mechanically pulled or beaten under air pressure to incorporate air into the mass, decreasing their density and obtaining a softer, yet chewy, texture. The pulling operation is essential to achieve this result. If, for example, we form candies out of prepulled chewy candy mass, the candy characteristics will be markedly different. The unpulled candy will not only be heavier, it will be stickier and harder to bite into. Moreover, its texture will be longer, and it will feel more glass-like than regularly pulled candy. This makes for difficulty in biting through with the teeth while eating. Also, because of the resistance and elasticity of gelatin, such candy will tend to shrink after being cut. Without proper pulling and curing, the candy will shrink back much more substantially than a pulled piece.

In my opinion, which I believe is shared by many in the confectionery industry, the mechanical energy put into the mass by the pulling operation helps to commence and enhance the graining process that makes the texture of the finished candy shorter, while still retaining its chewy characteristics.

Cooling Wheel

Figure 6

Today, the batch-pulling operation is the industry standard. However, the machinery market does offer continuous pulling machines that, while replicating the traditional mechanical pulling action, are designed to be continuously fed by a ribbon of product. As the pulling goes on, the pulled product is moved toward the discharge point. Existing continuous pullers perform a very similar pulling action as those of the traditional vertical pullers, therefore they can produce the same effect on the candy mass. The only limitation is with their maximum allowable pulling time, since this is directly proportional to the length and size of the continuous puller. For some very popular and traditional chewy candies that need to be pulled for very long time periods, up to 20 minutes, before achieving their required texture, the batch puller is still the only option (Figure 7).

The other important modification to the candy mass occurring during the pulling operation is a significant loss of specific weight, meaning, a growth in product volume arises because of the

Puller

Figure 7

incorporation of trapped air mixed between the layers of product which occurs each time the mass is stretched and folded on itself. The average specific weight of cooked, unpulled taffies is approximately 1.40. Should the only requirement be to reduce a product's specific gravity in order to increase its volume, this can also be achieved by adding some aerating agents such as beaten egg white or beaten milk proteins. The incorporation of these aerating or whipping agents needs to occur when the liquid product is coming off the cooker. The aeration effect is enhanced if the product is beaten under air pressure while the agents are mixed in. The process will reduce the product temperature and increase its viscosity. The incorporation of microscopic air bubbles contained in the whipping agents, as well as increased air bubble formation during the beating process, contributes to lowering the specific weight to approximately 1.20 to 1.15.

Forming And Cutting

So far I've discussed batch versus continuous cooking, batch versus continuous pulling and the differences between pulling and aerating systems. Now, as the taffy leaves the pulling stage with appropriate temperature and consistency characteristics, it is ready for the cutting or forming stage. Here, too, there are two kinds of forming processes available: the traditional configuration is a batch roller and rope sizer forming a feed rope for a cut-and-wrap machine; the other configuration is an extrusion system featuring an extruder forming a completely crystallized mass into one or more plastic and pliable ropes that are then fed through a rope sizer for diameter size control before being fed into either a cut-and-wrap machine or a die-forming candy line.

Because of different production procedures and recipes used in the extrusion process and because the product is completely crystallized before extrusion and only made pliable again by the friction and mixing action of the extruder, the rope that comes out of the extruder is more dimensionally stable than the rope produced by the combination batch roller and rope sizer system with a similar recipe mass. This is a good reason to prefer the extrusion process when die-formed chewy candy has to be produced. It is not so important for a standard cut-and-wrap taffy, as the rope-sizing and cutting actions do not stress the material as much as the die-forming, and the immediate wrapping of the cut piece helps it to retain its shape, preventing shrinkage and deformation.

From a factory automation point of view, we must keep in mind that, whether the process choice is for the standard batch roller, rope-sizer, cut-and-wrap line or for the extrusion system, the pulled mass can never be transferred directly from the pulling machines to the rope-forming stage. In all cases, the taffy mass must go through a cooling and stabilizing stage prior to being fed to the batch rollers, or through a curing (graining) stage prior to being fed into the extruders. For the first type of rope-forming system, in order to minimize the shrinkage and shape deformation, the taffy should reach the cut-and-wrap machine in a pliable and plastic consistency, at a temperature not exceeding 30°C (86°F).

When the extrusion rope-forming system is in use, the pulled taffy mass must be allowed to grain completely in order to be suitable for a good extrusion operation. Therefore, also in this case, one more stage must be fitted in after the pulling operation. Some machine manufacturers offer automatic equipment to cater to both needs.

Full Aerated Confections Panel
Questions & Answers

A panel discussion on aerated confections with John Cooke, Ralph Lee, Greg Johnson, Jim McGovern and Gianni Ruffinatti.

Q: How does water quality impact aerations? That is, does mineral content in water reduce stability?
A: I believe the basis of the water can lead to problems with foam structure. Hard water or the presence of a low or high pH may have an effect on the foam structure itself, which leads to breaking down the foam and that's the basic failure of any aerated product.

Q: Is there a preference in using cane or beet sugar when making aerated products?
A: Yes, typically cane sugar is a little bit whiter then beet. However, beet has higher mineral content in it so if you're concerned with minerals that might be a problem. Good hard candy is made with good processes and good cooking; you can't get away with just one.

Q: When you commented on mechanical seals in continuous aerators, how do you prevent sugar glazing the surfaces?
A: Most machines with mechanical seals have some type of continuous flush that keeps the seals clean, such as lantern rings. That's really the important part — to keep the seals themselves clean. But if you have a break in the protective seal and you start seeing sugar coming through your seal water, then you are messing up your mechanical seal. Keep an eye on that.

Q: Aren't we required to list air as an ingredient in aerated products?
A: Air is considered inherent in products; examples are ice cream and mayonnaise.

Q: How is pulled aeration density and pore shape/size affected by including fats in the candy?
A: In my experience, I must say that the inclusion of fat in the recipe, especially if it is accompanied by the introduction of an emulsifier like lecithin, does not affect the shape of the candy. The fat by itself, if well emulsified or well mixed into the candy, does not produce shrinkage or a change/deformation in a cut-and-wrap piece or a dye-form piece. Milk products tend to make the candy shrink more than fat.

Q: When aerating nougat, marshmallow or taffy at higher elevations such as Denver, Salt Lake City, etc., what are the effects? What do you have to watch for and what happens if you don't figure it out?
A: One of the things you have to understand is that the cook of the base candy is going to be affected by the elevation. High-elevation aerated products are going to be affected by outside atmospheric pressure so you have to adjust your processing parameters. At high elevation, you're probably going to have to increase your whip time to incorporate that much more energy into the product so that you have an aeration that is the same as you would get at sea level.

Q: Once a batch has been pulled, then cooled, can it be warmed and repulled?
A: Depending on the formulation of the batch, if in that batch you add enough glucose to prevent the crystallization or the graining of the batch, it can be warmed up carefully and re-pulled. I have seen in some companies where they keep the batch in a warm container or on a hot table and pull it two hours later. As long as it does not crystallize it can be pulled.

Q: What do you do with pulled candy rework? What precautions do you need to take?
A: With hard candy you wouldn't put ground aerated candy back into a batch directly. You might do it on a cold table once the cook candy is added to it and melted back down. The safest way to avoid crystallization is little centers of ground candy, especially once its pulled, would be melted down and retrieved as a rework syrup going back to the cooker. With soft and chewy candy, especially with extruded chewy candy, the crystallization is what you want to see happen because you want your mass to crystallize possibly early enough to have a continued production. The

use of rework, of already crystallized rework and the introduction of small percentages of this rework into the batch while you're pulling it will certainly help to achieve a very good crystallized texture of that batch, so it can be useful. If you're making a marshmallow where you're trying to control the crystallization, you should limit the addition of already aerated marshmallow. Backing in the batch can occur at two places. The best place would be at the beating stage where you could put small amounts back in. But once again, you can lose process control if you don't have it in a well-controlled environment.

Q: Can you use aerators to inject CO_2 when making "pop rock" hard candy? If so, what changes are made versus normal aeration?
A: If you add CO_2 with a standard aerated product it can give you a very odd flavor. Most of the aerators used for nougat and marshmallow cannot handle the temperature and pressure required for hard candy.

Q: When pulling in an open room, what are the temperature and humidity requirements?
A: Low humidity and reasonable temperature. Typically 70° to 75° is fine and you want as low humidity as you can get. You want to keep the dew point down certainly below the temperature of your cold tables when you're handling things. On the puller itself, just make sure to get it through while it's warm as it won't pick up humidity — it's when it starts cooling down that you have a problem.

Q: When making a pulled candy, is there anything that causes pulling to fail from an ingredient or contamination standpoint?
A: Only graining, which can happen if you make something like an after dinner mint which has a very high sucrose content and no glucose or very little glucose content. The ending of that product would have to be done very carefully or else it would grain, and if it grains you throw it away.

Q: How can you easily measure specific gravity of a pulled candy, hard candy,

marshmallow or nougat?
A: If you have a rinse cylinder with graduations and you weigh your candy and you throw it in the cylinder, you will see the increase in the volume of the liquid. If it is not water it is better because the water will dissolve the sugar. While you are trying to watch it rinse out, the sugar is dissolving and you lose your measurement.

Q: On marshmallow nougat what is the difference in foam structures, strengths, stability between the different whipping agents such as gelatin, soy, etc.?
A: I think gelatin would probably be the most stable whipping structure for marshmallow as it tends to be more stable due to a lower cook than that of nougat. Therefore, since you don't have the high syrup cook, you have to have a little bit more stability in the whipping agent. With egg albumen or some of the other ones that are very light and delicate, it might give you a light and fluffy whip, but doesn't necessarily have the stability and can break down easier with the incorporation of items such as fats, nut meats or anything that may disrupt the motion.

Q: What reaction causes the aeration after the addition of sodium bicarbonate to hard candy?
A: That's the reaction of the sodium bicarbonate with the slightly acidic candy. As that happens the CO_2 is produced and that causes an almost instantaneous reaction. So it's actually the pH difference that causes it.

Q: What is affected in pulling taffy when solids, such as cocoa powder, are included?
A: It might lead to crystallization; certainly the crystallization will not take place as fast, as you can see. Usually it doesn't take place during the pulling operation unless the pulling operation is carried out for 20 minutes. The introductions of ice and sugar or cocoa powder, and sometimes even the introduction of little pieces of nut, might, in a high-sugar-content recipe, lead to crystallization.

Q: Can compound coatings and chocolate be aerated? How do you do it?

A: Yes, they can be. Temperature control is the critical part. You can actually aerate it through continuous aerators and that works quite well. Temperature is critical, especially when using real chocolate. You need to aerate; with tempered chocolate you have to maintain temperature all the way through the process.

Q: Are there any additives that will reduce the likelihood of sugar inversion with a high cook?
A: Inversion is time, temperature and pH. Some ingredients such as polydextrose, if not neutralized, can cause your nougat to shorten and flatten out. You really need a long time for it to cause inversion; it's where somebody basically makes a batch and lets it sit in the kettle for hours and hours.

Q: Are there any candies made which combine a chewing gum base with the cooked candy ingredients?
A: There are certainly lollipops that are filled with bubble gum in the center. You usually don't see it in taffy but you can find it in the market. There are also specialty gum bases available which can be combined with cooked ingredients to produce a hybrid product.

Q: Why does candy turn white when we aerate it?
A: With hard candy it's the trapping of the air which forms long tubes of air and that changes the way light reflects from it. As you start to pull it, you change the way the light hits it and it reflects more, hence the white color.

Q: How do you know when to stop whipping, pulling, beating?
A: It depends on the product you are dealing with. With chewy candy, or taffy, you pull until you get that certain consistency that you want in the product. Of course, when you put together the formulation or production procedure you will test different pulling times and there is always going to be one pulling time that satisfies your characteristics for that product. For instance, one thing that you have to note is that when you pull taffy the temperature at which you pull the taffy is extremely important in relation to the amount of air that this taffy will retain. The product must not be too hot, of course, but warm enough that it does not break.

Q: In the slides there showed a clear coat of unpulled candy being put over a batch of pulled candy. Isn't the unpulled candy more hygroscopic and doesn't it cause problems?
A: I don't think so; in a pulled candy you're forming more surface area for moisture to attack. Hard candy, depending on the formulation, if you're going 45 percent sugar and 55 percent corn syrup, you're going to have more of a problem picking up moisture. If you go the other way and do high-sugar-content hard candy, there will be more of a seal or coating that will hold moisture longer.

Q: We know that free fat can cause an aerated structure to collapse. Exactly what is the physical chemistry mechanism that causes this?
A: The exact cause is worthy of a PhD thesis. The general answer is that the fat causes detrimental changes to the surface tension in the structure and results in collapse of the walls between the bubbles; this is called *lamellae rupture*. A good reference for understanding the mechanics and chemistry of foams is the paper by Mansvelt, *Aeration in Candy Technology*, presented at the PMCA Production Conference in 1964.

Q: What do you recommend as small-pilot-scale frappé equipment?
A: The simplest small-scale equipment is a small planetary mixer as used in the demonstration and in many kitchens. Pilot-scale (2,000 g to 3,000 g) batch pressure beaters work extremely well but are quite expensive (more than $25,000). Pilot-scale continuous pressure beaters also work well, but cost even more. There are a number of small beater manufacturers with batch, continuous or both. A few manufacturers that come to mind are Ter Braak, Chocotech, Oakes, Mondo Mix, Tanis Food Tec, Hansa and Trefa.

INDEX

INDEX

INDEX

INDEX

INDEX